COMPUTATIONAL ECONOMICS

Economic Modeling with Optimization Software

COMPUTATIONAL ECONOMICS

Economic Modeling with Optimization Software

by

Gerald L. Thompson
Carnegie Mellon University
Pittsburgh, Pennsylvania

Sten Thore
The University of Texas at Austin
Austin, Texas

The Scientific Press
651 Gateway Boulevard • Suite 1100 • South San Francisco, CA 94080-7014

COMPUTATIONAL ECONOMICS:
Economic Modeling with Optimization Software
by Gerald L. Thompson & Sten Thore

Printed in the United States of America

10 9 8 7 6 5 4 3 2 1

ISBN 0-89426-201-7 with 3.5″ disk
ISBN 0-89426-200-9 with 5¼″ disk

Publisher: The Scientific Press
Text design & production editor: Gene Smith
Cover design by Rogondino & Associates
Cover photograph by Thomas Lea

CONTENTS

FOREWORD

Our intent in writing this book is to provide a modern textbook on optimization in economics. In the 1960s and 1970s, nearly every economics department offered a course in operations research methods in economics, and the usual textbook used was *Economic Theory and Operations Analysis* by W. J. Baumol. An entire generation of economics students was familiar with this book which, however, has become outdated, so that many departments have ceased to offer such courses.

In order to write a modern version of the course it was necessary to take into account the vast changes that the fields of operations research and economics have undergone. First the array of operations research models that can be applied to economics and their diversity have grown dramatically. Second, personal computers and the software needed to quickly find numerical solutions to such models have only recently become widely available. Thus the course no longer must consist merely of descriptions of what kinds of models could be developed and solved *if* a computer and suitable software were available, but rather can discuss actual economic models and their solutions.

The name "computational economics" refers to economic models that pose computational challenges because of their scale and detail. The term applies to the new approaches to economic analysis and policy that are now becoming practical because of (a) the computational possibilities provided by new computer capabilities and algorithms, and (b) the greatly enhanced availability of data for use in such modeling.

Economics is sometimes defined as the science dealing with the attainment of good or desirable ends that make the best possible use of scarce means. Computational economics is therefore a way of spelling out this optimization problem explicitly, establishing constructive procedures to actually find a solution which achieves the desired optimum while staying within the scarce resource constraints.

The optimization problem will typically be cast in the form of a mathematical programming model. Mathematical programming, or operations research, is a branch of applied mathematics which was developed to find, with the aid of computers and large data sets, solutions to managerial and economic problems. Its best known subject is linear programming and other important areas are nonlinear and integer programming.

The purpose of this book on computational economics is to show how the techniques of operations research can be used to formulate economic problems, which usually involve large quantities of data, and to solve them by using optimization software. Emphasis is placed on the economic interpretations of the results, not on the mathematical techniques which are used by the software to actually find the solutions. In this way it is possible for students to solve a large variety of important economic applications, without requiring that they have an extensive mathematical or computer background.

The first step in applying operations research methods to an economic problem is to formulate a model of the situation being analyzed. A model is a set of mathematical expressions involving variables which represent the important quantities involved. Usually there is an objective function, that is, some mathematical expression which is to be optimized in the course of solving the problem. If all of the constraints and the objective function are linear in the variables, the problem can be solved by a linear programming code. If some of the constraints and objective functions are nonlinear in the variables then a nonlinear programming code is required. Finally, if some or all of the variables must take on integer values in the solution to the problem, then a (mixed) integer programming code is needed to solve the problem. Fortunately, software packages for solving such models have been developed and are easy to use. We shall make use of the GAMS (General Algebraic Modeling System) software package which is included on the diskette that comes with this book, for solving all of the text examples and homework exercises.

The material in the book is presented as it might be seen through the eyes of an economist. We have spent much effort in interweaving the material in our text with conventional economics material. For instance, the introductions to each part of the book provide stepping stones from conventional economics to the corresponding economic models. Also, each individual chapter begins with a general economic overview, preparatory to the statement of a model. The discussion of each model and its numerical solution emphasizes economic interpretations. We stress economic substance, not mathematical methods.

The bulk of the book is devoted to micro theory or theory of the firm (Part II) and macro theory or industry models (Part III). The one obvious omission in the latter is general equilibrium theory (which we plan to add in subsequent editions). A partial discussion of that topic is contained in part IV on financial modeling.

Because of its lack of elaborate mathematical or computational prerequisites, we have successfully used this book for beginning college freshmen up to and including masters and doctoral students. It turns out that each of these kinds of students has to spend a certain amount of time learning how to use the software, and after that they are on about equal footing.

We have found that the approach taken here enables students who are not highly technically trained, as well as those who are, to solve a wide variety of interesting economic problems. We also found that the mnemonic rules used to state the complementary slackness (see the front cover and Chapter 4) and the Kuhn-Tucker conditions (see Chapter 4) made them accessible to the whole range of students mentioned above. We welcome feedback from users of this book on ways it can be improved.

The authors would like to thank Dr. George Kozmetsky of the IC^2 Institute at the University of Texas for his encouragement and support during the preparation of this book. We would also like to thank Professor David Kendrick of the University of Texas for making early versions of GAMS available to us. We would like to thank Dr. Alexander Meeraus of the GAMS Development Corporation for giving us much useful advice on writing programs in the GAMS language, and for including our programs on the GAMS computer disk that comes with this book. Two members of The Scientific Press also deserve thanks for the contributions they made: Mr. Paul Kelly, the publisher, for his enthusiastic support and helpful advice; and Mr. Gene Smith, of the production department, who contributed much to the final format and appearance of the book. Thanks are also due to Ms. Guo Hua who ran the many versions of the GAMS programs. Finally, special thanks are due to Mrs. Eleanor Balocik who prepared numerous preliminary versions of the book during the five years in which we test taught the material both at Carnegie Mellon University and at the University of Texas.

G.L.T. and S.T.

June, 1991

A NOTE TO THE INSTRUCTOR

This computational economics book should be used in conjunction with a personal computer and a commercial software package which is capable of solving mathematical programming problems. Our current personal preference for a suitable software package is GAMS (General Algebraic Modeling System).[1] We like GAMS because it is relatively easy to learn, it can be purchased in other versions to handle problems of larger sizes, and also because it provides the user with complete documentation of the mathematical model of the economic situation being studied.

Although a course taught from this book does require some familiarity with elementary calculus, no prior experience with either a personal computer or operations research is required. The first one or two sessions of the course should be devoted to the explanation of how to use the software package. Preferably these sessions should be held in a computer laboratory room in which each students sits in front of a PC, and the instructor can project his or her own computer output. After initially copying and/or modifying some simple GAMS programs which are in the appendix, a student will be able to independently construct other programs.

Ours is a course in economics, not in mathematical programming or in operations research. The latter topics are used essentially as tools, and there is no attempt to give a systematic presentation to the student of the algorithms used by the software programs in solving the text and homework problems. However, much effort is devoted in this book to explaining the economic content of the solutions to the mathematical models involved, to interpret their dual variables, and to interpret the conditions they satisfy. What a student learns is how to formulate an economic problem using the format of one of a small number of model types, to enter the model into the computer, to use the software program to solve it, and finally to understand the economic meaning of its solution.

Each chapter in the book involves a simple economic application and an operations research model to analyze it. Because the chapters are largely independent, it is possible to pick and choose among them for use in any given course. Many of the problems can

---

[1] A Brooke, D. Kendrick, and A. Meeraus. *GAMS: A User's Guide*, The Scientific Press, South San Francisco, Calif., 1988. A copy of the student version of software from that book is included on the diskette attached to the back cover of this book.

be modeled as simple linear programming problems, and the student will learn how to formulate them by constructing a "data box," or else by entering a set of mathematical expressions that define the model. The student will also learn how to write the complementary slackness conditions for the model and to give their economic interpretations. The mathematical core of such models is given in the first four chapters, and the mnemonic rules for writing the complementary slackness conditions are given both there and also on the inside front cover of the book.

Only a few of our models involve nonlinear mathematics. The Kuhn-Tucker conditions for them are presented as complementary slackness conditions for an approximating linear program. By doing it in this way we have found that these conditions are easy to understand and use, even on the undergraduate level. However, an instructor who wishes to skip over the nonlinear material can do so without loss of continuity.

PART I

A Preview

INTRODUCTION

Economic Markets

An economic market is sometimes a physical location, such as a farmers' market, or a place where a cattle auction is held. But when economists use the term "a market," it is usually an abstraction which includes all of the many transactions between sellers and buyers for a certain group of goods. For instance, the market for vegetables in Texas encompasses all of the commerce in a wide array of different vegetables, both fresh produce and frozen vegetables, involving growers, shippers, wholesalers, retail outlets and consumers located in many different places. Here the product is an aggregate of many related individual products. The economic agents participating in the market are producers, middlemen, and consumers. The market is usually defined geographically. It also must be specified in a time interval, such as on a particular day or during a particular week.

As a result of market formation various prices are quoted: bid prices, asking prices, and actual prices at which transactions occur. Quantities change hands: suppliers are able to realize some or all of their selling intentions; consumers are able to realize some or all of their buying intentions.

In competitive markets, there are many buyers and many sellers collectively called agents. These agents compete in terms of price, delivery conditions, service, etc. The agents are free to negotiate these matters without outside intervention.

During earlier eras, most goods were uniform in appearance, quality and marketing. A consumer was not able to determine by inspection the identity of the manufacturer or grower who supplied it. There still are products like that today, such as sugar or wheat or sand sold in bulk.

Already by the 1930s, a broad range of products were sold under brand names, having distinctive features or characteristics that distinguish a seller's product from those of his competitors. Competition is then not just in price but also in quality, with each seller trying to offer superior quality in a given price range. In addition, through clever marketing efforts, a seller may be able to establish images in the consumers' minds of the product which are pleasurable or prestigious. In other words, what matters to motivate the consumer is not just objective quality but also very much his or her subjective perception of those qualities.

If a seller of a product is able to establish exclusivity in some aspect of his product for a limited time, it gives him an advantage relative to his competitors. He has created a "niche" in the market. If all sellers do likewise then, using the word of E. H. Chamberlin

(1933), the market becomes an instance of monopolistic competition, in which each seller offers a product that enjoys some actual or perceived advantage that his competitors' products do not possess.

In a modern economy, virtually every product or service offered in the marketplace is sold under a brand name, not just consumer goods but also producer goods such as steel and machinery. Also, the growing importance of services (such as software consulting, health care services, and tourism) has put in sharper focus the individual suppliers of the services. The quality of the service now depends upon the competence of the professional who delivers it.

In the present age of high technology a further evolution of the concept of a market is occurring as the quality of a product is coming to be measured in terms of an ever increasing array of technological characteristics. The "quality" of an ordinary home telephone service, for instance, depends upon the operating characteristics of the fiber optic cable, on software and hardware used in the national switching centers, and on the performance of communication satellites. Through technological advance and product development, each of the various players in the market attempts to gain a competitive edge. High technology products have a multiplicity of attributes (actual or perceived). It is the aim of product development to upgrade continuously the existing attributes of the product, or to introduce entirely new attributes (such as call tracing for telephones).

How is it possible to define a market in the face of such fragmentation and proliferation of goods? Perhaps the most reasonable approach is just to view the market as a convenient aggregate of transactions, that is, the sales and purchases of a number of closely related products which an economist finds helpful to group together for the purpose of study. In a competitive market there are many sellers and many buyers, not infinitely many but a reasonably large number. A product sold in the market is treated *as if* it were uniform, that is, for the purpose of the analysis the differences in product quality of the various products are disregarded.

Chains of Production and Distribution

When a consumer buys a good in a supermarket or a store, it is the last leg of a chain of production and distribution. That chain takes the good through different stages of production, and the shipment of raw materials and finished products frequently takes place over half the globe. The flow of commodities from the original suppliers to the ultimate consumers may be visualized as a network that has a vertical dimension, the chain of production stretching all the way from the employment of primary goods and services like natural resources and labor to the manufacture of the finished product, and its distribution to customers. This flow also has a spatial or geographical dimension, and a time dimension, because production and distribution activities take time.

Sometimes such a chain of production and distribution is operated by one single large corporation. For instance, integrated oil companies pump oil in the Middle East and in North Africa, and ship oil to the United States in tankers. Some integrated oil companies own their own fleet of tankers. An oil company may also own port facilities and storage tanks in several cities along the entire coastline of the United States, and refineries both abroad and in the United States. It may also own a fleet of trucks for the short-haul transportation of gasoline. Typically, it may also own a network of gasoline stations in the country.

In other instances, the production and distribution chains are divided among many individual producers and distributors. This is common in an agricultural area which has a great many individual farmers who are producers, and many competing food processors, wholesalers and retail distributors.

Thus, economic markets arise, or can be assumed to arise, at every stage of a production and distribution chain. For instance, there is a market for crude oil pumped in the Middle East and delivered to tankers calling at Middle Eastern ports. There is another market for crude oil delivered on the East Coast in the United States. There is a market for gasoline and other refined oil products delivered from United States refineries, etc. Whenever there is a bifurcation point on a chain of production and distribution, a manager must make a decision about the routing of the product flow, based on market prices and transportation costs.

As a result, the flow of goods and services in a market economy is directed by the prices that are quoted along the production and distribution chains: prices of raw materials and of labor, prices of semi-finished goods, and prices of consumer goods. Prices may also differ in different geographical areas and at different times.

An Overview of the Chapters in Part I

In Chapter 1 we take a first look at the system of production and distribution, using the well-known *transportation model* which usually deals with the physical shipment of a commodity from a number of origins to a number of destinations. However, the model can be employed in a much broader context. Production is also a kind of transportation (transportation through one stage of manufacture to the next) and so is storage of inventory and investment in capital goods (transportation from one time period to another).

One of the principal tasks of an economist is to understand how prices are formed in the setting of a free market economy. In Chapter 2 we turn to a study of *discrete auctions* as a means for determining prices in a competitive setting. The auction model is attractive, because it allows for considerably more realism than the standard assumptions of "competitive markets" usually employed in economic texts. In particular, we shall be able to determine the pricing of heterogeneous goods that may differ in their design, workmanship, or other characteristics that may seem important to the consumer.

In Chapter 3 we join together in one single model both the flow of goods through a transportation system and the formation of market prices through the interaction of supply and demand. Starting from a case in which the demands are constant but the supplies vary linearly with price, we imbed the transportation model into a larger setting of an entire nonlinear partial equilibrium model. As an example, in energy economics there is obviously the problem of determining the most efficient way of routing crude oil from the various oil fields located throughout the work to demand locations in the world. But there is also a larger problem of determining the amounts to be pumped at each oil field, and also in determining the locations at which new wells should be drilled to expand production. In such a generalized transportation problem the task is to simultaneously determine the optimal supply amounts and locations as well as the optimal shipments and the equilibrium market prices at each supply or demand location. In other models covered in this chapter we discuss two variants of the model: one in which the transportation costs are quadratic, and the other in which the size of each market demand varies linearly with price. In each of these cases the result is a small prototype specimen of a partial *equilibrium system* which we shall study more extensively in Part III of this book.

Chapter 4 concludes Part I with a discussion of the mathematical formulation of linear, nonlinear, and integer programs having linear constraints. This chapter should be read while reading and working with the other chapters in Part I. It will also be a useful reference for the remainder of the book.

Notes on Relevant Literature for Part I

The transportation problem dealt with in Chapter 1 was first mentioned in print, see [4], by a French mathematician, Gaspard Monge in 1781. While working on the construction of military fortifications for Napoleon, he had encountered a "cut and fill" problem, that of moving piles of dirt from locations where it wasn't needed to locations where it was needed. He stated that problem in mathematical form as a kind of transportation problem. In 1941 F. L. Hitchcock published a solution to the problem, see [2]. In the late 1940s, T. C. Koopmans applied the transportation problem to find an optimal way of shipping loads of cargo among several seaports, see [3]. For this and other work on the use of linear programming in economics some of which we will see in later chapters, Koopmans shared (with L. V. Kantorovitch) the 1975 Nobel prize in economics.

In 1891 the businessman and economist E. Böhm-Bawerk published a book which included an horse auction, see [1]. This model was used as an example of a market game by J. von Neumann and O. Morgenstern in their revolutionary book on game theory, see [5]. L. S. Shapley and M. Shubik in [8] described auctions, which included the horse auction, in which each buyer and each seller had only one unit to buy or sell, as assignment market games. G. L. Thompson, in [9] and [10], defined transportation market games, which include the sealed bid auctions covered in Chapter 2.

In Chapter 3 some simple instances of economic models in which supplies, transportation quantities, demands and prices are determined simultaneously. Such modelling arose first in the pioneering paper of P. A. Samuelson [7], written in 1952, which eventually was to lead to a vast body of literature on "spatial equilibrium." His model included an economic potential function which can be traced back to the earlier notion of "consumer surplus." However, Samuelson was quite explicit in rejecting all attempts at giving an economic interpretation for the economic potential function. For this and much other research in economics Samuelson received the 1970 Nobel prize in economics.

The "generalized transportation model" used in Chapter 3 to find the simultaneous solutions for supplies, transportation quantities, demands, and prices was formulated and studied by Rowse in [6].

Chapter 4 gives an overview of the notation to be used in this book. This chapter should be referred to whenever notational questions arise in other parts of the book. It is to be emphasized that the reader need not know the mathematical details behind the algorithms used to solve the problems considered in this book. However, for those who are interested, some references to the mathematical programming literature are given below in [11–15].

Economics References

1. Böhm-Bawerk, E., von, *Positive Theory of Capital*, translated by W. Smart. G. E. Steckert, N.Y., 1923. Originally published in 1891.
2. Hitchcock, F. L., "The Distribution of a Product from Several Sources to Numerous Localities," *Journal of Mathematics and Physics*, 20 (1941) 224–230.
3. Koopmans, T. C., and S. Reiter, "A Model of Transportation," in *Activity Analysis of Production of Allocation*, T. C. Koopmans, ed. Cowles Commission Monograph No. 13. John Wiley, Inc., New York, 1951.
4. Monge, G., "Dèblais et Remblais," *Memoires de l'Academie des Sciences*, 1781.
5. von Neumann, J., and O. Morgenstern, *Theory of Games and Economic Behavior*. Princeton University Press, Third Edition, 1953.
6. Rowse, J., "Solving the Generalized Transportation Problem," *Regional Science and Urban Economics*, 11 (1981) 57–68.
7. Samuelson, P. A., "Spatial Price Equilibrium and Linear Programming," *The American Economic Review*, 42 (1952) 283–303.
8. Shapley, L. S., and M. Shubik, "The Assignment Game I: The Core," *International Journal of Game Theory*, 1 (1972) 111–130.
9. Thompson, G. L., "Pareto Optimal, Multiple Deterministic Models for the Bid and Offer Auctions," *Methods of Operations Research*, 35 (1979), 517–530.
10. Thompson, G. L., "Auctions and Market Game," in *Essays in Game Theory and Mathematical Economics in Honor of Oskar Morgenstern*, edited by Aumon, R. J., *et al*. Bibliographisches Institut Mannheim, 1981, 181–196.

Mathematical Programming References

11. Charnes, A., and W. W. Cooper, *Management Models and Industrial Applications of Linear Programming*, 2 vols., Wiley, New York, 1961.
12. Dantzig, G. B., *Linear Programming and Extensions*, Princeton University Press, Princeton, N.J., 1963.
13. Hillier, F. S., and G. J. Lieberman, *Introduction to Mathematical Programming*, McGraw-Hill Publishing Co., 1990.
14. Luenberger, D. G., *Linear and Nonlinear Programming*, Addison-Wesley Publishing Co., 1984.
15. Garfinkel, R. S., and G. L.Nemhauser, *Integer Programming*. New York, John Wiley, 1972.

1

Transportation Problems

Economic models often involve many variables. For instance, in the production of an economic good there may be thousands of individual decisions and processing operations needed. Interspersed with these operations there may be hundreds of individual shipments of raw materials and semifinished or finished goods. Classical mathematics, including calculus and differential equations, which helped to propel spectacular advances in physics and chemistry, is not well suited to deal with many variable problems.

Economic models frequently also involve mathematical inequalities rather than equalities, which are the most commonly used form in classical mathematics. These arise from stating budget constraints, available resources constraints, demand constraints, production capacity constraints, etc.

Toward the end of the 1940s, a new kind of mathematics evolved that was designed to handle large numbers of unknowns and to handle inequalities as well as equalities. One of the first such problems to be stated and solved was the *transportation problem*, which asks for the minimum total cost way of shipping a homogeneous good located in various warehouses to many different customers located at various markets. Besides the shipment of goods to markets, many other interpretations of this model can be made, some of which will be illustrated in this chapter.

Early work on the transportation problem was carried out in the 1940s by T. C. Koopmans, a young Dutch economist who had written a dissertation on a shipping problem arising in the Dutch merchant marine. He presented his results in the United States in 1947 and subsequently accepted a position at Yale University where he was to stay for the rest of his career. Koopmans soon became one of the leaders in the application of linear programming of economic problems, including *activity analysis* which we will discuss in Chapter 17. Koopmans later was one of two recipients of the 1975 Nobel Prize in economics.

The development of these new mathematical techniques went together with rapid advances in hardware and software computer technology. Very efficient computer codes capable of solving problems having millions of variables and thousands of constraints are now available for solving transportation problems.

We will use the following notation:

m = the number of *warehouses*

n = number of *markets*

a_i = the *supply* at warehouse i, that is, the number of units of the good held in warehouse i.

b_j = the *demand* at market j, that is, the number of units of the good demanded at market j.

c_{ij} = the per unit *cost* of transporting the good from warehouse i to market j.

x_{ij} = the *quantity* to be shipped from warehouse i to market j.

There are several obvious conditions that the shipping quantities x_{ij} must satisfy in order that they give a feasible solution. The first condition is that they be nonnegative,

$$x_{ij} \geq 0 \qquad \text{for } i = 1, \ldots, m, \quad \text{and} \quad j = 1, \ldots, n. \tag{1.1}$$

The second condition is

$$\sum_{j=1}^{n} x_{ij} \leq a_i \qquad \text{for } i = 1, \ldots, m \tag{1.2}$$

which limits the total shipments from warehouse i to be at most a_i, the supply at that warehouse. The third condition is

$$\sum_{i=1}^{m} x_{ij} \geq b_j \qquad \text{for } j = 1, \ldots, n \tag{1.3}$$

which requires that the amount shipped to market j should be at least b_j, the demand at that market.

We want to find a feasible solution to constraints (1.1), (1.2), and (1.3) that also minimizes the following *objective function* which is the total transportation cost:

$$\text{Minimize} \quad \sum_{i=1}^{m} \sum_{j=1}^{n} c_{ij} x_{ij} \tag{1.4}$$

To see this note that x_{ij} is the number of units, and c_{ij} is the per unit cost of shipping between i and j. It follows that $c_{ij}x_{ij}$ is the total cost of shipping from i to j. Finally, the sum of all these products $c_{ij}x_{ij}$ over $i = 1, \ldots, m$ and $j = 1, \ldots, n$ gives the total shipping cost of the solution x_{ij}.

We next investigate a necessary condition that must be satisfied in order to find feasible solutions x_{ij} that satisfy (1.1), (1.2), and (1.3). If constraint (1.2) is summed for $i = 1, \ldots, m$ and constraint (1.3) is summed for $j = 1, \ldots, n$ the following chain of inequalities is obtained:

$$\sum_{j=1}^{n} b_j \leq \sum_{i=1}^{m} \sum_{j=1}^{n} x_{ij} \geq \sum_{i=1}^{m} a_i \tag{1.5}$$

Note that the term on the left of (1.4) is the total demand while the term on the right represents total supply. Intuitively constraint (1.5), which requires the total demand to be at most as large as the total supply, is clearly a *necessary condition* that feasible solutions to (1.1), (1.2), and (1.3) exist.

To summarize, we collect conditions (1.1) through (1.4) to state the *primal transportation problem:*

$$\text{Minimize} \quad \sum_{i=1}^{m} \sum_{j=1}^{n} c_{ij} x_{ij}$$

$$\text{Subject to} \quad \sum_{j=1}^{n} x_{ij} \le a_i, \qquad \text{for } i = 1, \ldots, m$$

$$\sum_{i=1}^{m} x_{ij} \ge b_j, \qquad \text{for } j = 1, \ldots, n$$

$$x_{ij} \ge 0, \qquad \text{for } i = 1, \ldots, m, \quad j = 1, \ldots, n$$

This is called the "primal" transportation problem to distinguish it from a closely related problem, the dual transportation problem which will be discussed after we consider a numerical example.

Example. To illustrate, consider a simple distribution system having three warehouses and three markets. The available supplies and demands are:

Warehouse	*Supply*	*Market*	*Demand*
1	$a_1 = 70$	*1*	$b_1 = 70$
2	$a_2 = 100$	2	$b_2 = 90$
3	$a_3 = 30$	*3*	$b_3 = 40$

The unit shipping costs are (in dollars):

To Market

$$\begin{array}{c} \textit{From} \\ \textit{Warehouse} \end{array} \begin{array}{c} \\ 1 \\ 2 \\ 3 \end{array} \begin{array}{c} \begin{array}{ccc} 1 & 2 & 3 \end{array} \\ \begin{bmatrix} 5 & 3 & 5 \\ 15 & 6 & 10 \\ 2 & 11 & 12 \end{bmatrix} \end{array} = \begin{bmatrix} c_{11} & c_{12} & c_{13} \\ c_{21} & c_{22} & c_{23} \\ c_{31} & c_{32} & c_{33} \end{bmatrix}$$

Next, the information about the problem is organized in the *data box*:

	x_{11}	x_{12}	x_{13}	x_{21}	x_{22}	x_{23}	x_{31}	x_{32}	x_{33}	
u_1	1	1	1	0	0	0	0	0	0	≤ 70
u_2	0	0	0	1	1	1	0	0	0	≤ 100
u_3	0	0	0	0	0	0	1	1	1	≤ 30
v_1	1	0	0	1	0	0	1	0	0	≥ 70
v_2	0	1	0	0	1	0	0	1	0	≥ 90
v_3	0	0	1	0	0	1	0	0	1	≥ 40
	5	3	5	15	6	10	2	11	12	

Figure 1.1

Graph of the distribution network. Unit transportation costs are shown in the boxes.

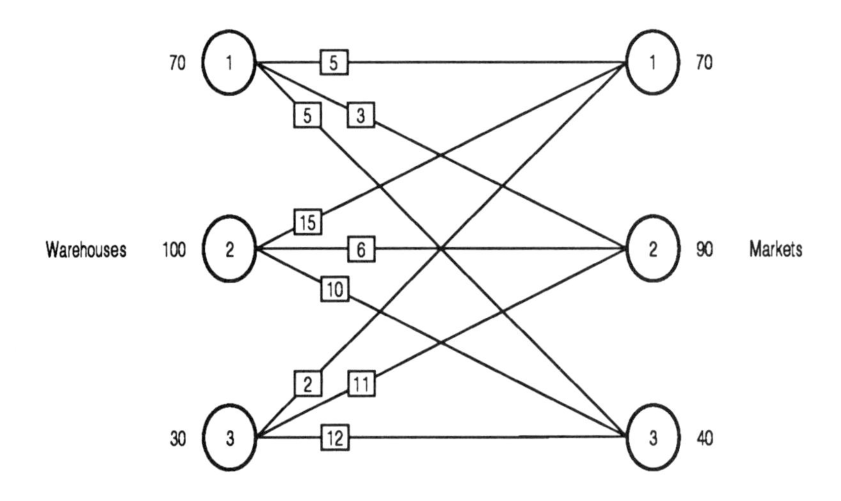

The unknown shipments, to be determined, are entered at the top of the data box. The supply constraints are entered in the first three rows with supply amounts on the right of the data box. The demand constraints are entered in rows 4 through 6 with the demand amounts on the right of the data box. Finally, the shipping costs on each link are listed along the bottom of the data box. Note that there are variables u_1, u_2, and u_3 and v_1, v_2, v_3 listed on the left of the data box. You may ignore them for the time being. They will be explained later in this section when we take up the dual problem.

The optimal solution to the distribution problem of Figure 1.1 can be found by using the GAMS program TRANS on page 303. If you run that program it will return the answer shown below:

i	j	x_{ij}^*
1	1	40
1	3	30
2	2	90
2	3	10
3	1	30

Total shipping cost = 1050

The graph of this solution is shown in Figure 1.2. The total cost of this solution can be calculated by multiplying the shipping amount on each arrow times the unit cost in the arrow, giving

Figure 1.2

Graph of optimal solution. Costs are in boxes, shipping amounts below connecting lines.

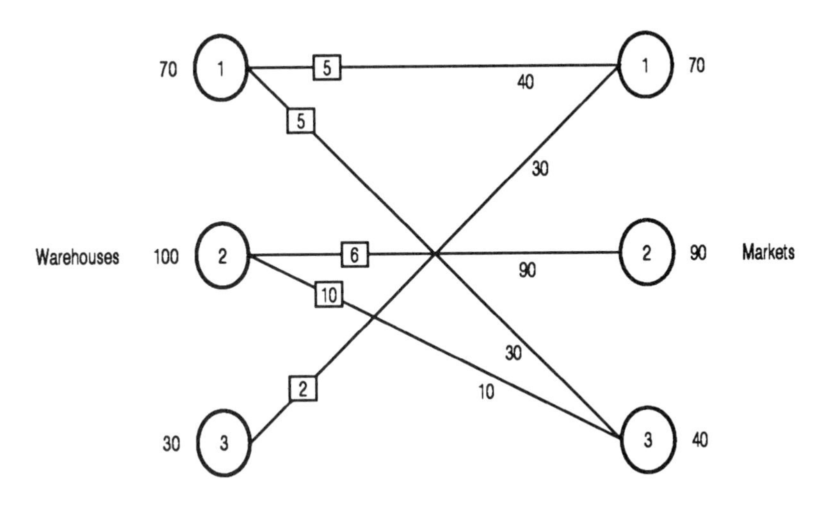

$$\text{Total Cost} = 40 \cdot 5 + 30 \cdot 5 + 90 \cdot 6 + 10 \cdot 10 + 30 \cdot 2$$
$$= 1{,}050$$

The total cost is also printed by your software program.

Dual Variables and the Dual Program

A linear program typically asks for an optimal allocation or utilization of one or more scarce commodities. A scarce commodity is a resource that is available in limited quantities or an output that must be supplied to customers. In the linear program such limitations are stated as constraints. For instance, in the transportation problem there is a given supply at each warehouse, and a given demand at each market.

The concept of scarcity is perhaps the most fundamental of all economic concepts. In an Elysian world, where no scarcity exists and all economic goods and services are freely available as required, there would be no need for a science of economics. As a matter of fact, an attractive way of defining economics is to say that it is the science that is concerned with how scarce means can be optimally combined in order to achieve desired ends.

The linear programming formulation of the distribution problem (as well as other problems) provides an evaluation of the scarcity of resources by means of *dual variables*. Each constraint in the problem has an associated dual variable, and optimal values of these dual variables are given by the computer program as part of the solution.

For a problem whose objective function is minimization, such as the transportation problem, dual variables associated with less than or equal to ($\leq$) constraints are *nonpositive* while dual variables associated with greater than or equal to ($\geq$) constraints are *nonnegative*. In the case of a maximization problem the signs of these dual variables are reversed. For either kind of problem, dual variables associated with equality ($=$) constraints (if any) can be of either sign, positive or negative. For a summary of these rules read the first five pages of Chapter 4.

In order to derive the conditions that these dual variables must satisfy, we assume that an optimal solution denoted by x_{ij}^* to the primal problem (1.1)–(1.4) is known. Rewriting (1.2) and (1.3) gives

$$\sum_{j=1}^{n} x_{ij}^* - a_i \leq 0 \tag{1.6}$$

$$\sum_{i=1}^{n} x_{ij}^* - b_j \geq 0 \tag{1.7}$$

Now define a dual variable u_i associated with each constraint (1.6); it is nonpositive. The optimal duals u_i^* should indicate the presence of slack in the constraints; hence we require that at the optimum they satisfy

$$u_i^*\left(\sum_{j=1}^{n} x_{ij}^* - a_i\right) = 0, \qquad u_i^* \leq 0, \text{ for all } i \tag{1.8}$$

In words these conditions say two things: (a) if an equation has slack, i.e.,

$$a_i - \sum_{j=1}^{n} x_{ij}^* > 0,$$

indicating that ith resource is available in excess, then $u_i^* = 0$. In this case we say that the supplies in warehouse i are *free goods*. Also, (b) if $u_i^* < 0$, that is, if the ith resource has an *imputed cost*, then

$$a_i - \sum_{j=1}^{n} x_{ij}^* = 0,$$

indicating that the ith resource is completely used up. Conditions (1.8) are called *complementary slackness conditions*.

Letting v_j for $j = 1, \ldots, n$ be the nonnegative dual variables associated with each constraint (1.7), we require that at the optimum they should satisfy the complementary slackness conditions

$$v_j^*\left(\sum_{i=1}^{m} x_{ij}^* - b_j\right) = 0, \qquad v_j^* \geq 0, \text{ for all } j \tag{1.9}$$

In words these conditions say two things: (a) if there is excess supply or slack in the jth market, signaled by the fact that $\sum_{i=1}^{m} x_{ij}^* - b_j > 0$, then $v_j^* = 0$ indicating that the imputed value of the good at market j is 0, again a free good. Otherwise, (b) if $v_j^* > 0$, that is, the good at the jth market has positive imputed value, then $\sum_{i=1}^{m} x_{ij}^* - b_j = 0$, meaning demand at market j is satisfied exactly.

Next, we require that the dual variables satisfy the following conditions, called the *dual constraints*,

$$u_i^* + v_j^* \leq c_{ij}, \qquad \text{for all } i \text{ and } j \tag{1.10}$$

There is one such dual constraint for each link (i,j) between warehouse i and market j. Constraint (1.10) states that the imputed appreciation in value, caused by shipping the good from warehouse i to market j, cannot exceed the unit shipping cost. Thus a hypothetical shipper who buys the good at a warehouse for a price equal to the dual variable there, and then transports it to a market and sell it at a price equal to the dual variable there, can never make a profit after paying the transportation costs. At best he can break even.

We also note that the dual variables satisfy the following dual complementary slackness conditions:

$$x_{ij}^*(c_{ij} - u_i^* - v_j^*) = 0, \qquad \text{for all } i \text{ and } j \tag{1.11}$$

In words these conditions say: (a) if a positive quantity is shipped from warehouse i to market j, then the imputed profit to the shipper is 0. Also (b) if $c_{ij} - u_i^* - v_j^* > 0$ so that the shipper would lose money on the link (i,j), then $x_{ij}^* = 0$, i.e., no shipment on that link will be made.

For a summary of the rules for deriving complementary slackness conditions, see pages 48–49 of Chapter 4.

Exhaustion of Costs Interpretation of Dual Variables

Notice that the dual variables establish an imputation scheme so that all the imputed values are associated with costs. The costs *exhaust* the values. Thus for each shipping link (i,j), the *imputed value* of one unit of the commodity at destination j is exactly exhausted by its imputed cost at the origin plus the unit transportation cost on the link. This is the *exhaustion of costs* interpretation of the optimal dual variables.

Later in this chapter we will give another interpretation of these dual variables.

Since the exhaustion of values occurs along each link, it follows that the total of all values delivered by the entire transportation system to the markets will be exhausted by total of the imputed costs at all the warehouses plus the total transportation costs. We can show this by rearranging the complementary slackness conditions (1.8), (1.9), and (1.11) and summing over all i and j, giving

$$\sum_{i=1}^{m} \sum_{j=1}^{n} c_{ij} x_{ij}^* = \sum_{i=1}^{m} a_i u_i^* + \sum_{j=1}^{n} b_j v_j^* \tag{1.12}$$

Total shipping costs = total imputed costs + total imputed values

This equation tells us that, at the optimum, the total net appreciation of value equals the total transportation cost.

We can deduce even more from (1.12) by making use of the dual constraints (1.10) which say that the appreciation of value along links not used in the optimal distribution scheme falls short of (or at most equals) the transportation cost on those links. Hence it is clear that the net appreciation of value that takes place with the optimal transportation scheme is, in fact, the maximum total net appreciation than can take place in any other

Figure 1.3

Imputed unit costs at warehouses and imputed unit values at markets. (Boxes show unit shipping costs.).

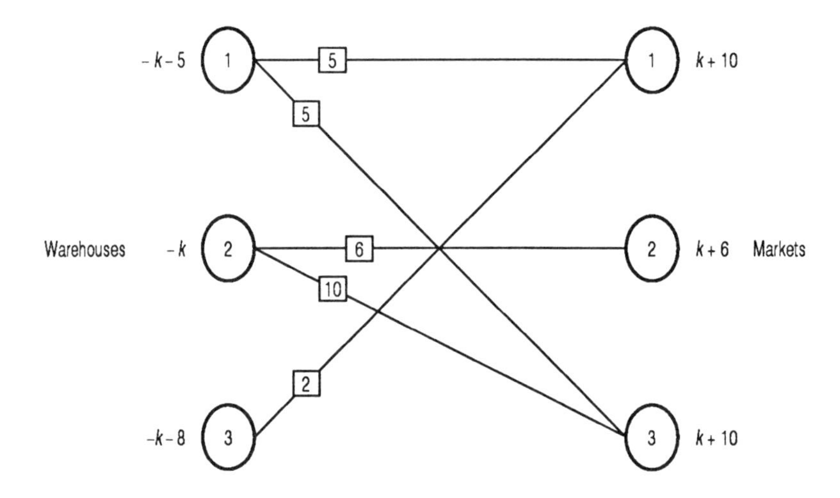

transportation scheme satisfying (1.10). The dual variables therefore solve the following *dual transportation problem:*

$$\text{Maximize} \quad \sum_{i=1}^{m} u_i a_i + \sum_{j=1}^{n} v_j b_j$$

$$\begin{aligned} \text{Subject to} \quad u_i + v_j &\le c_{ij}, & i &= 1, \ldots, m, \quad j = 1, \ldots, n \\ u_i &\le 0, & i &= 1, \ldots, m \\ v_j &\ge 0, & j &= 1, \ldots, n \end{aligned}$$

Example (continued). The dual transportation problem for the numerical example can also be seen in the data box shown on page 11 by observing that the dual constraint coefficients correspond to columns of the data box, and the objective function coefficients to the numbers on the right. (See Chapter 4, page 47.)

The computer software program prints the optimal solution to the dual transportation problem as

$$\begin{aligned} u_1^* &= -k - 5 \qquad & v_1^* &= k + 10 \\ u_2^* &= -k & v_2^* &= k + 6 \\ u_3^* &= -k - 8 & v_3^* &= k + 10 \end{aligned}$$

where k is some nonnegative number chosen by the computer. Because any nonnegative k is a correct choice it follows that there are infinitely many sets of optimal dual solutions. Note that the interpretation given above of the shipper buying at a price u_i^* and selling at a price v_j^* still is correct regardless of the value of k, because the k's cancel out.

The imputed unit costs and values along the transportation routes actually used in the primal solution are shown in Figure 1.3. Note that the imputed appreciation of value along any shipping route in actual use equals exactly the unit transportation costs on that route. On shipping routes *not used*, the imputed appreciation of value is less than (or equal to) the unit transportation cost.

Capacity Conditions

Transportation systems usually provide only limited capacity on given links. Thus a truck, an airplane, or a ship has limited capacity and only limited quantities of each are available (in the short run) for each link. Denote $\bar{x}_{ij}$ the maximal capacity along each link, so that any feasible transportation plan must satisfy the capacity condition

$$x_{ij} \leq \bar{x}_{ij} \qquad \text{for } i = 1, \ldots, m, \quad j = 1, \ldots, n \tag{1.13}$$

The complete *capacitated transportation problem* then is

$$\begin{aligned}
\text{Minimize} \quad & \sum_{i=1}^{m} \sum_{j=1}^{n} c_{ij} x_{ij} \\
\text{Subject to} \quad & \sum_{j=1}^{m} x_{ij} \leq a_i \qquad \text{for } i = 1, \ldots, m \\
& \sum_{i=1}^{n} x_{ij} \geq b_j \qquad \text{for } j = 1, \ldots, n \\
& x_{ij} \leq \bar{x}_{ij} \qquad \text{for } i = 1, \ldots, m, \quad j = 1, \ldots, n \\
& x_{ij} \geq 0
\end{aligned} \tag{1.14}$$

Because of the additional constraints the dual problem must be changed as well. Define a dual variable w_{ij} corresponding to each capacity constraint (1.13). Its interpretation is an imputed cost, or surcharge, that is assessed on shipments along link (i,j). The complementary slackness conditions w_{ij}^* must satisfy are

$$w_{ij}^*(\bar{x}_{ij} - x_{ij}^*) = 0, \qquad w_{ij}^* \leq 0 \tag{1.15}$$

for $i = 1, \ldots, m$ and $j = 1, \ldots, n$. Condition (1.15) asserts two things: (a) if $\bar{x}_{ij} - x_{ij}^* > 0$, that is, if route (i,j) has surplus capacity, then the imputed surcharge w_{ij} must be 0 which makes unused transportation vehicles on that route free goods; and (b), if $w_{ij}^* < 0$, that is there is a surcharge on the use of link (i,j), then $x_{ij}^* = \bar{x}_{ij}$, so that all the capacity on that link is used.

The capacitated dual problem is then

$$\begin{aligned}
\text{Maximize} \quad & \sum_{i=1}^{m} u_i a_i + \sum_{j=1}^{n} v_j b_j + \sum_{i=1}^{m} \sum_{j=1}^{n} w_{ij} \bar{x}_{ij} \\
\text{Subject to} \quad & u_i + v_j + w_{ij} \leq c_{ij} \\
& u_i, w_{ij} \leq 0, \; v_j \geq 0 \qquad \text{for } i = 1, \ldots, m, \quad j = 1, \ldots, n
\end{aligned} \tag{1.16}$$

The new dual constraints require the imputed appreciation $u_i + v_j$ along link (i,j) plus the surcharge w_{ij} to not exceed the unit transportation charges c_{ij}. The mythical shipper then pays $u_i + w_{ij}$ when he buys one unit of good at warehouse i, and collects v_j when he delivers it to market j. Again the imputed costs exactly exhaust the imputed value, so that the shipper just breaks even.

Example (continued). Let us return to the previous numerical example and add capacity upper bound constraints. The values of $\bar{x}_{ij}$ are given in (1.17)

$$\begin{bmatrix} 40 & 40 & 40 \\ 35 & 35 & 35 \\ 50 & 50 & 50 \end{bmatrix} = \begin{bmatrix} \bar{x}_{11} & \bar{x}_{12} & \bar{x}_{13} \\ \bar{x}_{21} & \bar{x}_{22} & \bar{x}_{23} \\ \bar{x}_{31} & \bar{x}_{32} & \bar{x}_{33} \end{bmatrix} \tag{1.17}$$

Notice that the previous optimal shipping pattern is no longer feasible because it requires $x_{22}^* = 90$ which violates the new upper bound constraint $x_{22} \leq \bar{x}_{22} = 35$.

The program CAPTRANS on page 304 is TRANS modified to include upper bounds. Solving the problem again using CAPTRANS gives the optimal shipping pattern shown below. Note that all but one of the links has some quantity shipped on that link. Also three of the links, $(1,2)$, $(2,2)$, and $(2,3)$, are at capacity. Observe that the total shipping cost has increased to 1,475.

i	j	x_{ij}^*
1	1	25
1	2	40
1	3	5
2	1	30
2	2	35
2	3	35
3	1	15
3	2	15

Total shipping cost = 1,475

The optimal dual solution has also changed as shown below. Notice that surcharges of 11, 18, and 5 are assessed for the use of routes $(1,2)$, $(2,2)$ and $(2,3)$, respectively. All dual variables not shown are zero.

$$u_1^* = -k - 10 \qquad v_1^* = k + 15 \qquad w_{12}^* = -11$$
$$u_2^* = -k \qquad v_2^* = k + 24 \qquad w_{22}^* = -18$$
$$u_3^* = -k - 13 \qquad v_3^* = k + 15 \qquad w_{23}^* = -5$$

If we set $k = 0$, the appreciation of value along link $(1,2)$ is $u_1^* + v_2^* + w_{12}^* = -10 + 24 - 11$ which exactly equals the unit transportation cost of 3. Along link $(2,3)$ the appreciation is $u_2^* + v_3^* + w_{23}^* = 0 + 15 - 5 = 10 = c_{23}$.

Managerial Interpretation of Dual Variables

Suppose the manufacturer who makes and distributes the product also owns the transportation facilities (e.g., a fleet of trucks). Looking at the above numerical solution he observes that the capacity of link (2,2) is completely used up and also that there is a unit surcharge of \$18 charged to send goods on this link. He asks the question: "What if I add one unit of capacity to link (2,2); by how much will my total shipping costs be reduced?" It is easy to make this change, replacing $\bar{x}_{22} = 35$ by $\bar{x}_{22} = 36$, and re-solve the problem; you will be asked to do this in Exercise 3. You will find that the total shipping cost of the solution to the new problem is $1457 = 1475 - 18$, so that the value of the dual variable (-18) associated with the capacity constraint correctly predicts the amount total costs will decrease if that constraint is relaxed by 1, keeping all other constraints the same. By comparing the new and the old solutions it is possible to see exactly how these savings are achieved.

The use of dual variables to give answers to "What if . . . " questions gives what we will call the *managerial interpretation of dual variables*. It should be noted that the predicted change will hold only for a *sufficiently small* (perhaps 0) change in the right hand side of the constraint.

In this chapter we have found two interesting economic interpretations for dual variables, namely, the exhaustion of costs, and the managerial interpretations. In later chapters we will see still other economic interpretations for these quantities.

Exercises

1. For the optimal primal and dual solutions to the numerical example on page 11,
   (a) Verify that the complementary slackness conditions (1.8) and (1.9) hold.
   (b) Verify that the complementary slackness conditions (1.11) hold.
   (c) Verify that the exhaustion of values condition (1.12) holds.
2. Assume $k = 0$, and verify the fact that shipping links in Figure 1.1 that are not used in the optimal solution shown in Figure 1.2 are not profitable.
3. Change the capacities in (1.17) as shown below and re-solve the capacitated transportation problem. Does the dual variable of the capacity constraint predict the new total cost correctly? Why or why not?
   (a) Change $\bar{x}_{22}$ from 35 to 36.
   (b) Change $\bar{x}_{11}$ from 40 to 41 (after restoring $\bar{x}_{22}$ to 35).
4. One of the earliest descriptions of a transportation problem is due to a French mathematician Gaspard Monge, in 1781. He was employed by Napolean in the construction of military fortifications and he formulated the following "cut and fill" problem: Suppose there are m cut locations that have excess amounts of dirt $a_1, \ldots, a_m$, and there are n fill locations that need dirt in amounts $b_1, \ldots, b_n$. Let c_{ij} be the distance from cut i to fill j. How can the dirt be transported from the cuts to the fills with least effort? (Civil engineers today encounter the same problem in their construction projects.)
   (a) Show that this is a transportation problem.

(b) Interpret the dual variables for the optimal solution to such a problem.

(c) Solve the cut and fill problem with the following data:

	Fills			
Cuts	7	10	6	20
	4	8	11	30
	12	28	10	

(d) Do the same for the following problem:

	Fills			
Cuts	13	26	13	22
	28	29	11	10
	22	21	12	15
	33	27	23	12
	34	18	33	11
	21	22	27	

5. An *assignment problem* is a square $(n \times n)$ transportation problem all of whose supplies and demands are one. The classical interpretation for this problem is that of assigning n people to n jobs, where c_{ij} is the cost of assigning person i to job j. Solve the following two assignment problems, and interpret the solutions.

(a)

	Purchasing	*Sales*	*Advertising*	*Receiving*
Sally	13	9	12	10
Bill	9	12	13	8
John	5	9	8	9
Dorothy	11	13	5	11

(Each person can fill one job and each job needs one person.)

(b)

	Lathe	*Milling Machine*	*Drill Press*	*Router*	*Shaper*
Henry	26	15	21	13	22
June	11	19	24	34	17
George	26	33	19	32	29
Mary	33	18	28	26	21
Jim	18	13	28	23	20

(Each operator can run one machine and each machine needs one operator.)

6. A company has eight sales regions in a state, A, B, C, D, E, F, G, H to which it wishes to assign eight salespeople. It calculates the cost, c_{ik}, of assigning salesman i to sales region k which includes travel cost, meals and accommodations as shown in the table below. What is the minimum cost way of making the assignment of salespeople to sales territories?

Territories

People	*A*	*B*	*C*	*D*	*E*	*F*	*G*	*H*
1	4	12	16	13	14	11	9	3
2	5	17	13	10	17	7	17	13
3	8	5	14	11	9	3	14	10
4	11	41	12	6	9	4	10	3
5	11	17	7	12	17	8	16	14
6	7	9	13	6	14	13	17	16
7	10	5	10	12	7	6	11	15
8	4	5	13	10	16	12	11	13

7. A company has four manufacturing locations for a given product and six major markets. Each manufacturing center has different costs, and each market has different prices for the product. In addition the distances between manufacturing locations and markets varies and so does the transportation cost. The company has calculated the net profit, c_{ij}, of producing the good at location i and selling it in market j. These net profit figures, together with the maximum manufacturing capability at each location and demand at each market are shown in the table below.

Markets

Plants	*1*	*2*	*3*	*4*	*5*	*6*	
1	29	51	59	54	56	27	1200
2	44	43	29	63	53	46	1800
3	63	37	63	62	46	47	1100
4	51	53	54	51	43	38	1900
	1000	1200	700	1500	500	1100	

(a) What is the optimal way for the company to produce and sell its product? [*Hint:* Remember that the company is a profit maximizer.]

(b) What is the interpretation of the dual variables?

(c) Which plant (if any) would you recommend expanding?

(d) Which plant (if any) would you recommend reducing in size?

(e) Which sales territory is the most profitable?

(f) Which sales territory is the least profitable?

2

Discrete Auctions

In the retail marketing sector of the United States economy, sellers state selling prices for their goods and buyers either buy at that price or don't buy. In the rest of the economy goods are frequently exchanged by means of auctions. There are many different kinds of auctions. We shall consider only one kind, a *sealed bid auction*, which can be described as follows: The sellers arrive at the auction building with the objects (such as farm animals, paintings, etc.) that they wish to sell. Each buyer examines each object and writes on a piece of paper the amount he would be willing to pay for that object. These bids are placed in an envelope and handed to the auctioneer. When all bids have been received the auctioneer decides who the buyer of each object shall be and the price which the buyer must pay to the seller for the object.

In this chapter a solution method for the auction model just described is given, which makes use of a linear programming problem to provide an optimal way of exchanging the objects. We assume that there are m sellers; the amounts they have to sell are

$$a_i > 0 \qquad \text{for } i = 1, 2, \ldots, m \tag{2.1}$$

Similarly there are n buyers who wish to buy amounts

$$b_j > 0 \qquad \text{for } j = 1, 2, \ldots, n \tag{2.2}$$

Each seller brings his or her own brand of products to the auction, say cattle or mink fur. This brand may show typical characteristics of the producer. The buyers can easily identify the origin of each unit put up for auction, but all units offered for sale by each single seller are identical. The good is thus homogeneous for each individual seller, but it is in general heterogeneous among sellers.

Although auctions are most common for certain specific commodities, such as agricultural products, works of art, treasury bonds, etc., the auction model to be developed here actually has theoretical interest that transcends these applications. It throws considerable light on the marketing of standard brand products sold in supermarkets. Different brands compete in design and consumer appeal just as much as in price. The market for breakfast cereal, or for toothbrushes, or even for butter and margarine, consists of a large number of different brands. In the real world, a "market" is made up of many heterogeneous goods. In order to understand how markets function, we need to understand how prices are formed for heterogeneous goods.

Let buyer j make a sealed bid of

$$c_{ij} \geq 0 \tag{2.3}$$

(dollars), which is the maximum amount j is willing to pay for one unit of seller i's goods. Suppose the result of the auction indicates that seller i sells

$$x_{ij} \geq 0 \tag{2.4}$$

units to buyer j at a *price* of

$$u_i \geq 0 \tag{2.5}$$

dollars. Note that if x_{ij} units are exchanged between seller i and buyer j, the total bid value is $c_{ij}x_{ij}$ while the total cost is $u_i x_{ij}$. We now discuss how prices u_i and amounts x_{ij} exchanged can be determined.

The actual price u_i which seller i receives, which is related to but not necessarily the same as the individual buyers' sealed bids $c_{i1}, \ldots, c_{in}$, is determined by the rules of the auction and/or the auctioneer. If buyer j actually buys from seller i at price u_i then the quantity

$$v_j = c_{ij} - u_i \tag{2.6}$$

is defined to be buyer j's *surplus*. Because c_{ij} was the maximum amount that buyer j was willing to pay, it follows that we should require

$$v_j \geq 0 \tag{2.7}$$

Is it possible to determine exchanges of goods, a set of actual seller's prices, and hence actual buyer's surplus, satisfying (2.3) through (2.7) so that all buyers and sellers are satisfied with the outcome? Clearly both groups must feel that they have been treated fairly in order to be satisfied. We list some fairness requirements below:

Seller i	*Buyer j*
(i) Doesn't sell more than a_i	(i) Doesn't buy more than b_j
(ii) Gets the same price, u_i, (≥ 0), for each unit sold	(ii) Gets the same surplus, v_j, (≥ 0), for each unit bought
(iii) If $u_i > 0$, then he sells all a_i units	(iii) If $v_j > 0$, then he buys all b_j units
(iv) If he doesn't sell all a_i units, then $u_i = 0$	(iv) If he doesn't buy all b_j units, then $v_j = 0$

Clearly condition (i) for the seller i is reasonable because he made the decision to bring to the auction only those a_i units that he wanted to sell. Condition (i) for the buyer can be justified similarly. Condition (ii) for the seller is needed because if he were required to sell identical units of his good at two different prices, he would prefer withholding the sale to the lower bidder and make it instead to the higher bidder. Similarly, condition (ii) for the buyer is needed, for otherwise, after the auction he would try to exchange goods on which his surplus was low for goods giving him a larger surplus. Conditions (iii) and (iv) for the seller simply states that goods left unsold at the end of the auction are free; to have a positive price they must be sufficiently in demand that all are bought. (This condition will be modified later in this chapter to permit the seller to have reservation prices.) Conditions (iii) and (iv) for the buyer are similar; in order for buyer j to have a positive surplus his bids must be high enough that his demands are completely fulfilled. Otherwise his surplus is zero.

Several questions now present themselves. Are conditions (2.4) through (2.7) and conditions (i) through (iv) for buyers and sellers enough to determine a set of seller prices and buyer surpluses? Is this solution unique? How can it be calculated?

In order to answer these questions, we present a linear programming problem and its dual problem which give answers x_{ij}, u_i and v_j satisfying all of these conditions.

$$\begin{aligned} &\text{Maximize} && \sum_{i=1}^{m}\sum_{j=1}^{n} c_{ij}x_{ij} \\ &\text{Subject to} && \sum_{j=1}^{n} x_{ij} \le a_i \qquad \text{for } i = 1, \ldots, m \\ &&& \sum_{i=1}^{m} x_{ij} \le b_j \qquad \text{for } j = 1, \ldots, n \\ &&& x_{ij} \ge 0 \qquad \text{for } i = 1, \ldots, m, \quad j = 1, \ldots, n \end{aligned} \tag{2.8}$$

Note that the nonnegativity condition on x_{ij} is (2.4). Also the first constraint states condition (i) for the seller i, and the second constraint states condition (i) for the buyer j.

The objective function of (2.8) requires the exchange should be made so that the total bid value of all goods exchanged should be maximized. One way of interpreting this objective is that it provides an "invisible hand" that causes the goods for sale to go to as many of the highest bidders as possible. Another way of looking at it is that the maximand is an *economic potential function* that just happens to peak at the auction outcome having the desired properties. The mathematical developments to follow will demonstrate that this in fact occurs.

Since (2.8) is a linear program it possesses a dual program. Let u_i be dual variables associated with the first set of constraints in (2.8) and let v_j be dual variables associated with the second set. Their optimal values u_i^* and v_j^* will turn out to be the sellers' prices (2.5) and buyers' surpluses (2.6), respectively. When optimal solutions x_{ij}^*, u_i^*, and v_j^* are found for both the primal and dual problems, the following primal complementary slackness conditions hold:

$$\sum_{j=1}^{n} x_{ij}^* - a_i \le 0, \qquad u_i^* \ge 0, \qquad u_i^*\left(\sum_{j=1}^{n} x_{ij}^* - a_i\right) = 0 \qquad \text{for } i = 1, \ldots, m \tag{2.9}$$

$$\sum_{i=1}^{m} x_{ij}^* - b_j \le 0, \qquad v_j^* \ge 0, \qquad v_j^*\left(\sum_{i=1}^{m} x_{ij}^* - b_j\right) = 0 \qquad \text{for } j = 1, \ldots, n \tag{2.10}$$

Observe that the first inequality in (2.9) is also the first constraint in (2.8). Also recall that condition (i) in the first column of list of fairness requirements (page 24) is that the ith seller sells no more than a_i units. The second inequality in (2.8) is that his price is nonnegative and independent of j which is (ii) in the list of fairness requirements. The third assertion in (2.9) has two parts: if $u_i^* > 0$ then seller i sells all of his goods which is condition (iii) in the list; and, if the ith seller does not sell all of his goods, then his price is zero which is condition (iv) in the list. Similar remarks hold for the relationship between (2.10) and the column labeled buyer j in the list of the fairness requirements.

The dual variables also satisfy the dual constraints

$$u_i + v_j \geq c_{ij} \qquad \text{for } i = 1, \ldots, m \quad \text{and} \quad j = 1, \ldots, n \tag{2.11}$$

Since the variable x_{ij} acts as a "dual variable" to these constraints we also have the following dual complementary slackness conditions at the optimum:

$$u_i^* + v_j^* - c_{ij} \geq 0, \qquad x_{ij}^* \geq 0, \qquad x_{ij}^*(u_i^* + v_j^* - c_{ij}) = 0 \tag{2.12}$$
$$\text{for } i = 1, \ldots, m \quad \text{and} \quad j = 1, \ldots, n$$

In words, these conditions say: If a positive transaction $x_{ij}^* > 0$ occurs from seller i to buyer j, then the market price of seller i plus the surplus of buyer j exactly equal the bid c_{ij}. But if the bid price by buyer j is short of the sum of the market price for seller i's goods plus buyer j's surplus, then no transaction takes place between seller i and buyer j.

Since these interpretations hold for individual transactions, they hold for the sums of all transactions. If we multiply out the equality in (2.12) and sum over all i and j we obtain

$$\sum_{i=1}^{m} \sum_{j=1}^{n} c_{ij} x_{ij}^* = \sum_{i=1}^{m} \sum_{j=1}^{n} u_i^* x_{ij}^* + \sum_{i=1}^{m} \sum_{j=1}^{n} v_j^* x_{ij}^* \tag{2.13}$$

Total value of all bids = Total seller receipts + Total buyer surpluses

which shows how the total bid value is divided among buyers and sellers. Note that, in this case, all of the value is distributed.

Example. Consider an auction of tulip bulbs in Amsterdam. There are two growers who have the following quantities of tulip bulbs available:

grower 1	100 cases
grower 2	140 cases

Also, there are four buyers who have the following demands for tulip bulbs:

buyer 1	30 cases
buyer 2	60 cases
buyer 3	80 cases
buyer 4	70 cases

After examining the goods available the buyers submit the following sealed bids in guldens to the auctioneer:

		buyer 1	buyer 2	buyer 3	buyer 4
grower	1	22	18	21	25
grower	2	25	23	22	20

The data box of the resulting linear program is displayed below.

	x_{11}	x_{12}	x_{13}	x_{14}	x_{21}	x_{22}	x_{23}	x_{24}	
u_1	1	1	1	1	0	0	0	0	≤ 100
u_2	0	0	0	0	1	1	1	1	≤ 140
v_1	1	0	0	0	1	0	0	0	≤ 30
v_2	0	1	0	0	0	1	0	0	≤ 60
v_3	0	0	1	0	0	0	1	0	≤ 80
v_4	0	0	0	1	0	0	0	1	≤ 70
	22	18	21	25	25	23	22	20	

The optimal solution, obtained by solving the GAMS program TULIP on page 305, is shown below.

grower i	buyer j	x_{ij}^*
1	3	30
1	4	70
2	1	30
2	2	60
2	3	50

Total bid value of sales = 5,610

The computer output also contains a dual solution of the form shown below. Note that these optimal solutions involve an arbitrary constant k, which must satisfy $0 \leq k \leq 21$ to keep all the prices and surpluses nonnegative. Your computer will supply a value for k, but any other value in the required range is equally good.

growers' prices	sellers' surpluses
$u_1^* = 21 - k$	$v_1^* = 3 + k$
$u_2^* = 22 - k$	$v_2^* = 1 + k$
	$v_3^* = 0 + k$
	$v_4^* = 4 + k$

The choice of k in an actual situation depends on other factors such as: whether sellers have reservation prices (to be discussed next); whether the auction is organized by the buyers or by the sellers; whether there are competing auctions or national markets where other sales or purchases can be made; whether total supply is greater or lesser than total demand; and so on.

You will note that we chose in this example to have the total number of cases of tulips offered for sale be exactly equal to the total number of cases demanded. It is not necessary that this always be true. Several of the exercises involve situations where the total supply is greater than or less than total demand.

Reservation Prices

Suppose we choose $k = 21$ in the numerical example. Then the grower prices and buyer surpluses are:

growers' prices	*buyers' surpluses*
$u_1^* = 0$	$v_1^* = 24$
$u_2^* = 1$	$v_2^* = 22$
	$v_3^* = 21$
	$v_4^* = 25$

Although the buyers might be pleased with this solution which gives them very large surpluses, certainly grower 1 would be very unhappy to get 0 as a price. And grower 2 would be nearly as unhappy with his price of 1.

A common feature in real-life auctions is that each seller specifies in advance a *reservation price*, being the lowest price at which that seller is willing to sell. If the price set by the auctioneer is higher than the reservation price, a seller will obviously sell the entire amount of the commodity that he brought to the market. But if the market price turns out to equal the reservation price, it may happen that some portion of the supply that he brought to the market remains unsold.

Disregarding transaction costs charged by the auctioneer, the outcome then is the same as what would have happened had the seller "sold the goods to himself" at the reservation price. We shall make use of this observation when we turn to the mathematical formulation in a moment.

The phenomenon of a reservation price has considerable theoretical interest, because it is an example of *price rigidity* that can cause the market formation to fail to reach an equilibrium in which the market clears and all goods are sold. The unsold quantity that the prospective seller brings back home from the auction is *excess supply* that no buyer wanted to buy at the quoted price.

The concept of a reservation price has been much debated by economists in relation to the analysis of labor markets and unemployment. For example, a reservation wage rate is the lowest wage for which a worker is willing to enter into employment.

Labor is of course not sold at auctions, but the mathematical model that we have developed clearly still goes a long way toward explaining the formation of wage rates and employment in the labor market. Labor is a heterogeneous good and workers may be characterized in economic terms by their occupation, their education and training, etc. Worker i seeking employment may contact various potential employers j and inquire about the highest wage c_{ij} that they would be willing to offer. If no offer c_{ij}, equals or exceeds the worker's reservation wage rate, then he will withdraw from the labor market and will be unemployed. Similarly a worker who currently has a low paying job may seek one with better pay, while using his or her current wage rate as a reservation wage.

In order to state the auction model in which sellers have reservation prices, we use the extended mathematical notation below:

m = the number of sellers

n = the number of buyers

a_i = the quantity brought to the market by seller i

b_j = the demand by buyer j

c_{ij} = the amount bid by buyer j on one unit of the goods brought to the market by seller i

π_i = the reservation price stipulated by seller i

x_{ij} = the quantity actually bought by buyer j from seller i

y_i = unsold quantity brought back home from the market place by seller i (his excess supply)

We may then formulate the model as the linear program in (2.14)

$$\text{Maximize} \quad \sum_{i=1}^{m} \sum_{j=1}^{n} c_{ij} x_{ij} + \sum_{i=1}^{m} \pi_i y_i \tag{2.14}$$

$$\begin{aligned} \text{Subject to} \quad & \sum_{j=1}^{n} x_{ij} + y_i = a_i, \qquad i = 1, 2, \ldots, m \\ & \sum_{i=1}^{n} x_{ij} \le b_j, \qquad j = 1, 2, \ldots, n \\ & x_{ij} \ge 0, \quad y_i \ge 0, \qquad i = 1, 2, \ldots, m, \quad j = 1, 2, \ldots, n \end{aligned}$$

The maximand represents the total bid value of all transactions that actually take place at the auction, as before. The expression now includes the value of all unsold goods y_i that the prospective sellers buy back for themselves at the reservation prices, π_i. The constraints have also the same meaning as before. Specifically, the first set of constraints states that the total sales of seller i, including the wares that he buys back for himself at the reservation price, cannot exceed (actually, must equal) his total supply. The second set of constraints asserts that buyers do not buy more than their stated demands.

The dual constraints are:

$$u_i^* + v_j^* \ge c_{ij} \qquad \text{for } i = 1, \ldots, m, \quad j = 1, \ldots, n \tag{2.15}$$

$$u_i^* \ge \pi_i \qquad \text{for } i = 1, \ldots, m \tag{2.16}$$

We are already familiar with the constraints in (2.15). The constraints in (2.16) assert that each seller will not accept less than the stated reservation price. The corresponding complementary slackness condition is

$$(u_i^* - \pi_i) y_i^* = 0 \qquad \text{for } i = 1, \ldots, m \tag{2.17}$$

Condition (2.17) says two things: (a) if $y_i^* > 0$, that is, if seller i buys back a positive amount of his own good, then his selling price equals his reservation price; and (b) if his selling price exceeds his reservation price, then $y_i^* = 0$ so that he sells everything he brought to the auction.

Example (continued). We return to the tulip bulb auction with the assumption that the reservation prices of growers 1 and 2 are 22 and 23 guldens, respectively. The new data box now is:

	x_{11}	x_{12}	x_{13}	x_{14}	x_{21}	x_{22}	x_{23}	x_{24}	y_1	y_2	
u_1	1	1	1	1					1		$= 100$
u_2					1	1	1	1		1	$= 140$
v_1	1				1						≤ 30
v_2		1				1					≤ 60
v_3			1				1				≤ 80
v_4				1				1			≤ 70
	22	18	21	25	25	23	22	20	22	23	

The optimal solution obtained by solving the GAMS program RESERVE on page 305 is shown below.

grower i	*buyer j*	x^*_{ij}	y^*_1	y^*_2
1	4	70	30	
2	1	30		50
2	2	60		

Total value of sales $= 5{,}690$

Note that neither grower is able to sell all of his goods to the buyers, since grower 1 returns home with 30 unsold cases, and grower 2 returns home with 50 unsold cases. (The total value of sales includes the value of these unsold cases.) Because both y_1 and y_2 are positive we know that the selling prices are equal to the growers reservation bids.

The optimal dual solution with reservation prices is shown below.

growers' prices	*buyers' surpluses*
$u_1{}^* = 22$	$v_1{}^* = 2$
$u_2{}^* = 23$	$v_2{}^* = 0$
	$v_3{}^* = 0$
	$v_4{}^* = 3$

Notice now the prices are completely determined by the auction mechanism because the reservation prices of the growers are relatively high. In the exercises you will be asked to solve the same problem with other reservation prices. You will see that when reservation prices are sufficiently low, a degree of arbitrariness in prices again becomes possible.

Exercises

1. Show that in the tulip auction with reservation prices of 22 and 23 for the growers the following in an alternative optimal solution:

grower i	*buyer j*	x^*_{ij}	y^*_1	y^*_2
1	4	70	30	
2	1	30		0
2	2	60		
2	3	50		

Show that the objective function is unchanged.

2. Rework the tulip auction with reservation prices of 22 for both growers. Show that grower 2 can now sell all of his tulips, but grower 1 must buy back 30 cases.

3. Rework the tulip auction with reservation prices 21 and 23 for growers 1 and 2, respectively. Show that grower 1 can sell all of his tulips but grower 2 must buy back 50 cases.

4. If both growers have reservation prices of 20 show that now there is a range of prices for both growers that satisfy all of the auction solution conditions.

5. A cattle auction having two large sellers, *A* and *B* is to be conducted by sealed bids instead of the usual auctioneer method. The two sellers have the following cattle to sell:

   A has 200 head of cattle
   B has 300 head of cattle

   There are three prospective buyers *C*, *D*, and *E* whose demands are:

   C wants 225 head
   D wants 125 head
   E wants 150 head.

   The buyers examine the cattle of each seller and submit the following sealed bids in dollars/head.

	C	*D*	*E*
A	1,000	800	1,500
B	1,200	900	1,300

   None of the sellers is willing to sell at a price less than $900/head.

   (a) Construct a linear programming model that can be used to determine the optimal solution.

   (b) Solve the problem.

   (c) What are the optimal prices for each seller?

   (d) What are the optimal buyer surpluses?

6. A certain academic department has nine students each of whom is trying to take one of three popular electives. Each elective has exactly three openings. In order to prevent quarrels the department head has instituted a sealed bid auction in which each of the students is given 100 points and allowed to allocate them in any way to bid for the courses. The bidding gave the following data:

		Students									
		1	*2*	*3*	*4*	*5*	*6*	*7*	*8*	*9*	
	A	100	10	33	20	50	16	100	5	15	3
Course	*B*	0	80	33	40	20	32	0	90	5	3
	C	0	10	34	40	30	52	0	5	80	3
		1	1	1	1	1	1	1	1	1	

(a) Set up and solve the problem.

(b) Interpret the primal solutions.

(c) What is the "price" of each course.

(d) What is the "surplus" of each student.

7. Describe an auction mechanism for solving another similar problem such as: choice of vacation weeks; choice of group members; choice of work schedules; etc.

3

A Prototype Partial Equilibrium System

The neoclassical school of economics was developed around the turn of the century in an effort to understand the formation of competitive markets through the interactions of consumers and producers. The building blocks of this school were the theory of consumer demand, the theory of production, and the notion of competitive equilibrium.

The equilibrium models that we shall encounter in this book are all *partial* in that they relate only to one or a few sectors of the economy. In the present chapter we shall take a look at a prototype model of the production, the distribution and demand for one single product. Production occurs at several different plants; the product is thereupon shipped from the plants to a number of different retail outlets. The cost function at each plant will be assumed to be given and known. The transportation from plants to retail outlets will be modeled through a standard transportation model (Chapter 1). Finally, on the demand side, we simply assume fixed and given demands at each location (vertical demand curves). So, what we propose to do is to bring together a set of cost functions and a transportation model, and to solve for the resulting equilibrium pattern of supply, distribution and equilibrium prices.

Rather than spelling out in detail the institutional characteristics of the market formation (such as those in the auction model discussed in the preceding chapter) we shall from now on simply deal with cases where each local market involves the transaction of homogeneous product and that competitive forces see to it that the market "clears." The conventional assumption is that there is present in each market an "Edgeworth auctioneer" (after the English economist F. Y. Edgeworth, whose main work, *Mathematical Physics*, was published in 1881) who sets prices to clear the markets.

What does it mean to say that a market "clears?" The most immediate interpretation simply is that the total quantity demanded equals the total quantity supplied, so that the market clearing condition becomes satisfied as an equality. The neoclassical system originally expounded by L. Walras ((in his *Eléments d'Économie Politique Pure*, definitive edition 1900) consisted of a system of equations, with one equation for each market.

With the advent, around 1930, of modern mathematical economics, a more sophisticated view of the clearing condition took hold, which suggested that the market clearing relation should be written as an *inequality*, stating that the total demand is less than or equal to the total supply. In the case that a positive market price ensues, the equality sign will hold. But, it may also occur that total demand is less than total supply. In that case, due to the complementary slackness condition, the market price of the commodity must be zero, and the commodity is a "free good."

The conditions just spelled out can be brought together in the mathematical conditions

$$\text{demand} \leq \text{supply} \tag{3.1a}$$

$$\text{price (supply} - \text{demand)} = 0 \tag{3.1b}$$

We have already encountered the inequality approach to market clearing in the formulation of the transportation model (Chapter 1). There were market relations of type (3.1a) at each supply origin, stating that the shipments from the origin could not exceed its local supply. And there was a complementary slackness condition of type (3.1b) at each origin, tying the imputed price (the dual variable at the origin) to the gap between supply and total shipments. Similarly, there were market relations of type (3.1a) at each demand destination, stating that the shipments in to each destination must suffice to cover the local demand there. And there were complementary slackness condition of type (3.1b) at each destination, tying the imputed price (the dual variable at each destination) to the gap between the total shipments to the destination.

The prototype equilibrium system to follow can be seen as a generalization of the transportation model (it is a "generalized transportation model") involving "price sensitive" (i.e., price dependent) supply quantities at each origin rather than fixed and given supplies. As we shall see, the mathematical programming model to be used involves *non-linear programming* rather than just linear programming. At the point of optimality, there will still be conditions of type (3.1a) and (3.1b) at each origin and at each destination, stating that the markets at all plants and the markets at all retail outlets will all be cleared.

We begin the outline of the model by discussing the cost relationships and supply at each plant (each origin). For simplicity, the supply curve at each plant is assumed to be linear (see Figure 3.1). Supply at plant i, say s_i, is taken to be a linear function of the price. Conversely, solving for the *supply price*, the supply price function is also linear, say $\gamma_i + \delta_i s_i$ with $\delta_i > 0$. The supply price is defined as the lowest price that the owner of the plant requires in order to be willing to supply the quantity s_i. (The supply price function is the inverse function of the supply function.)

Whereas we earlier assumed that the supply function was vertical, we now allow for the possibility that the owner of the plant may be willing to respond to a higher price by supplying an increased quantity.

The amount supplied is also related to costs of production. The equilibrium solution that we shall be looking for will not permit the presence of any positive profits (beyond the payments to all productive factors). The supply price is therefore the same as the *marginal cost* of production.

Figure 3.1

Supply price curve.

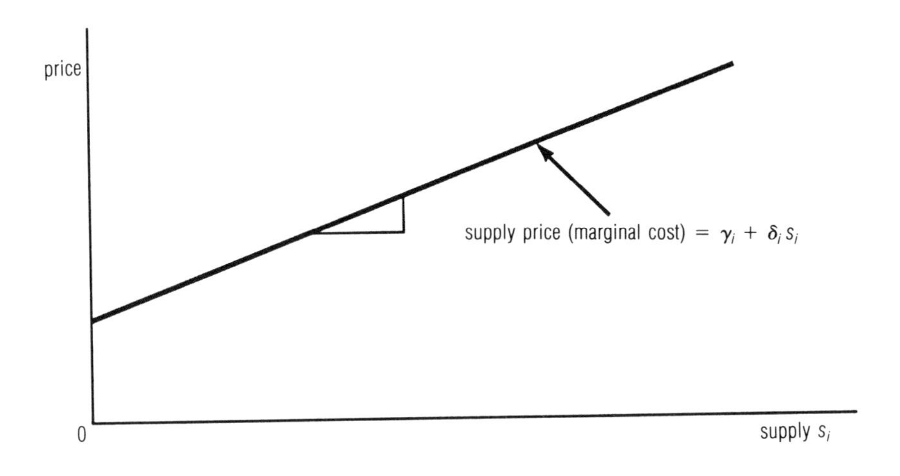

To see this, consider a hypothetical expansion of the supply of plant i by one unit, the "last" unit supplied by the plant. The cost of that last unit is the marginal cost of the plant. The supply price of the same unit is the lowest price that the owner of the plant requires in order to be willing to supply it. Hence, that lowest price is the marginal cost of production.

The realization that prices in a competitive economy are brought into equality with marginal costs belongs to the so called "marginal revolution" which occurred in economics in the 1870s. Ever since, it has become one of the fundamental tenets of economics.

One interesting consequence of this relationship is that it is possible to form *total costs* of plant i by integrating the production marginal cost curve $\gamma_i + \delta_i s_i$. Carrying out the integration, one finds

$$f(s_i) = \text{total costs of plant } i = \gamma_i s_i + 0.5\delta_i s_i^2 + \text{integration constant} \qquad (3.2)$$

The integration constant can be interpreted as a fixed cost, which is incurred even if production is zero. Note that the total cost function (3.2) is convex provided $\delta_i \geq 0$ which we will assume. Because $f(s_i)$ depends only on s_i it is a separable function.

For the definitions of convexity and separability see Chapter 4, pages 50–55.

For the reference purposes, all notation to be used is brought together below:

m = number of plants.

n = number of retail marketing regions.

s_i = supply at plant i (to be determined).

$\gamma_i + \delta_i s_i$ = supply price (marginal cost) at plant i, where γ_i and δ_i are constants with $\delta_i > 0$.

b_j = demand in marketing region j (given and fixed)

c_{ij} = unit cost of transporting the good from plant i to market j

x_{ij} = the quantity to be shipped from plant i to market j

We are now ready to spell out the various market constraints of the model, which have already been discussed in a general fashion. The supply balance conditions, one for each plant, state that the shipments from a plant cannot exceed the local supply.

$$\sum_{j=1}^{n} x_{ij} - s_i \leq 0 \qquad \text{for } i = 1, 2, \ldots, m \tag{3.3}$$

On the demand side, the total shipments to each market must not fall short of the local demand,

$$\sum_{i=1}^{m} x_{ij} \geq b_j \qquad \text{for } j = 1, 2, \ldots, n \tag{3.4}$$

Thus prepared, we form the nonlinear programming problem,

$$\begin{aligned} \text{Minimize} \quad & \sum_{i=1}^{m} \left(\gamma_i s_i + 0.5\delta_i s_i^2\right) + \sum_{i=1}^{m} \sum_{j=1}^{n} c_{ij} x_{ij} \\ \text{Subject to} \quad & \sum_{j=1}^{n} x_{ij} - s_i \leq 0, \qquad i = 1, 2, \ldots, m \\ & \sum_{i=1}^{m} x_{ij} \geq b_j, \qquad j = 1, 2, \ldots, n \\ & x_{ij}, s_i \geq 0, \qquad i = 1, 2, \ldots, m, \quad j = 1, 2, \ldots, n \end{aligned} \tag{3.5}$$

The objective function equals the sum of total production costs at all plants, and all transportation costs. (The fixed costs have been suppressed.) The first sets of constraints are market clearing constraints at each plant, and the second set of constraints are market clearing conditions in each retailing region.

The objective function is convex, and the constraints are linear, so that the program is actually an instance of quadratic programming. It has a unique optimal solution.

In order to verify that program (3.5) accomplishes what we have set out to do, we turn to the Kuhn-Tucker conditions (see Chapter 4). Let the Lagrange multipliers of the two sets of constraints be u_i and v_j, respectively. The multipliers u_i are nonpositive and the multipliers v_j are nonnegative.

Denoting the optimal solution by an asterisk (*), the multiplier u_i^* may be interpreted as the negative of the imputed unit cost of one unit of the commodity available at the factory loading dock. It is the *imputed equilibrium price* of the commodity at the factory dock of plant i. The multiplier v_j^* may be interpreted as the *equilibrium price* of the commodity in retail market j.

In order to motivate these interpretations, we now turn to the Kuhn-Tucker conditions which are listed below. First, corresponding to the two sets of market balances in program (3.5), one has

$$u_i^* \le 0, \qquad \sum_{j=1}^{n} x_{ij}^* - s_i^* \le 0, \qquad u_i^*\left(\sum_{j=1}^{n} x_{ij}^* - s_i^*\right) = 0, \qquad \text{for } i = 1, 2, \ldots, m \tag{3.6}$$

$$v_j^* \ge 0, \qquad \sum_{i=1}^{m} x_{ij}^* - b_j^* \ge 0, \qquad v_j^*\left(\sum_{i=1}^{m} x_{ij}^* - b_j^*\right) = 0, \qquad \text{for } j = 1, 2, \ldots, n \tag{3.7}$$

The first set of constraints (3.6) state: The optimal shipments from each plant cannot exceed the supply of the plant. If the imputed unit cost u_i^* of the supply is positive, then those shipments will exactly equal the supply. But if the shipments fall short of the available supply, the imputed unit cost must have fallen to zero.

The second set of constraints (3.7) state: The optimal shipments arriving at each market must suffice to cover the local demand. If the equilibrium price of the commodity at market j, measured by the Lagrange multiplier v_j^*, is positive, then those shipments equal total demand. But if the shipments exceed the demand, the equilibrium price must have fallen to zero.

Next we have the dual conditions,

$$u_i^* + v_j^* \le c_{ij}, \qquad x_{ij}^*(c_{ij} - u_i^* - v_j^*) = 0, \qquad \text{for } i = 1, 2, \ldots, m \text{ and } j = 1, 2, \ldots, n \tag{3.8}$$

The expression $u_i^* + v_j^*$ measures the appreciation that occurs when a unit of the good is transported from plant i (where the implied unit cost is $-u_i^*$) to market j (where the market price is v_j^*). Relations (3.8) state that the appreciation can never exceed the unit transportation cost. If a positive quantity x_{ij}^* is shipped from plant i to market j, the appreciation must exactly equal the unit transportation cost. A shipper, buying the commodity at the factory dock of plant i and shipping it to market j and selling it again, would then make zero profit. But if the price appreciation were to fall short of the unit transportation cost, so that such a hypothetical shipper would suffer a unit loss, and no shipments would occur.

The last set of Kuhn-Tucker conditions is (see Chapter 4, pages 56–57):

$$-u_i^* \le \gamma_i + \delta_i s_i^*, \qquad s_i^*(\gamma_i + \delta_i s_i^* + u_i^*) = 0, \qquad \text{for } i = 1, 2, \ldots, m \tag{3.9}$$

These relations spell out the association between the imputed market price $-u_i^*$ at the factory dock of plant i, and the supply price $\gamma_i + \delta_i s_i^*$. The market price can never exceed the supply price. If a positive quantity s_i^* is supplied, then the market price equals the supply price. But if the imputed market price falls short of the supply price, the supply must have dropped to zero.

Example. The numerical example solved below involves three plants and three retail areas. The data are:

Plant	*Supply Price Function*	*Retailing Region*	*Demand*
1	$\gamma_1 + \delta_1 s_1 = 42 + 0.3 s_1$	1	$b_1 = 300$
2	$\gamma_2 + \delta_2 s_2 = 35 + 0.25 s_2$	2	$b_2 = 150$
3	$\gamma_3 + \delta_3 s_3 = 50 + 0.5 s_3$	3	$b_3 = 200$

The unit shipping costs (in dollars) to the retail regions are:

$$\text{From Plant}\quad \begin{array}{c} \\ 1 \\ 2 \\ 3 \end{array} \begin{array}{c} \begin{array}{ccc} 1 & 2 & 3 \end{array} \\ \begin{bmatrix} 0 & 1 & 1.5 \\ 1 & 0 & 2 \\ 1.5 & 2 & 0 \end{bmatrix} \end{array} = \begin{bmatrix} c_{11} & c_{12} & c_{13} \\ c_{21} & c_{22} & c_{23} \\ c_{31} & c_{32} & c_{33} \end{bmatrix}$$

The production and distribution system can also be illustrated by the network diagram given in Figure 3.2.

In the simple numerical example shown here, it is assumed that plant 1 is located in the immediate vicinity of marketing region 1, plant 2 of region 2 and plant 3 of region 3. The diagonal unit transportation costs c_{ij} in the matrix are therefore zero.

The nonlinear objective programming problem may now be organized as in the data box shown below. (Notice that the fixed cost term has been omitted.)

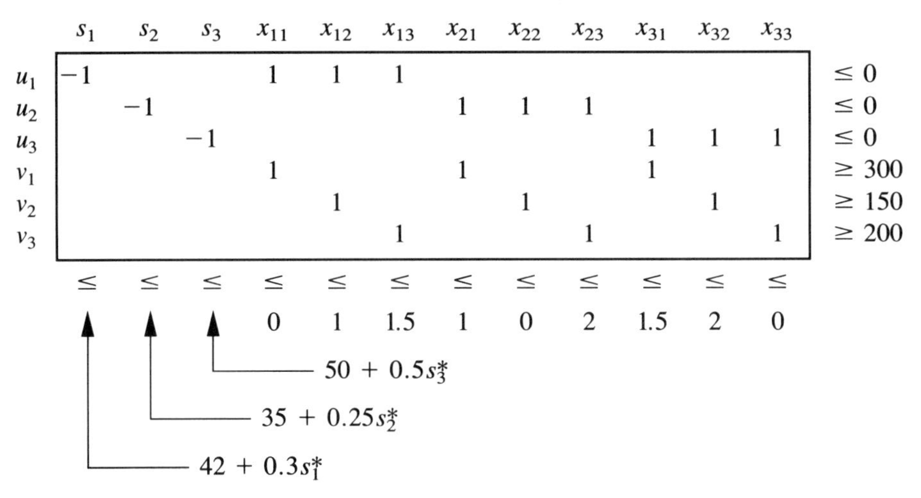

	s_1	s_2	s_3	x_{11}	x_{12}	x_{13}	x_{21}	x_{22}	x_{23}	x_{31}	x_{32}	x_{33}	
u_1	−1			1	1	1							≤ 0
u_2		−1					1	1	1				≤ 0
u_3			−1							1	1	1	≤ 0
v_1				1			1			1			≥ 300
v_2					1			1			1		≥ 150
v_3						1			1			1	≥ 200
	≤	≤	≤	≤	≤	≤	≤	≤	≤	≤	≤	≤	
	$42 + 0.3s_1^*$	$35 + 0.25s_2^*$	$50 + 0.5s_3^*$	0	1	1.5	1	0	2	1.5	2	0	

The main body of the data box displays the coefficients of the various market constraints in the manner that we have already encountered several times. The bottom row deserves special explanation. The objective function of the nonlinear programming problem is the quadratic function

$$\begin{aligned} &42s_1 + 0.15s_1^2 + 35s_2 + 0.125s_2^2 + 50s_3 + 0.25s_3^2 \\ &\quad + x_{12} + 1.5x_{13} + x_{21} + 2x_{23} + 1.5x_{31} + 2x_{32} \end{aligned} \tag{3.10}$$

As will be explained in more detail in Chapter 4 in the section on nonlinear programming, the entries in the bottom row in the data box above are the *slope*

Figure 3.2

Production and distribution system. Unit costs are in boxes.

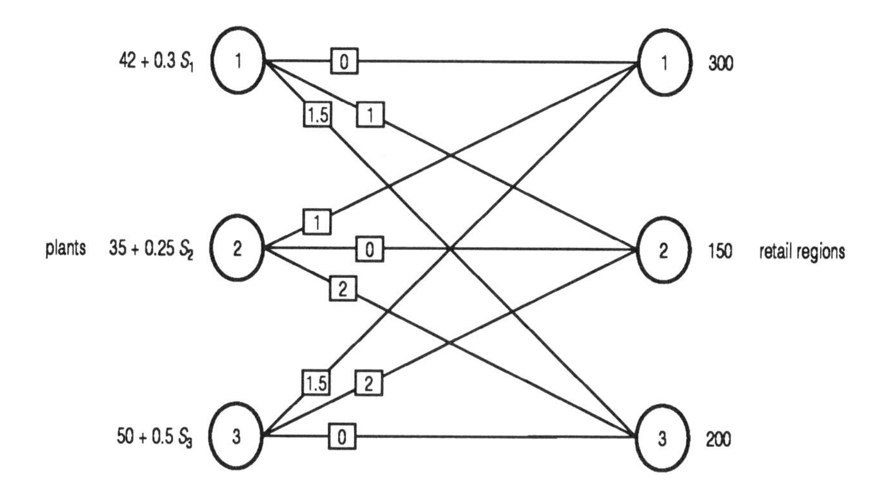

coefficients of this function at the point of optimum. Each slope coefficient is obtained as a partial *derivative*. In the nonlinear case, these slope coefficients are tangential approximations to the linear unit cost coefficients.

The optimal solution to the production and distribution problem now outlined can be found by solving the GAMS program EQUILIB on page 306. The output will provide the following answer:

$$\begin{aligned} s_1^* &= 228.6 & x_{11}^* &= 228.6 \\ s_2^* &= 298.3 & x_{21}^* &= 71.4 \\ s_3^* &= 123.1 & x_{22}^* &= 150.0 \\ & & x_{23}^* &= 76.7 \\ & & x_{33}^* &= 123.1 \end{aligned}$$

(all other x_{ij}^* are zero).

The solution is illustrated in Figure 3.3.

The GAMS software also lists the optimal values of the Lagrange multipliers of the constraints at the point of optimum. These multipliers have been denoted u_i (for the supply constraints) and v_j (for the demand constraints). Refer to the left hand rim entries in the data box on page 38. The optimal values are:

$$\begin{aligned} u_1^* &= -110.6 & v_1^* &= 110.6 \\ u_2^* &= -109.6 & v_2^* &= 109.6 \\ u_3^* &= -111.6 & v_3^* &= 111.6 \end{aligned}$$

The u_i^* can be interpreted as the negative values of the optimal imputed supply prices holding at the factory dock of the three plants. The v_j^* are the market prices in the three retailing regions.

Figure 3.3

Graph of the optimal solution. Unit shipping costs are in boxes, and shipments are on lines.

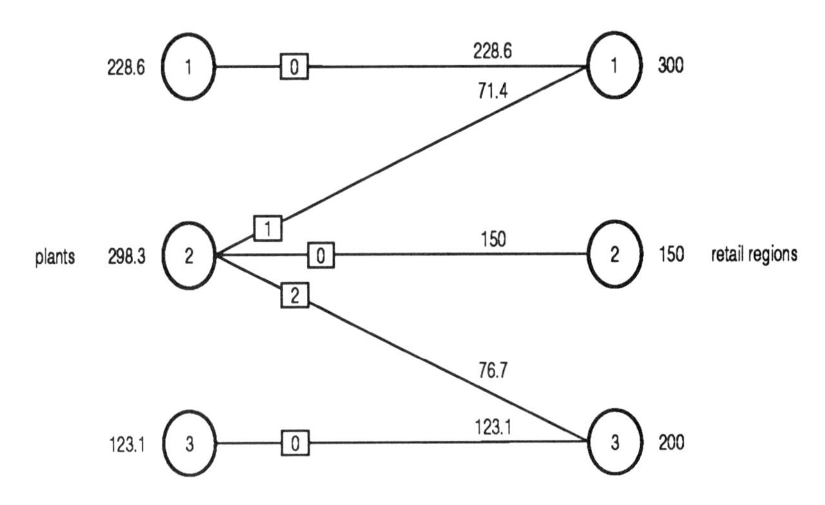

The reader is now asked to refer back to the theoretical discussion of the Kuhn-Tucker conditions. First note that all supply constraints are *tight*, as indeed they must when the implied supply prices are positive. Also the demand constraints are tight because the market prices are also positive. Next, there was a set of Kuhn-Tucker conditions [relations (3.8)] that stated that the imputed price appreciation of the commodity along any link could not exceed the unit cost. Now check the imputed price appreciation along *all* links in the distribution network, both those shown in Figure 3.4 and those that are *not* utilized. If a link is used for shipments, the imputed appreciation exactly equals the unit cost. If the imputed appreciation falls short of the unit cost, the link is not used.

Finally, let us also look at the Kuhn-Tucker relations (3.9). Calculate the supply price at each plant:

$$\text{supply price at plant 1} = 42 + 0.3s_1^* = 42 + 0.3 \cdot 228.6 = 110.6$$
$$\text{supply price at plant 2} = 35 + 0.25s_2^* = 35 + 0.25 \cdot 298.3 = 109.6$$
$$\text{supply price at plant 3} = 50 + 0.5s_3^* = 50 + 0.5 \cdot 123.1 = 111.6$$

The supply price at each plant equals the imputed market price at the factory doors, as indeed the theoretical analysis has shown that it must when a positive quantity is being supplied.

In the present instance, the Kuhn-Tucker conditions happen to throw light on the *decentralization* properties of the direct program (3.5). The program minimizes the sum of all production costs and all transportation costs. That may indeed be a fair objective of an economic planner charged with the task

Figure 3.4

Imputed prices at the factory loading docks, and at the retailing regions.

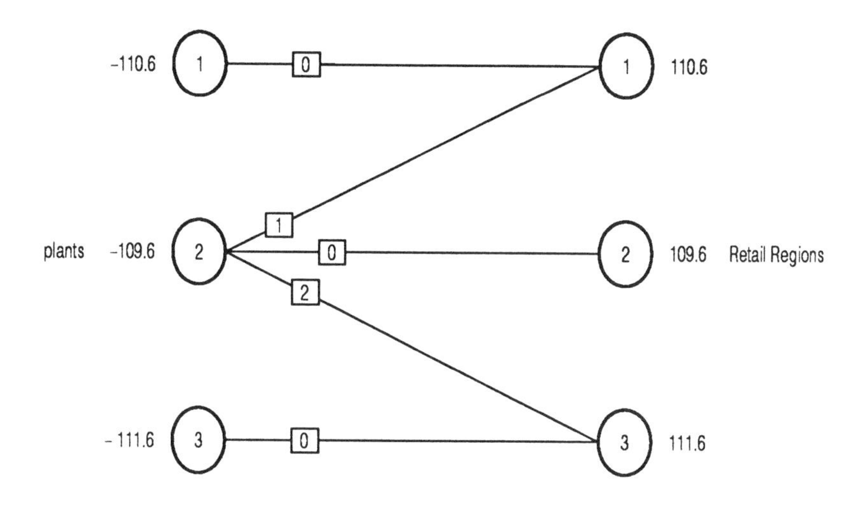

of drawing up an optimal plan for the entire partial economy under consideration. But what assurance do we have that the individual plant managers and the individual shippers will adhere to this master plan? In a competitive economy there exists no all-powerful planning secretariat (such as the Soviet Gosplan agency) that sees to it that the master plan becomes implemented. Instead, a competitive economy relies on decentralized decision-making.

In a later chapter (Chapter 7), we shall bring up the subject of decentralization in some detail. For the moment, it will suffice to consider the Kuhn-Tucker conditions (3.6–9). They tell us that the optimal master plan can be implemented if all imputed prices are established as market prices, and if all agents, both plant managers and shippers, are asked to cover costs.

Nonlinear Shipping Costs

The underlying reason why we were able to use the technique of nonlinear programming to solve the generalized transportation model was that all of the cost functions were convex. Production costs at plants were convex (they were quadratic) and transportation costs were convex (they were actually linear). The combined costs arising in the model therefore had a minimum.

The cost function at each plant was convex because the marginal cost always increased as output increased. Had marginal costs been decreasing over some interval, we would not have been able to solve the problem in the same way.

It seems obvious that it must be a quite straightforward to extend the model to include the case of convex transportation costs. To accomplish this, assume that

$$\text{total shipping costs along link } (i,j) = c_{ij}x_{ij} + d_{ij}x_{ij}^2$$

with the coefficients d_{ij} being nonnegative.

Program (3.5) would then read:

$$\begin{aligned} &\text{Minimize} \quad \sum_{i=1}^{m} \left(\gamma_i s_i + 0.5\delta_i s_i^2 \right) + \sum_{i=1}^{m} \sum_{j=1}^{n} \left(c_{ij} x_{ij} + d_{ij} x_i^2 \right) \\ &\text{Subject to} \quad \sum_{j=1}^{n} x_{ij} - s_i \le 0, \qquad i = 1, 2, \ldots, m \\ &\qquad\qquad \sum_{i=1}^{m} x_{ij} \ge b_j, \qquad j = 1, 2, \ldots, n \\ &\qquad\qquad x_{ij}, s_i \ge 0, \qquad i = 1, 2, \ldots, m, \quad j = 1, 2, \ldots, n \end{aligned} \tag{3.11}$$

The Lagrange multipliers u_i^* and v_j^* may be interpreted as before. The quantity u_i^* is an imputed equilibrium price (with negative sign) at the factory dock of plant i; the v_j^* is the market price in retailing area j. Each such imputed price brings about the clearing of the corresponding market. The Kuhn-Tucker conditions (3.6) and (3.7) hold as before. But the conditions (3.8) must be replaced by

$$u_i^* + v_j^* \le c_{ij} + 2d_{ij}x_{ij}^*, \qquad x_{ij}^*(c_{ij} + 2d_{ij}x_{ij}^* - u_i^* - v_j^*) = 0 \qquad \text{for } i = 1, 2, \ldots, m \text{ and } j = 1, 2, \ldots, n \tag{3.12}$$

The expression $c_{ij} + 2d_{ij}x_{ij}^*$ is the *marginal shipping cost* along link (i,j). Hence, relations (3.12) state that the appreciation from plant i to market j cannot exceed the marginal shipping cost. In other words, the mythical shipper evaluating the possible profitability of shipping a unit along a given link, will carry out this evaluation *at the margin*. The price appreciation of the "last" unit cannot exceed the cost of shipping of the same unit.

If a positive quantity is shipped, the appreciation of the last unit is exactly exhausted by the cost of shipping that unit. But if the appreciation were to fall short of the shipping cost, no shipment would occur.

Conditions analogous to those in (3.9) can be stated and interpreted as before.

Nonlinear Market Demand

We now also briefly discuss the case when transportation costs are linear but market demand in each retailing region is price-sensitive, the demand price in each region being given by the linear expression

$$\text{demand price in region } j = \alpha_j - \beta_j d_j \tag{3.13}$$

where the letter d_j is a variable representing the quantity demanded in region j and α_j and β_j are positive constants. See the demand price curve in Figure 3.5.

The demand price is defined as the highest price that the consumers would be willing to pay to buy quantity d_j. (The demand price function is the inverse function of an ordinary demand function.) In this case, rather than assuming a fixed and given demand in each retailing region, we now allow for the possibility that sales may be increased in a region by lowering the retail price.

Figure 3.5

Demand price curve.

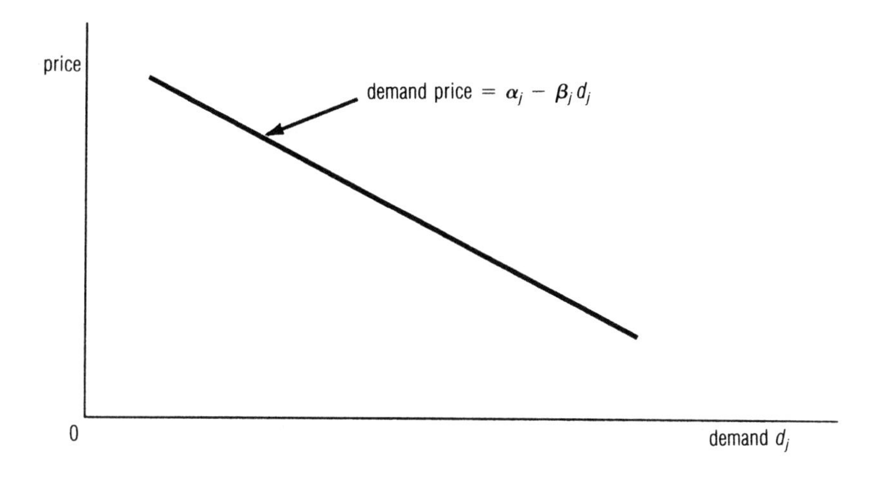

In order to solve for equilibrium in the entire production and distribution system, we resort to a technique already encountered in the preceding chapter: the optimization of an *economic potential function*, designed so that it has a minimum at the desired point of solution. The general procedure that we are about to apply here was originally suggested by P. A. Samuelson (Nobel prize 1970) in solving a problem of spatial equilibrium. The potential function has no direct economic interpretation and is used as a mathematical artifact only.

The entire nonlinear program reads (maintaining price sensitive supplies as in the main section of this chapter, but reverting to the case of constant and known unit transportation costs c_{ij} along each link of the network):

$$\text{Minimize} \quad \sum_{i=1}^{m}\left(\gamma_i s_i + 0.5\delta_i s_i^2\right) + \sum_{i=1}^{m}\sum_{j=1}^{n} c_{ij}x_{ij} - \sum_{j=1}^{n}\left(\alpha_j d_j - 0.5\beta_j d_j^2\right)$$

$$\text{Subject to} \quad \sum_{j=1}^{n} x_{ij} - s_i \leq 0, \qquad i = 1, 2, \ldots, m \tag{3.14}$$

$$\sum_{i=1}^{m} x_{ij} - d_j \geq 0, \qquad j = 1, 2, \ldots, n$$

$$x_{ij}, s_i, d_j \geq 0, \qquad i = 1, 2, \ldots, m \quad \text{and} \quad j = 1, 2, \ldots, n.$$

The new feature in this program is the third term in the minimand. It has been obtained through a mathematical procedure that is entirely analogous to the previous treatment of the supply side: each demand price function has been integrated and the resulting integrals are all summed together. On the supply side, the result of this operation had an obvious and direct economic interpretation: the resulting term simply stands for total costs. On the demand side, there is no obvious economic interpretation of the result, and none is needed.

What matters is that the program now formulated will provide the Kuhn-Tucker conditions that characterize the desired point of optimum. In order to see this, note that we will now (in addition to retrieving relations (3.6) and (3.8) also find, first:

$$\sum_{i=1}^{m} x_{ij}^* - d_j^* \geq 0, \qquad v_j^*\left(\sum_{i=1}^{m} x_{ij}^* - d_j^*\right) = 0 \qquad \text{for } j = 1, 2, \ldots, n \tag{3.15}$$

which states that each retail market must clear, and second:

$$v_j^* - \alpha_j + \beta_j d_j^* \geq 0, \qquad d_j^*(v_j^* - \alpha_j + \beta_j d_j^*) = 0 \qquad \text{for } j = 1, 2, \ldots, n \tag{3.16}$$

In words: the demand price in each market cannot exceed the market price. If a positive quantity is purchased by the consumers, the demand price equals the market price.

Exercises

1. Solve the prototype equilibrium model with your software and check that the primal and dual solutions on the bottom of page 39 are correct.

2. Modify the example problem by making the transportation cost on each route i, j be a nonlinear function, namely $c_{ij}x_{ij}^2$ instead of $c_{ij}\, x_{ij}$, in the problem given in (3.5). Modify the code you used in Exercise 1 to reflect this change and re-solve. Compare the new solution to the previous one and comment.

3. Modify the problem in Exercise 2 to the case where the demand is nonlinear as well as the supply and the transportation cost. The demand function is like that in (3.14) with the following values for α_j and β_j:

j	α_j	β_j
1	175	0.49
2	190	0.37
3	181	0.61

Re-solve the new problem and compare its solution with the previous two sections. Observe that the second plant sends all of its output to the second market.

4

Linear, Nonlinear & Integer Programming

During the last few decades a number of mathematical techniques, collectively termed *mathematical programming*, have been developed which are well suited for formulating and solving problems in economics and management. One of these techniques, linear programming, has been utilized in Chapters 1 and 2. Another, nonlinear programming, was used in Chapter 3. A third technique, integer programming, will be used to solve capital budgeting and investment problems in Chapters 11 and 16. The purpose of the current chapter is to summarize the rules for setting up problems for solution by means of these techniques, and for interpreting the answers they provide.

The methods of infinitesmal calculus (differential and integral) which were instrumental in aiding the natural sciences in the finding of spectacular results in Newtonian physics, relativity theory, chemical structures, engineering, and so on, frequently are not well suited for the needs of the economist. Typical problems in economics involve large (instead of small) numbers of variables which occur in inequality (instead of equality) constraints. The methods of mathematical programming were developed to meet these needs.

Linear Programming

Linear programming problems can be stated in either maximizing or minimizing form. In either case, the originally formulated problem is called the *primal linear program*. Every primal linear program has an associated *dual linear program*. If the primal problem has a *maximizing objective* then the dual problem has a *minimizing objective*. Similarly, if the primal has a *minimizing objective* then the dual problem has a *maximizing objective*.

When the objective function of a primal or dual linear program is maximizing we say that $\leq$ inequalities are *right way inequalities* and $\geq$ inequalities are *wrong way inequalities*. For a minimizing objective $\geq$ are *right way inequalities* and $\leq$ are *wrong*

Figure 4.1

Sign rules for dual variables for different objective functions.

Objective Function	*Right Way Constraint*	*Wrong Way Constraint*
Maximizing	$\leq$	$\geq$
Minimizing	$\geq$	$\leq$

Rules for signs of dual variables:

(a) The dual variable of a right way constraint is nonnegative.
(b) The dual variable of a wrong way constraint is nonpositive.
(c) The dual variable of an equality constraint is unconstrained.

---

way inequalities. Every constraint has a dual variable. The rule for the sign of a dual variable can be summarized as: *the sign of the dual variable of a right way inequality is nonnegative* whereas *the sign of the dual variable of a wrong way constraint is nonpositive*. Some linear programs have equality constraints. The *dual variable of an equality constraint is unconstrained* regardless of whether the objective function is maximizing or minimizing.

The above sign rules for dual variables are summarized in Figure 4.1.

Example 1: Consider the linear program

$$\begin{aligned} \text{Maximize} \quad & 5x_1 - 6x_2 \\ \text{Subject to} \quad & x_2 \leq 2 \\ & 3x_1 + 5x_2 = 1 \\ & x_1, x_2 \geq 0 \end{aligned}$$

The first step is to determine the "detached coefficient tableau" or "data box" of the problem, which contains just the coefficients of the variables and the right hand sides of the constraints, as shown below:

	x_1	x_2	
u_1	0	1	≤ 2
u_2	3	5	$= 1$
	$\geq$	$\geq$	
	5	-6	

Note that the 0 coefficient of x_1 in the first constraint has been inserted. Also the coefficients of the objective function appear at the bottom. The nonnegativity constraints on x_1 and x_2 have been omitted, but cause the $\geq$ signs above the objective function coefficients. The dual variables $u_1$and u_2 on the left will be explained below. The general rule for deriving the data box for a maximizing primal problem having nonnegativity constraints is:

x_1	x_2			
a_{11}	a_{12}	$\leq b_1$	→	$a_{11}x_1 + a_{12}x_2 \leq b_1$
a_{21}	a_{22}	$= b_2$	→	$a_{21}x_1 + a_{22}x_2 = b_2$
a_{31}	a_{32}	$\geq b_3$	→	$a_{31}x_1 + a_{32}x_2 \geq b_3$
$\geq$	$\geq$			
c_1	c_2		→	$c_1x_1 + c_2x_2 =$ Maximum

(because both dual constraints are $\geq$) → $x_1, x_2 \geq 0$

The general rule for deriving the dual problem from the primal problem when the primal objective is maximizing is:

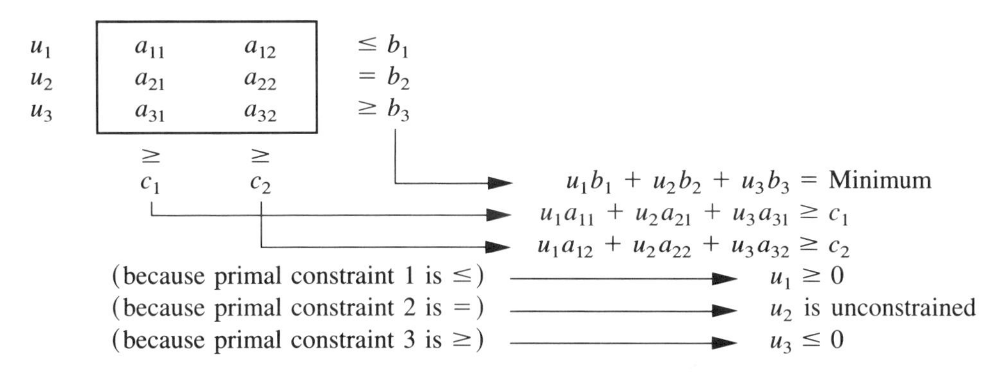

When primal objective is minimizing, reverse the signs of the dual inequalities.

Using the general rule, we derive the dual problem of this example as follows:

$$
\begin{aligned}
\text{Minimize} \quad & 2u_1 + u_2 \\
\text{Subject to} \quad & 3u_2 \geq 5 \\
& u_1 + 5u_2 \geq -6 \\
& u_1 \geq 0 \\
& u_2 \text{ unconstrained}
\end{aligned}
$$

Example 2. Let us consider the minimizing problem:

$$
\begin{aligned}
\text{Minimize} \quad & 3x_1 + 4x_2 + 6x_3 \\
& -x_1 + 3x_2 + 2x_3 \leq 100 \\
& 5x_1 - 2x_2 \geq 20 \\
& x_1, x_2, x_3 \geq 0
\end{aligned}
$$

The data box for this problem is:

	x_1	x_2	x_3	
u_1	-1	3	2	≤ 100
u_2	5	-2	0	≥ 20
	$\leq$	$\leq$	$\leq$	
	3	4	6	

The dual linear program is:

$$\begin{aligned}
\text{Maximize} \quad & 100u_1 + 20u_2 \\
& -u_1 + 5u_2 \leq 3 \\
& 3u_1 - 2u_2 \leq 4 \\
& 2u_1 \leq 6 \\
& u_1 \leq 0 \\
& u_2 \geq 0
\end{aligned}$$

The data box also gives a useful mnemonic for writing the primal and dual complementary slackness conditions. The rules for deriving these conditions are demonstrated below. Note that there is a primal complementary slackness condition for each row of the data box, and there is a dual complementary slackness condition for each column.

First, the primal complementary slackness conditions when the primal objective function is maximizing:

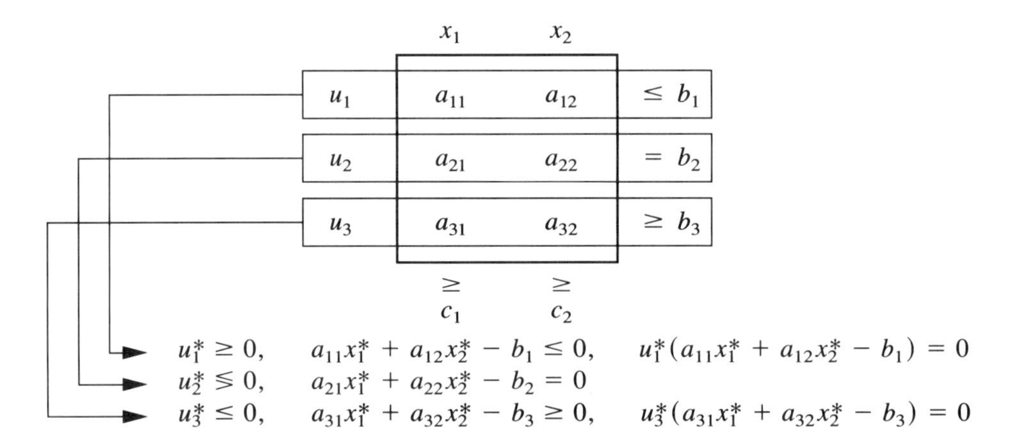

When the objective function is minimizing, reverse the signs of the u_i's.

Second, the dual complementary slackness conditions when the primal objective function is maximizing:

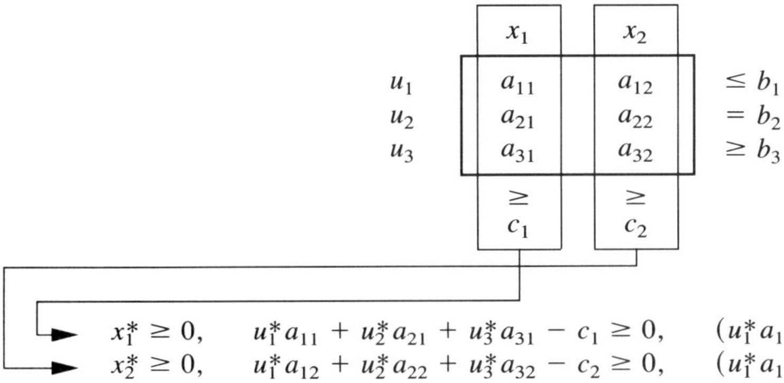

	x_1	x_2	
u_1	a_{11}	a_{12}	$\leq b_1$
u_2	a_{21}	a_{22}	$= b_2$
u_3	a_{31}	a_{32}	$\geq b_3$
	$\geq$	$\geq$	
	c_1	c_2	

$$x_1^* \geq 0, \quad u_1^* a_{11} + u_2^* a_{21} + u_3^* a_{31} - c_1 \geq 0, \quad (u_1^* a_{11} + u_2^* a_{21} + u_3^* a_{31} - c_1)x_1^* = 0$$
$$x_2^* \geq 0, \quad u_1^* a_{12} + u_2^* a_{22} + u_3^* a_{32} - c_2 \geq 0, \quad (u_1^* a_{12} + u_2^* a_{22} + u_3^* a_{32} - c_2)x_2^* = 0$$

When the objective function is minimizing, reverse direction of the dual inequalities.

Example 1 (continued). The primal complementary slackness conditions for the first example can be read from the data box on page 46 as:

$$u_1^* \geq 0, \quad x_2^* - 2 \leq 0, \quad u_1^*(x_2^* - 2) = 0$$
$$u_2^* \lessgtr 0, \quad 3x_1^* + 5x_2^* - 1 = 0,$$

Similarly the dual complementary slackness conditions are:

$$x_1^* \geq 0, \quad 3u_2^* - 5 \geq 0, \quad x_1^*(3u_2^* - 5) = 0$$
$$x_2^* \geq 0, \quad u_1^* + 5u_2^* + 6 \geq 0, \quad x_2^*(u_1^* + 5u_2^* + 6) = 0.$$

Example 2 (continued). Using the data box on page 48, we see that the primal complementary slackness conditions are:

$$u_1^* \leq 0, \quad -x_1^* + 3x_2^* + 2x_3^* - 100 \leq 0, \quad u_1^*(-x_1^* + 3x_2^* + 2x_3^* - 100) = 0$$
$$u_2^* \geq 0, \quad 5x_1^* - 2x_2^* - 20 \geq 0, \quad u_2^*(3x_1^* - 2x_2^* - 20) = 0.$$

The dual complementary slackness conditions are:

$$x_1^* \geq 0, \quad -u_1^* + 5u_2^* - 3 \leq 0, \quad x_1^*(-u_1^* + 5u_2^* - 3) = 0$$
$$x_2^* \geq 0, \quad 3u_1^* - 2u_2^* - 4 \leq 0, \quad x_2^*(3u_1^* - 2u_2^* - 4) = 0$$
$$x_3^* \geq 0, \quad 2u_1^* - 6 \leq 0, \quad x_3^*(2u_1^* - 6) = 0$$

Matrix Notation

Frequently it is convenient to write linear programs in matrix notation as follows:

Maximize cx

Subject to $Ax \leq b$

$u \geq 0$

where A is an $m \times n$ matrix, b is an $m \times 1$ vector, c is a $1 \times n$ vector and x is an $n \times 1$ vector. Then the dual variables are written as a $1 \times m$ vector and the dual problem becomes:

$$\begin{aligned} &\text{Minimize} && ub \\ &\text{Subject to} && uA \geq c \\ & && u \geq 0 \end{aligned}$$

In the case that there are some $\leq$, some $=$, and some $\geq$ constraints it is convenient to divide the matrix and the vectors into parts and express these separately. We will use the following notation from time to time.

Signs of the dual variables for a maximizing primal objective function:

$$\begin{array}{lc|c|l} & & x & \\ \cline{3-3} u^{(1)} & (\geq 0) & A^{(1)} & \leq b^{(1)} \\ u^{(2)} & (\lessgtr 0) & A^{(2)} & = b^{(2)} \\ u^{(3)} & (\leq 0) & A^{(3)} & \geq b^{(3)} \\ \cline{3-3} & & \geq & \\ & & c & \end{array}$$

Signs of the dual variables for a minimizing primal objective function:

$$\begin{array}{lc|c|l} & & x & \\ \cline{3-3} u^{(1)} & (\leq 0) & A^{(1)} & \leq b^{(1)} \\ u^{(2)} & (\lessgtr 0) & A^{(2)} & = b^{(2)} \\ u^{(3)} & (\geq 0) & A^{(3)} & \geq b^{(3)} \\ \cline{3-3} & & \geq & \\ & & c & \end{array}$$

Nonlinear Programming

Although many of the economic models we consider in this book can be analyzed by means of a linear programming model, others will require nonlinear analysis. However we will consider only relatively simple nonlinear functions such as quadratics or exponentials. What follows is a necessarily brief introduction to nonlinear programming.

If x and y are n-component vectors corresponding to points in n-space and θ is a real number satisfying $0 \leq \theta \leq 1$, then the point y given by

$$z = \theta x + (1 - \theta)y \qquad \text{for } 0 \leq \theta \leq 1 \tag{4.1}$$

is a point on the *line segment* connecting x and y. A set S of points in n-space is said to be a *convex set* if whenever x and y belong to S, then all points z given by (4.1) also belong to S. For example the two sets shown in Figure 4.2 are both convex.

In Figure 4.3 two examples of *non-convex* sets are illustrated. In each case points x and y in S together with a point z not in S on the line segment connecting them are shown. A set is either convex or non-convex. (There is no such thing as a concave set.)

An important example of a convex set is a *half space*, consisting of all the points on one side of a line (in two space) or hyperplane (in n space). Figure 4.4(a) shows

Figure 4.2

Examples of two-dimensional convex sets are shown shaded.

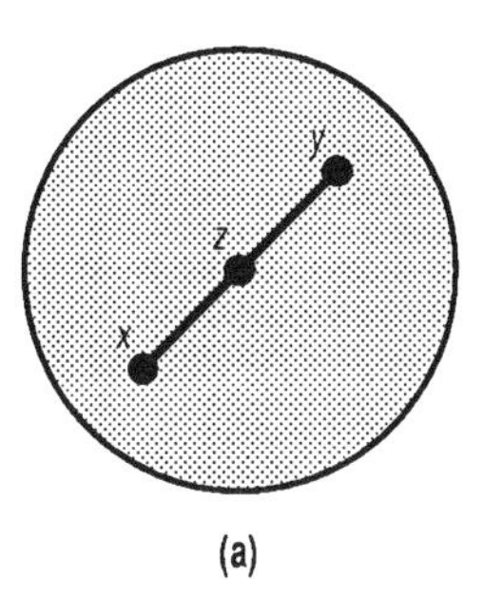

(a)

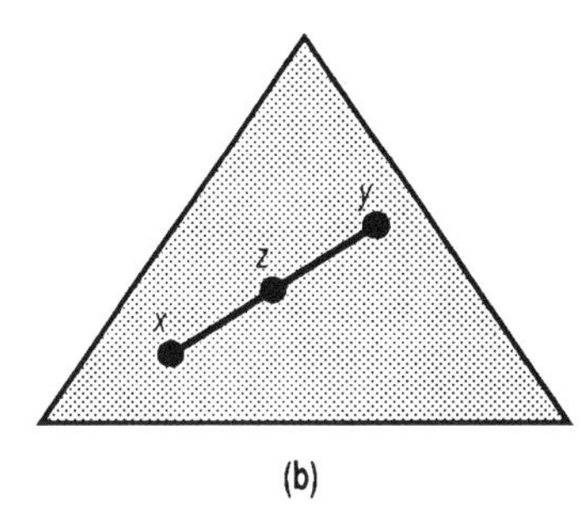

(b)

a half plane in two space. Such a half plane can be defined as the set of solutions $x = (x_1, x_2)$ to a linear inequality of the form:

$$a_{11}x_1 + a_{12}x_2 \leq b_1 \tag{4.2}$$

In n space a half space is defined as the set of solutions $x = (x_1, \ldots, x_n)$ to a linear inequality of the form:

$$\sum_{k=1}^{n} a_{1k} = a_{11}x_1 + \cdots + a_{1n}x_n \leq b_1 \tag{4.3}$$

The intersection of two convex sets is also a convex set. The following argument shows this to be true. Let S and T be convex sets and x and y be two points both of which belong to both S and T; then any point z as in (4.1) on the line segment between x and y will also belong to both S and T, and hence will belong to their intersection. Therefore the intersection $S \cap T$ must also be convex. (To make this argument complete, note that the empty set ϕ, which contains *no* points, *is* a convex set, since it satisfies the definition vacuously.)

Figure 4.3

Examples of non-convex sets shown shaded. Note that in each case x and y belong to the set, but z does not.

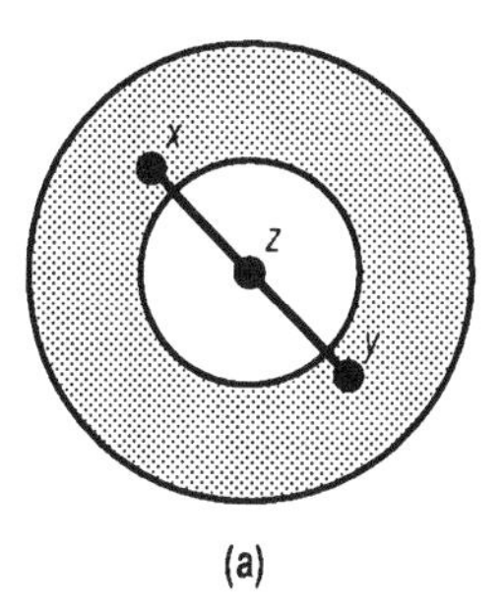

(a)

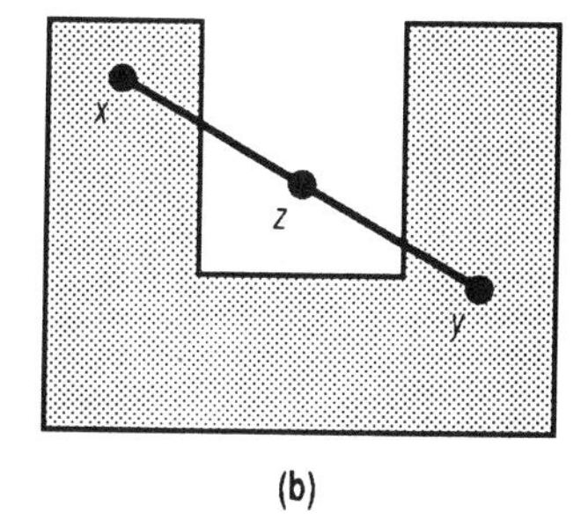

(b)

Figure 4.4

In (a) a half space is shown shaded. In (b) the intersection of two half spaces is shaded. Both are convex sets.

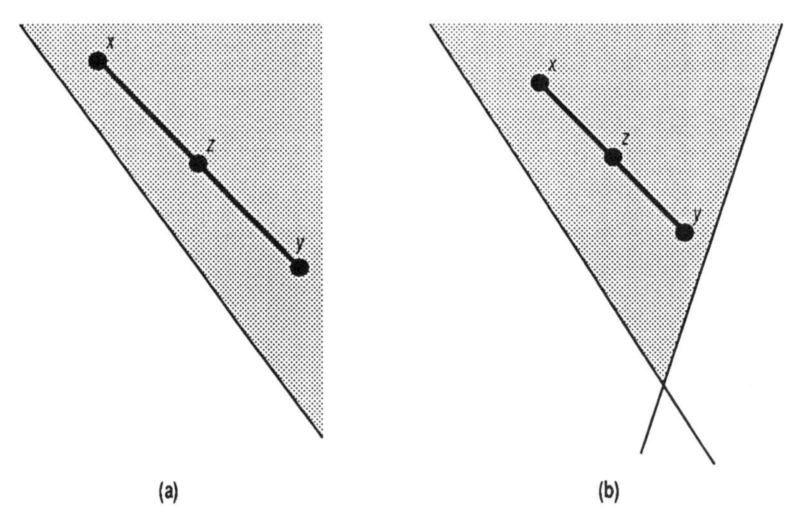

From this we see that the intersection of two half spaces, illustrated in Figure 4.4(b) is a convex set. Such an intersection is also the set of solution $x = (x_1, x_2)$ to a pair of linear inequalities of the form:

$$\begin{aligned} a_{11}x_1 + a_{12}x_2 &\leq b_1 \\ a_{21}x_1 + a_{22}x_2 &\leq b_2 \end{aligned} \tag{4.4}$$

This argument can be extended to show that the set of solutions to n inequalities in n unknowns

$$\begin{aligned} a_{11}x_1 + \cdots + a_{1n}x_n &\leq b_1 \\ \cdot \quad \cdots \quad \cdot \quad &\quad \cdot \\ a_{m1}x_1 + \cdots + a_{mn}x_n &\leq b_m \end{aligned} \tag{4.5}$$

is also a convex set.

We turn now to the definitions of linear, convex, and concave functions. Let $f(x)$ be a function of one variable defined in an *interval* (a, b) which is the set of x such that $a \leq x \leq b$ where $a \leq b$. If the first and second derivatives $f'(x)$ and $f''(x)$ are defined in the same interval then:

(a) $f(x)$ is *linear in* (a, b) if $f'(x) =$ constant throughout (a, b).

(b) $f(x)$ is *convex* in (a, b) if $f''(x) \geq 0$ throughout the interval;
it is *strictly convex* in (a, b) if $f''(x) > 0$ throughout (a, b).

(c) $f(x)$ is *concave* in (a, b) if $f''(x) \leq 0$ throughout the interval;
it is *strictly concave* if (a, b) if $f''(x) < 0$ throughout (a, b).

Figure 4.5

Convex functions. Both have unique minima. The function in (b) is monotone decreasing. Note that the points on the graph lie below the corresponding point on the chord.

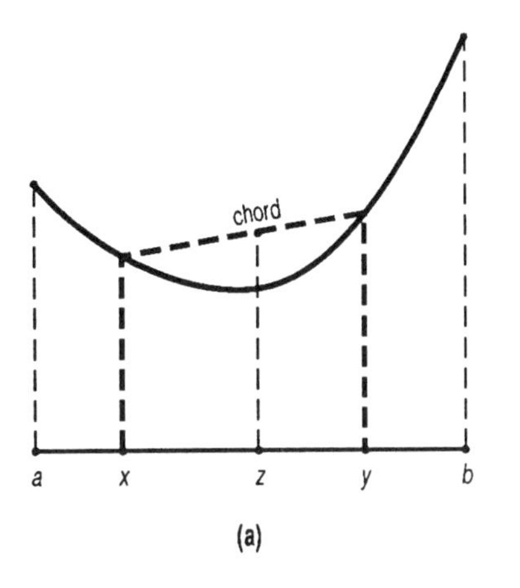

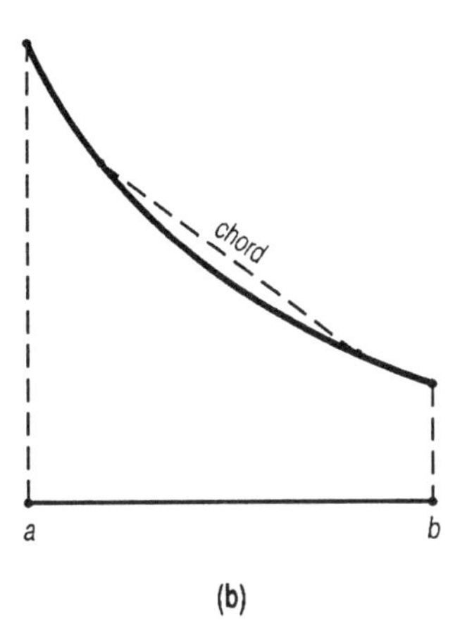

Clearly a linear function in (a, b) has $f''(x) = 0$ throughout the interval so that it is both convex and concave (but not strictly so) throughout the interval.

Example 3.

(a) The functions $f(x) = 2x + 1$, $g(x) = -x$, and $h(x) = 5$ are linear and both convex and concave (but not strictly so) for all x.

(b) The functions $f(x) = x^2 + 4x + 6$ and $g(x) = 1 + e^x$, and $h(x) = e^{-x}$ are strictly convex in any interval.

(c) The functions $f(x) = -x^2 - 4x + 6$, $g(x) = 1 - e^{-x}$, and $h(x) = -e^x$ are strictly concave in any interval.

It is easy to see that the following statements are true:

1. The negative of a convex function is concave (check the second derivatives). The negative of a concave function is convex.
2. The sum of two or more convex functions is convex. The sum of two or more concave functions is concave.
3. A quadratic function of the form $f(x) = ax^2 + bx + c$ is strictly convex if $a > 0$. It is strictly concave if $a < 0$.

Other results are given in the exercises.

Another way to characterize convex and concave functions is by means of chords. A *chord* of function $f(x)$ is the straight line (shown dotted in Figures 4.5 and 4.6)

Figure 4.6

Concave functions. Both have unique maxima. The function in (b) is monotone increasing. Note that the points on the graph lie above the corresponding point on the chord.

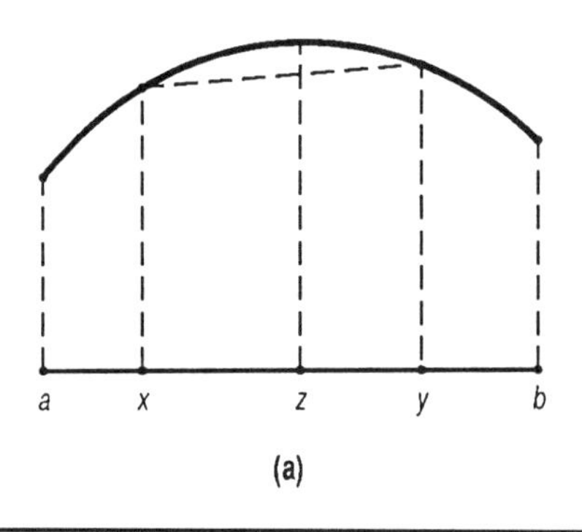

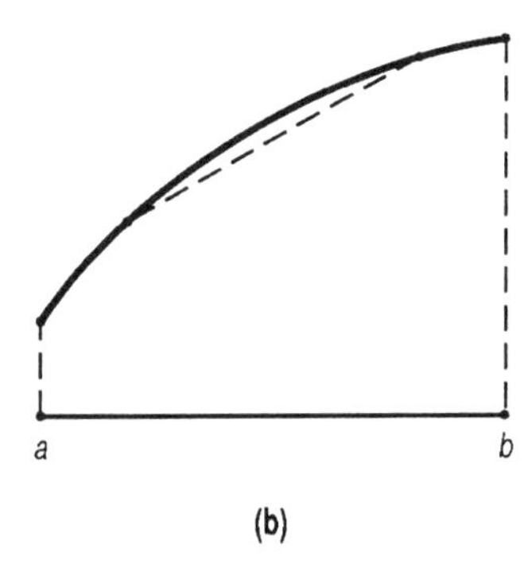

connecting two points on the graph of the function. Note that in the case of a convex function points on its graph always lie below (or on) the corresponding point on any chord, see Figure 4.5. To state this condition precisely, let x and y be points such that $a \leq x < y \leq b$ and let θ be a number satisfying $0 \leq \theta \leq 1$, then

$$f[\theta x + (1 - \theta)y] \leq \theta f(x) + (1 - \theta)f(y) \tag{4.6}$$

In the case of a concave function, the inequality should be reversed, see Figure 4.6.

Let us consider cases in which the chord is horizontal, see Figures 4.7 and 4.8. In Figure 4.7(a) there are two solutions to $f(x) = k$ where k is a fixed number; and in Figure

Figure 4.7

The set of x in (a,b) for which a convex function satisfies $f(x) \leq k$ is a convex set.

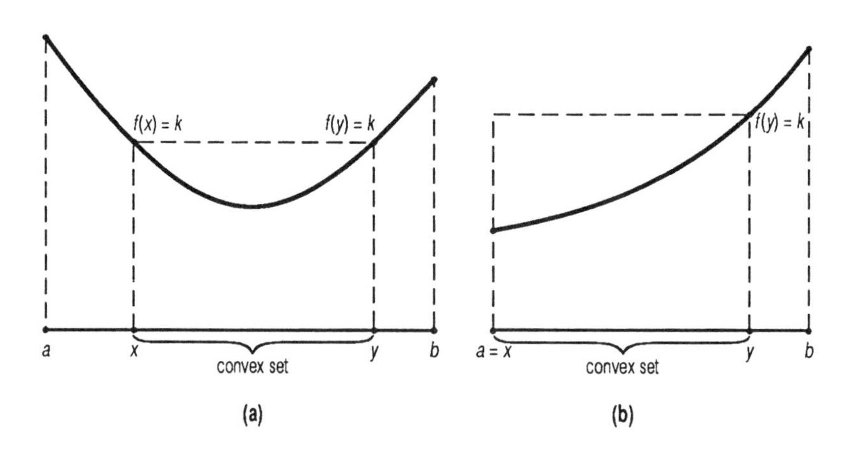

Figure 4.8

The set of x in (a,b) for which a concave function satisfies $f(x) \geq k$ is a convex set.

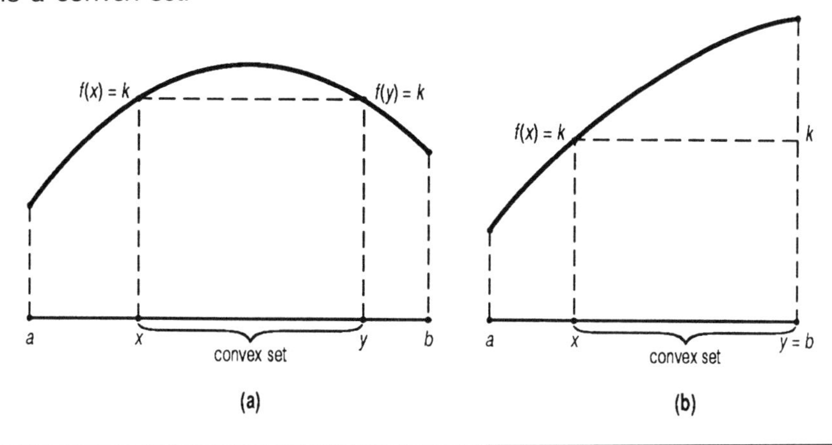

4.7(b) there is only one solution to $f(x) = k$. In either case the set of x such that $f(x) \leq k$ is a convex set when $f(x)$ is a convex function.

The situation when $f(x)$ is a concave function is illustrated in Figure 4.8. Here, the set of x such that $f(x) \geq k$ is a convex set when $f(x)$ is a concave function.

Before we can state the kinds of nonlinear programming problems we want to solve we need one more concept, that of a separable function. A *separable function* of several variables is one that can be expressed as a sum of separate functions of its individual variables. Thus, for a function of two variables a separable function $f(x_1, x_2)$ can be written as

$$f(x_1, x_2) = f_1(x_1) + f_2(x_2) \tag{4.7}$$

where $f_1(x_1)$ and $f_2(x_2)$ are each functions of a single variable. More generally, for a separable function of n variables we have

$$\begin{aligned} f(x_1, \ldots, x_n) &= f_1(x_1) + \cdots + f_n(x_n) \\ &= \sum_{j=1}^{n} f_j(x_j) \end{aligned} \tag{4.8}$$

Example 4.

(a) Let $f(x_1, x_2)$ be the objective function of a linear program. Then

$$\begin{aligned} f(x_1, x_2) &= c_1x_1 + c_2x_2 \\ &= f_1(x_1) + f_2(x_2) \end{aligned} \tag{4.9}$$

where $f_1(x_1) = c_1x_1$ and $f_2(x_2) = c_2x_2$. Thus the objective function is linear and separable.

(b) The linear programming objective function in n variables can be stated similarly as a separable function as:

$$
\begin{aligned}
f(x_1, \ldots, x_n) &= c_1x_1 + \cdots + c_nx_n \\
&= f_1(x_1) + \cdots + f_n(x_n) \\
&= \sum_{j=1}^{n} f_j(x_j)
\end{aligned} \tag{4.10}
$$

where $f_j(x_j) = c_jx_j$ for $j = 1, \ldots, n$.

(c) Consider the case when

$$
\begin{aligned}
f(x_1, x_2) &= (9 + x_1^2) + (4 - x_2)^2 \\
&= f_1(x_1) + f_2(x_2)
\end{aligned}
$$

where $f_1(x_1) = (9 + x_1^2)$ and $f_2(x_2) = (4 - x_2)^2$. Note that both $f_1(x_1)$ and $f_2(x_2)$ are convex functions so that by earlier results $f(x_1, x_2)$ is also a convex function.

Given this background we can now state the two kinds of nonlinear programming problems that we will solve in this book.

(a) ***Maximizing a concave separable function subject to linear constraints.*** We state this problem for $m = 3$ and $n = 2$:

$$
\begin{aligned}
\text{Maximize} \quad & f_1(x_1) + f_2(x_2) \\
\text{Subject to} \quad & a_{11}x_1 + a_{12}x_2 \leq b_1 \\
& a_{21}x_1 + a_{22}x_2 = b_2 \\
& a_{31}x_1 + a_{32}x_2 \geq b_3 \\
& x_1, x_2 \geq 0
\end{aligned}
$$

where $f_1(x_1)$ and $f_2(x_2)$ are concave functions. The data box and Kuhn-Tucker constraints for the problem are shown below. Comparing the data box and constraints on pages 48 and 49, we see that the primal Kuhn-Tucker constraints and the complementary slackness conditions are the same except that c_j is replaced by $f_j'(x_j^*)$. Also the u_i variables are called *Lagrange multipliers* instead of dual variables, but they play an entirely analogous role to that played by the dual variables.

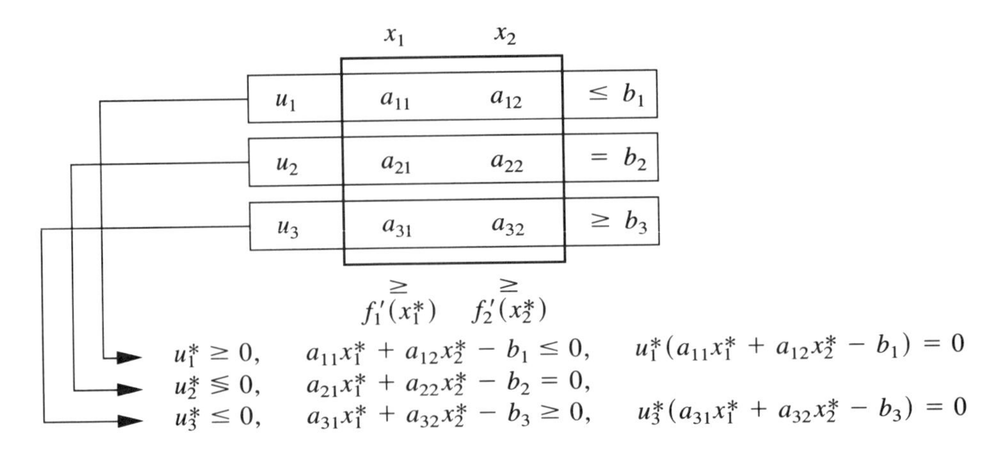

When the objective function is to minimize a convex separable function, reverse the signs of the u_j's.

Comparing the data box and constraints on pages 48 and 49, we see that the dual Kuhn-Tucker constraints and the complementary slackness conditions are again the same except that c_j is replaced by $f_j'(x_j)$.

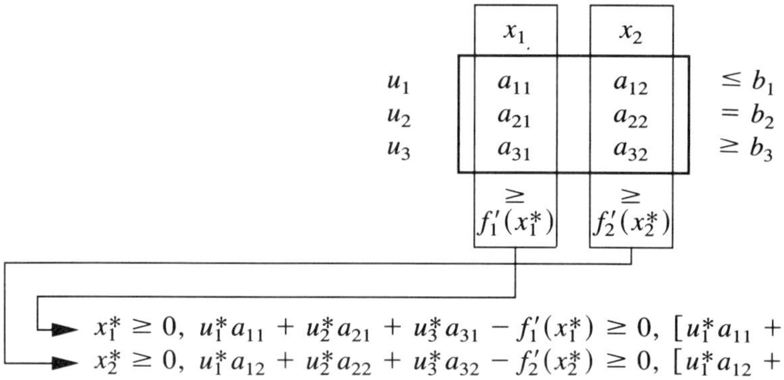

<table>
<tr><td></td><td>x_1</td><td>x_2</td><td></td></tr>
<tr><td>u_1</td><td>a_{11}</td><td>a_{12}</td><td>$\le b_1$</td></tr>
<tr><td>u_2</td><td>a_{21}</td><td>a_{22}</td><td>$= b_2$</td></tr>
<tr><td>u_3</td><td>a_{31}</td><td>a_{32}</td><td>$\ge b_3$</td></tr>
<tr><td></td><td>$\ge$
$f_1'(x_1^*)$</td><td>$\ge$
$f_2'(x_2^*)$</td><td></td></tr>
</table>

$$x_1^* \ge 0,\ u_1^* a_{11} + u_2^* a_{21} + u_3^* a_{31} - f_1'(x_1^*) \ge 0,\ [u_1^* a_{11} + u_2^* a_{21} + u_3^* a_{31} - f_1'(x_1^*)]x_1^* = 0$$

$$x_2^* \ge 0,\ u_1^* a_{12} + u_2^* a_{22} + u_3^* a_{32} - f_2'(x_2^*) \ge 0,\ [u_1^* a_{12} + u_2^* a_{22} + u_3^* a_{32} - f_2'(x_2^*)]x_2^* = 0$$

When the objective function is to minimize a convex separable function, reverse the direction of the dual inequalities.

(b) ***Minimizing a convex separable function subject to linear constraints.*** We also state this problem for $m = 3$ and $n = 2$:

$$\begin{aligned} \text{Minimize} \quad & f_1(x_1) + f_2(x_2) \\ \text{Subject to} \quad & a_{11}x_1 + a_{12}x_2 \le b_1 \\ & a_{21}x_1 + a_{22}x_2 = b_2 \\ & a_{31}x_1 + a_{32}x_2 \ge 0 \\ & x_1, x_2 \ge 0 \end{aligned}$$

where $f_1(x_1)$ and $f_2(x_2)$ are convex functions. The rules for writing the primal and dual Kuhn-Tucker constraints are given above.

Example 5(a). Consider the problem

$$\begin{aligned} \text{Maximize} \quad & (9 - x_1^2) + (4 - x_2^2) \\ \text{Subject to} \quad & 2x_1 + 3x_2 \le 6 \\ & x_1 \ge 2 \\ & x_1, x_2 \ge 0 \end{aligned}$$

Check to see that the objective function is concave.

The data box for the problem is

	x_1	x_2	
u_1	2	3	≤ 6
u_2	1	0	≥ 2
	$\geq$	$\geq$	
	$-2x_1$	$-2x_2$	

By using the Kuhn-Tucker primal conditions above, we easily find the primal Kuhn-Tucker constraints to be:

$$\begin{array}{lll} u_1^* \geq 0, & 2x_1^* + 3x_2^* - 6 \leq 0, & u_1^*(2x_1^* + 3x_2^* - 6) = 0 \\ u_2^* \leq 0, & x_1^* - 2 \geq 0, & u_2^*(x_1^* - 2) = 0 \end{array}$$

Using the Kuhn-Tucker dual conditions above, we find the dual Kuhn-Tucker constraints to be:

$$\begin{array}{lll} x_1^* \geq 0, & 2u_1^* + u_2^* + 2x_1^* \geq 0, & (2u_1^* + u_2^* + 2x_1^*)x_1^* = 0 \\ x_2^* \geq 0, & 3u_1^* + 2x_2^* \geq 0, & (3u_1{}^* + 2x_2^*)x_2^* = 0 \end{array}$$

Example 5(b). Consider the problem

$$\text{Minimize} \quad 4e^{x_1} + (2x_2^2 - 8x_2 + 15)$$

$$\begin{array}{rl} \text{Subject to} & x_1 \leq 20 \\ & 2x_1 - x_2 = 10 \\ & x_2 \geq 5 \\ & x_1, x_2 \geq 0 \end{array}$$

The data box for the problem is

	x_1	x_2	
u_1	1	0	≤ 20
u_2	2	-1	$= 10$
u_3	0	1	≥ 5
	$\leq$	$\leq$	
	$4e^{x_1^*}$	$4x_2^* - 8$	

Again using the Kuhn-Tucker primal conditions, we can easily find the primal Kuhn-Tucker constraints to be:

$$\begin{array}{lll} u_1^* \leq 0, & x_1^* - 20 \leq 0, & u_1^*(x_1^* - 20) = 0 \\ u_2^* \gtrless 0, & 2x_1^* - x_2^* - 10 = 0, & \\ u_3^* \geq 0, & x_2^* - 5 \geq 0, & u_3^*(x_2^* - \ 5) = 0 \end{array}$$

Using the Kuhn-Tucker dual conditions, we find the dual Kuhn-Tucker constraints to be:

$$\begin{array}{lll} x_1^* \geq 0, & u_1^* + 2u_2^* - 4e^{x_1^*} \leq 0, & (u_1^* + 2u_2^* - 4e^{x_1^*})x_1^* = 0 \\ x_2^* \geq 0, & -u_2^* + u_3^* - 4x_2^* + 8 \leq 0, & (-u_2^* + u_3^* - 4x_2^* + 8)x_2{}^* = 0 \end{array}$$

Integer Programming

Many economic problems involve decisions about the allocation of indivisible objects such as automobiles, houses, art objects, people, investment projects, etc. If a mathematical program is written to analyze such a problem an additional requirement on the variables of the problem must be made, namely, that they take on *integer values*. An example will make this clear.

Example 6. A host and hostess are planning beverages to be served at an afternoon party. They have settled on the following rules:

(a) either tea or coffee will be served;

(b) if tea is served then it must be accompanied by lemon or milk;

(c) if coffee is served then it must also be accompanied by cream;

(d) tea must be served with sugar;

(e) coffee must be served with sugar;

(f) pop will be served.

The hosts wish to minimize their costs for the party so they set up an integer programming problem having the following variables and costs;

x_1 = tea is served	cost $c_1 = 2$
x_2 = coffee is served	cost $c_2 = 1.9$
x_3 = sugar is served	cost $c_3 = 1$
x_4 = lemon is served	cost $c_4 = 0.8$
x_5 = cream is served	cost $c_5 = 0.9$
x_6 = milk is served	cost $c_6 = 1$
x_7 = pop is served	cost $c_7 = 2.5$

Each of these is a 0/1 variable where $x_j = 1$ means the corresponding statement is true while $x_j = 0$ means the statement is false. Let us translate conditions (a) through (f) into mathematical constraints involving the x_j variables:

$$
\begin{array}{llr}
(a') & x_1 + x_2 & \geq 1 \\
(b') & -x_1 + x_4 + x_6 & \geq 0 \\
(c') & -x_2 + x_5 & \geq 0 \\
(d') & -x_1 + x_3 & \geq 0 \\
(e') & -x_2 + x_3 & \geq 0 \\
(f') & & x_7 = 1
\end{array}
$$

To check the correctness of the translation let us look at condition (a) and inequality (a′). If we remember that x_1 and x_2 each can take on only the values 0 and 1, we can see that constraint (a′) rules out the possibility that $x_1 = 0$ and $x_2 = 0$ which is the event that *neither* tea *nor* coffee is served. However, it permits the three other possibilities $x_1 = 0$ and $x_2 = 1$, $x_1 = 1$ and $x_2 = 0$, and $x_1 = x_2 = 1$. In each of these cases either tea or coffee or both is served.

As another instance let us check the equivalence of statement (b) and inequality (b′). Note that if $x_1 = 0$, that is if tea is not served, then (b′) imposes no constraint on variables x_4 and x_6. However, if $x_1 = 1$ then (b′) becomes $x_4 + x_6 \geq 1$, which is analogous to (a′), and asserts that either $x_4 = 1$ or $x_6 = 1$, or both.

You should check that the translations of the other statements into constraints are also correct.

Now consider the cost of any 0/1 solution of the variables $x_1, \ldots, x_7$ satisfying constraints (a′) through (f′).

It is:

$$(g') \quad z = 2x_1 + 1.9x_2 + x_3 + 0.8x_4 + 0.9x_5 + x_6 + 2.5x_7.$$

The minimum cost solution for the afternoon party can now be stated as a 0/1 integer programming problem: find 0/1 solutions for $x_1, \ldots, x_7$ that minimize the objective (g′) subject to constraints (a′) through (f′).

Your software can solve this problem, and it will find one of the following two answers:

1. $x_1 = x_3 = x_4 = x_7 = 1, \quad x_2 = x_5 = x_6 = 0, \quad z = 6.3$

In this solution tea with lemon and/or sugar and pop will be served at a total cost of \$6.30.

2. $x_2 = x_3 = x_5 = x_7 = 1, \quad x_1 = x_4 = x_6 = 0, \quad z = 6.3$

Here coffee with cream and/or sugar and pop will be served at a total cost of \$6.30.

Notice that the minimizing objective ruled out serving both milk and lemon with the tea, and also ruled out serving both tea and coffee even though these possibilities were permitted by the constraints. Obviously, such possibilities would add to the cost of the optimal solution.

Variables x_j which take on the value 1 when statement j is true and 0 when it is false are sometimes called truth variables for the statement. One common use of such statements is in solving the problem of selecting a set of investments subject to a budget constraint, as the following example illustrates.

Example 7. A firm has \$100 thousand dollars to invest and is considering the following set of possible projects each of which has (in thousands of dollars) a cost and a Net Present Value (NPV) expected return:

Project	*1*	*2*	*3*	*4*	*5*	*6*
NPV	22	37	51	67	102	117
Cost	10	20	30	40	50	60

What is the best way for the firm to invest its money?

To set up this problem we define the 0/1 variable x_j as:

$$x_j = \begin{cases} 1 & \text{invest in project } j, \\ 0 & \text{don't invest in project } j. \end{cases}$$

Then the mathematical programming problem to be solved is:

$$\begin{aligned} \text{Maximize} \quad & z = 22x_1 + 37x_2 + 51x_3 + 67x_4 + 102x_5 + 117x_6 \\ \text{Subject to} \quad & 10x_1 + 20x_2 + 30x_3 + 40x_4 + 50x_5 + 60x_6 = 100 \\ & x_j = 0 \text{ or } 1 \qquad \text{for } j = 1, \ldots, 6. \end{aligned}$$

Your software program will return the following optimal answer:

$$x_1 = x_4 = x_5 = 1, \qquad x_2 = x_3 = x_6 = 0, \qquad z = 191.$$

In other words, the optimal action is to invest the hundred thousand dollars in projects 1, 4, and 5 whose total NPV is 22 + 67 + 102 = 191 thousands of dollars. (In Exercise 5, you will be asked to solve this problem by hand to verify its correctness.)

Exercises

1. Which of the following sets are convex:
   (a) The set of x such that $1 \le x \le 5$.
   (b) The set of x such that $x \le 1$ and $x \ge 5$.
   (c) The set of x such that $x \le 1$ or $x \ge 5$.
   (d) The set of (x_1, x_2) such that $x_1^2 + x_2^2 \le 4$.
   (e) The set of (x_1, x_2) such that $x_1^2 + x_2^2 \ge 4$.

2. Classify the following functions as being convex, concave, or neither in the specified intervals.
   (a) $f(x) = x^3$ in $(0, 10)$
   (b) $f(x) = x^3$ in $(-10, 10)$
   (c) $f(x) = 1 - e^{-x}$ in $(-\infty, \infty)$
   (d) $f(x) = -10x^2 + 25x + 5$ in $(0, 1)$
   (e) $f(x) = 15x^2 - 30x + 10$ in $(-\infty, \infty)$
   (f) $f(x) = 1 + e^{2x}$ in $(-\infty, \infty)$

3. Write the primal and dual Kuhn-Tucker conditions for the following problem: (First show the objective function to be concave or convex as required.)
   (a)
$$\begin{aligned} \text{Maximize} \quad & \ln(x_1) + (1 - e^{-x_2}) \\ \text{Subject to} \quad & 3x_1 + 4x_2 \le 12 \\ & x_1 - x_2 \ge 0 \\ & x_1, x_2 \ge 0 \end{aligned}$$

(b) Minimize $(16 - 8x_1 + x_1^2) + (25 - 10x_2 + x_2^2)$

Subject to
$$-x_1 + x_2 \geq 10$$
$$5x_1 + 10x_2 \leq 100$$
$$x_1, x_2 \geq 0$$

4. Re-solve Example 6 if the price of milk is \$.70 instead of \$.90. Explain the difference in the solution.

5. Answer the following questions concerning Example 7.

   (a) Show that the equation
   $$10x_1 + 20x_2 + 30x_3 + 40x_4 + 50x_5 + 60x_6 = 100$$
   has exactly 5 different solutions with $x_j = 0$ or 1.

   (b) Find the NPV of each of the solutions you found in (a) and show that the best one has a NPV of \$191,000.

6. In Example 7 show that if the NPV of project 4 changes from 67 to 62, there are now two optimal solutions, each having a NPV of \$190,000.

7. Solve the NPV value problem with eight projects a maximum total investment of \$200 and the following data:

Project	*A*	*B*	*C*	*D*	*E*	*F*	*G*	*H*
NPV	58	152	69	93	143	78	23	37
Cost	25	70	35	40	65	30	15	20

8. A problem very similar to the NPV problem is the *knapsack problem*. An example is the problem faced by a hiker going on a camping trip who is willing to carry up to 90 pounds, but has a list of 10 objects whose total weight is 119 pounds. In order to select a subset of items whose total weight is less than or equal to 72 pounds, the hiker assigns a value to each as follows:

Object	*1*	*2*	*3*	*4*	*5*	*6*	*7*	*8*	*9*	*10*
Value	75	46	16	55	6	52	75	24	13	6
Weight	14	7	15	11	16	12	14	10	10	8

Let x_j be a variable that is 1 if the hiker takes object j and 0 if he doesn't take it. The hiker must then solve the problem:

$$\text{Maximize} \quad \sum_{j=1}^{10} V_j x_j$$
$$\text{Subject to} \quad \sum_{j=1}^{10} W_j x_j \leq 72$$
$$x_j = 0 \text{ or } 1 .$$

Solve this problem showing that in the optimal solution the hiker takes six items whose total weight is 68 and total value is 327.

9. Re-solve Exercise 8 if the hiker has the following logical constraints on the choice of the objects:
   (i) at most one of objects 6, 7, and 8 will be chosen;
   (ii) if 1 is chosen, then 3 must also be chosen;
   (iii) if 3 is chosen, then either 8 or 9 must be chosen.
10. Re-work problem 9 if the hiker decides he can carry 90 pounds.

PART II

Production, Inventories, Capital Budgeting & Personnel Planning

INTRODUCTION

The second part of this book deals with a business organization (a firm) which is engaged in economic activities that create economic values. Such creation of value economists call *production*. This is a somewhat inappropriate name because many other activities other than factory production also create value for business organizations. Among such activities are organizational change, innovative activities, new product research and development, and portfolio management. Also many of the economic values created today are services and software rather than industrial goods.

The material to be presented in Part II has been brought into economics from the closely related fields of operations research and management science. During the last 35 years a vast body of knowledge in those fields has been discovered which relates to the nature of the operations of the modern business organization. In the following chapters a series of mathematical programming models that have been developed to analyze the managerial problems of firms will be discussed.

A student who is familiar with *the theory of the firm* as taught in a principles of economics textbook should regard the material to follow as a complementary rather than a competing body of knowledge. One way to characterize the operations research and management science approach is to say that it deals with the business organization in much greater detail than is customary in economics texts. In so doing, it is able to employ concepts which are operationally meaningful and which relate to the actual management and conduct of the business organization.

Revenues and Costs

The purpose of the micro theory of production is to discuss the input decisions that a producer must make in order to convert inputs into outputs. Typically, the producer is assumed to be a "price taker," that is, he will assume that the market prices of all inputs such as raw materials, semifinished products, labor, and capital are given and known. He also assumes that the prices that his outputs will fetch upon delivery are given and known. An individual producer is supposed to be "small" in relation to the total volume of transactions in the markets both for inputs and outputs so that his production does not influence their market prices.

Assuming that the producer manufactures a single good, total revenue then is proportional to the output of that good. The total revenue curve in Figure II-1(a) is a ray

Figure II-1

Total revenue and marginal revenue curves.

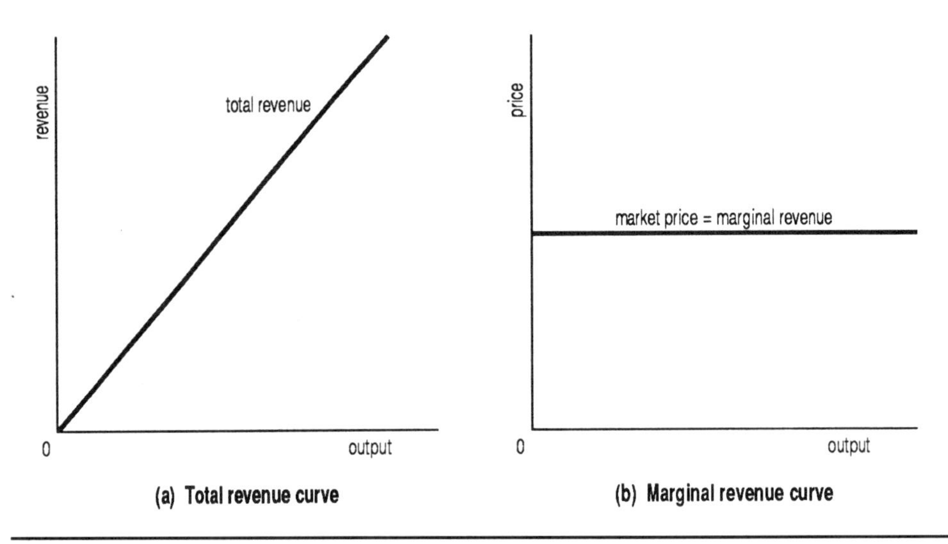

(a) Total revenue curve **(b) Marginal revenue curve**

through the origin. Marginal revenue, the revenue from the "last" unit of output, is constant and is equal to the market price; see Figure II-1(b).

Turning to the cost side, total costs consist of fixed costs and variable costs. Let us first discuss the cost structure illustrated in Figure II-2. Fixed costs, such as the costs of machinery and other fixed equipment, have to be paid regardless of the scale of operations. They can be read off the diagram in the Figure II-2(a) as the intercept on the vertical axis of the total cost curve.

The diagram shows a case where variable costs grow only slowly as operations get under way. Eventually, however, capacity limits of various kinds are encountered (defined by the size of the current plant, the availability of qualified management and skilled labor, etc.) and costs escalate quickly. The total cost curve in Figure II-2(a) is convex. Marginal costs are increasing; the marginal cost curve is forward sloping.

As the diagram in Figure II-2(a) shows, there is an output interval in which total revenue exceeds total costs. Clearly, the optimal production point is located at point A at which the slope of the total cost curve equals the slope of the total revenue curve. At that point, the surplus of total revenue above total costs (the profit) is maximal. The same point A can be located in Figure II-2(b) where the marginal cost curve intersects the price line.

Furthermore, the optimal production point determined in this fashion is *stable*: that is, a small deviation away from it will set up incentives that cause the producer to return to it. Assume that the producer happens to overshoot the optimal output OA. If the overshooting is not excessive, total revenues will still exceed total costs. But the cost of manufacturing the "last" unit of output will now exceed the price that it fetches [see Figure II-2(b)]. That last unit is therefore unprofitable and should never have been manufactured. The producer will voluntarily curtail output in order to reestablish equality between marginal cost and the market price.

Figure II-2

Total and marginal revenues and costs.

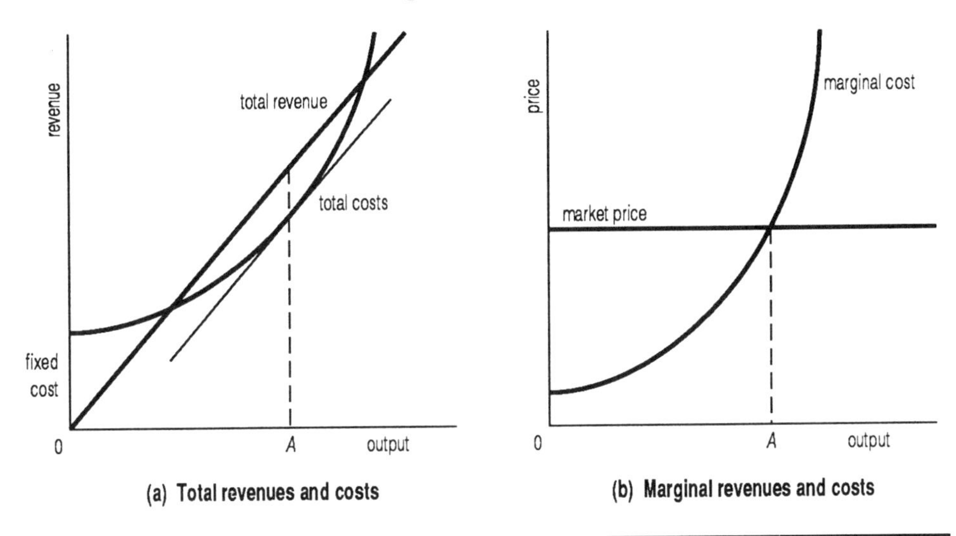

(a) Total revenues and costs

(b) Marginal revenues and costs

An entirely different picture is the one represented in Figure II-3(a). Here the total cost curve rises rapidly at the outset, but eventually flattens out. The total cost curve is concave. As the scale of operations is being increased, marginal costs fall.

There may still exist a point at which the marginal cost equals the market price (point A). But this point is no longer a solution to the production problem. For one thing, at

Figure II-3

Revenues and costs, case of decreasing marginal costs.

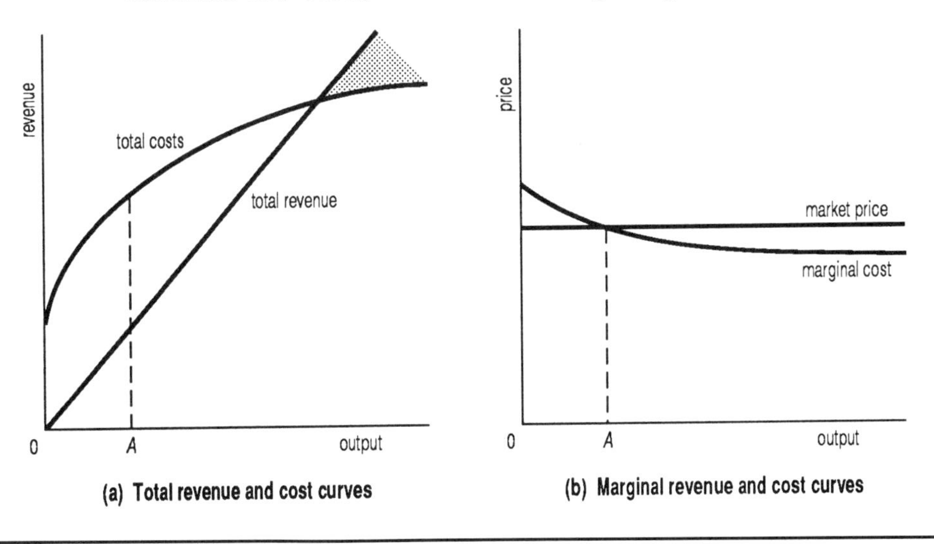

(a) Total revenue and cost curves

(b) Marginal revenue and cost curves

Figure II-4

Revenues and costs, case of constant marginal costs.

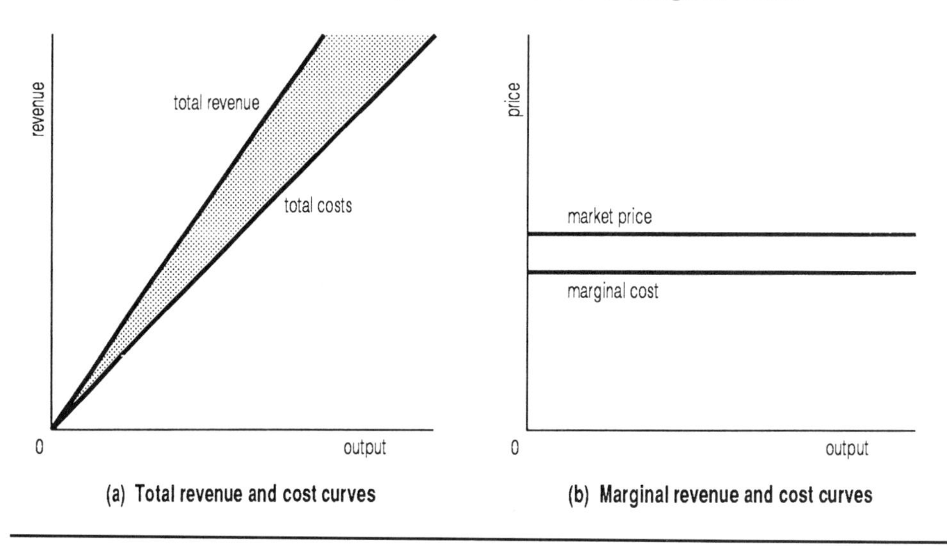

(a) Total revenue and cost curves **(b) Marginal revenue and cost curves**

this point the producer would suffer a loss. For another, point *A* is unstable. For consider a slight displacement from point *A*, letting the producer obtain a volume of output slightly greater than *OA*. The cost of manufacturing that "last" unit of output falls short of the price that it fetches [Figure II-3(b)]. That unit yields a positive profit. The producer will step up production even further, moving toward the right in the diagram, away from point *A*.

Where will this movement away from *A* stop? Soon the producer will reach output levels at which total revenue exceeds total cost, which is the shaded region in Figure II-3(a). Provided the total cost curve continues to flatten, the producer can reach even larger profits by moving further to the right in the diagram. There exists no stable static solution for this case. The producer will engage on a path of extended growth.

There is considerable empirical evidence that total cost curves for many real life corporations may indeed by comparatively flat at least over a limited range. One mechanism at work which causes this to be true is the "learning effect." Learning has been observed in a wide range of industrial operations, such as building airplanes, assembling computers, or even performing open heart surgery. Through learning, marginal costs come down, pulling down both average costs and total costs. Indeed, the downward sloping marginal cost curve in Figure II-3 may be thought of as being traced by a producer who is gradually expanding output, at each time seeing a short term prospective upward sloping curve ahead of him but actually, because of learning, following a downward sloping cost curve.

In most industries there are examples of maverick corporations which, beating all odds and outperforming their competitors, are engaged in paths of spectacular growth. Apple Computer once was an example of such rapid growth; there are many others. Indeed, in the present high technology era there seems to be promise of rapid evolution in entire industries, such as the biotechnology industry. Nonconvergent dynamic processes of growth in emergent industries certainly are part of the reality with which the student of economics must grapple.

Figure II-5

Input isoquant curve. (Refer to Figure 6.1 in Chapter 6 for a numerical example.)

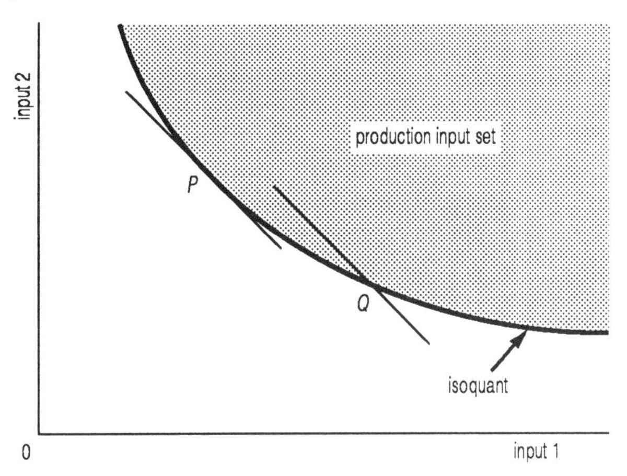

Consider also the limiting case shown in Figure II-4. Here the total cost curve is neither strictly concave nor stictly convex—it is linear, a ray through the origin. Marginal costs (and average costs) are constant. Assuming that revenue covers cost, the producer will make a profit. In this case as well, the final solution is indeterminate.

Using an obvious term, the case now mentioned may be referred to as *constant returns to scale*. If the total cost curve is strictly convex, there are *decreasing returns to scale*; and if it is strictly concave, there are *increasing returns to scale*.

Isoquants and Isocosts

When a producer employs two or more outputs, such as several kinds of specialized labor, or labor and capital, there is usually some possibility of substituting, at the margin, the use of one input for another. For instance, some use of labor may be replaced by the use of labor-saving machinery. Obviously, such possibilities will vary from industry to industry. The assembly of a motorcar, for instance, obviously requires one engine and one body and four wheels for each car. But there are substitution possibilities between the use of steel and plastics in making certain parts.

An *isoquant* (Figure II-5) is a locus of alternative input points in the input space that yield a given or fixed amount of output (or, in the case of several outputs, given and fixed amounts of each of the entire list of outputs). Varying that fixed amount of output parametrically, one obtains the entire map of isoquants, of which only one is shown in Figure II-5.

Consider the set of input points in Figure II-5 that yield at least a given and fixed amount of output. It is assumed that the set (called the "production input set") is convex. The isoquant curve is the lower boundary of this convex set.

Expressed in another way, convexity assures that the production input set will always be located in its entirety above any tangent to the isoquant curve.

Figure II-6

Isocost curve.

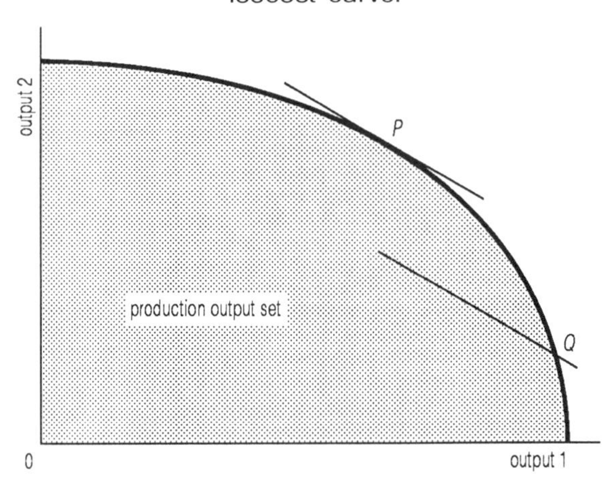

The producer being a price taker, the prices of inputs are fixed and known. At any point in the input space one can then calculate the total cost of inputs. In the case of two inputs, total cost is obtained as (the price of first input) × (use of first input) + (price of second input) × (use of second input). Starting from an arbitrary point on the isoquant such as point Q in Figure II-5, one may proceed to identify all other input combinations that have the same cost. They are all located along a straight line that passes through Q. The slope of the line equals (the negative of) the price ratio between the two inputs, say $-q_1/q_2$ (using the letter q to denote an input price).

Now consider the problem of locating the particular point along the isoquant at which *total input cost is minimal*. It is point P in Figure II-5. A straight line having a slope equal to $-q_1/q_2$ is tangent to the isoquant at point P.

The tangency condition can be further elaborated as follows: The isoquant gives the rate of substitution between the two inputs that is possible given the existing technology. The straight line is a budget line, joining together all input combinations that can be purchased with that input budget. At P, the point of optimum, the rate of substitution between the two inputs which is possible at the margin, must equal the negative of the ratio between the prices of those inputs.

An *isocost* curve (Figure II-6) is the locus of alternative output points in the output space that can be reached, employing those combinations of inputs whose total cost is a constant. By varying that total cost parametrically, one can obtain an entire map of isocost curves, of which only one is shown in Figure II-6.

Consider the production output set shown in Figure II-6 consisting of all output points that can be attained using inputs whose total cost is at most equal to a given amount. It is assumed that the output set is convex. The isocost curve is the upper boundary of this convex set. The output set, and its boundary, is located in its entirety below each tangent to the isocost curve.

The isocost curve illustrates the possibilities of substitution between the two inputs that a given input budget allows.

At any point in the output space one can calculate the total revenue obtained from manufacturing and selling that combination of outputs. In the case of two outputs, total revenue is obtained as (price of the first output) × (quantity of first output sold) + (price of the second output) × (quantity of the second output sold). Starting out from an arbitrary point on the isocost such as point Q, one can identify all other output combinations which would fetch the same revenue. They are all located along a straight line passing through Q. The slope of the line equals (the negative of) the price ratio between the two outputs, say $-p_1/p_2$ (using letter p to denote an output price.)

At the point of optimum, point P, the rate of substitution which is possible by substituting one output by the other at the margin, is equal to the negative of the ratio between the prices of those outputs.

If all the optimality conditions in the input space and in the output space stated above are satisfied, the producer is said to be "optimally adjusted," or simply "adjusted."

An Overview of the Chapters in Part II

The underlying reason why any good can command a positive price in the market place is that it is scarce. Chapter 5 gives an account of the basic linear programming model of production by the use of scarce factors such as labor and resources.

One of the basic tenets of modern economics is that economic agents will behave rationally, that is, they will maximize some objective function while staying within resource constraints. They will then be looking for an optimal point located on the production frontier where inputs are efficiently converted into outputs. In order to test this theory, and in order to establish the production frontier empirically, the methods of data envelopment analysis can be invoked. This technique, the subject of Chapter 6, was developed to compare different decision making units, with only those operating at the frontier being deemed efficient. This method has been used to compare efficiencies of both for profit and nonprofit organizations.

As the rash of corporate takeovers in the 1980s has demonstrated, sometimes the mere restructuring of ownership of or the change of management at a production facility, can dramatically change its production capabilities. What is at issue here is the organizational structure of the firm, the hierarchy of management responsibilities, and the delegation of production decisions to individual production units, see Chapter 7. The problems involved here are not only to coordinate the management decisions concerning individual production facilities, but also to manage the flows of one or several goods through a vertical chain of both production facilities and distribution channels, such as the flow of oil products through an integrated oil company, see Chapter 8.

The concept of vertical integration is studied in more detail in Chapter 9 in which a vertically integrated paper company is modelled by means of a linear program.

Economists have previously categorized the factors of production under two headings: capital and labor. There were two categories of real capital, inventories (circulating capital) and machinery and other fixed capital. In the last three chapters of Part II, we study all of these factors. These chapters also bring in the time dimension of the operation and management of enterprises. The problem is to determine the optimal employment of factors of production over time.

Chapter 10 discusses the management of inventory systems, which in the early 1960s became the showcase of successful operations research applications. A comparison is made between a "transactions motive" and a "speculation motive" for holding inventories, and mathematical programming models are developed that cover both situations.

The choice of a series of good investment projects is of crucial importance to maintain the continued vigor of a corporation over time. In Chapter 11 the solution to this problem, by means of an integer programming model of capital budgeting, is developed.

In Chapter 12 personnel systems in large private or public institutions are considered. Such systems may steadily increase or decrease or simply fluctuate. Examples are of personnel systems in military and industrial organizations.

Notes on Literature Relevant to Part II

From its inception by Leonid Kantorovich and George Dantzig in the 1930s and 1940s, linear programming has been employed to model problems of economics and the management of a firm, see [8,13]. The name programming means, "a statement of the actions to be performed, their timing, and their quantity, which will permit the system to move from a given status toward defined objective," see [8] page 2. An early example of a book that made significant connections between economics and mathematical programming is [10] by Robert Dorfman, Paul Samuelson, and Robert Solow published in 1958. Samuelson received (as noted earlier) the 1970 Nobel Prize in Economics; later Robert Solow received the 1987 Nobel Prize in Economics. Another, later book connecting economics and mathematical programming is [2] by William Baumol. The material in Chapter 5 is related to that contained in the above two books. The optimal machine loading problem in that chapter was contained in the translation (from Russian) of the paper [13] by Leonid Kantorovich who, as mentioned earlier, shared the 1975 Nobel Prize in Economics.

Data envelopment analysis, which is the subject matter of Chapter 6, is due to Abraham Charnes, William Cooper, and Edward Rhodes [7]. This idea, which is only a few years old, has already brought forth several hundred research and application papers. For earlier related developments, see Farrell [11] and Afriat [1]. The concept of bounded rationality mentioned in the chapter is due to Herbert Simon, who was the 1978 Nobel Laureate in Economics.

The decentralization theory of the firm presented in Chapter 7 is distilled from the decomposition method of George Dantzig and Phillip Wolfe for solving staircase linear programs [9]. The text in Chapter 7 discusses only the economics of decentralization and the problems of control that arise between the headquarters and the divisions. (Algorithmic matters are not touched on at all.) The concept of coherent decentralization is due to Abraham Charnes, R. Clower, and Kenneth Kortanek [4], as does the theorem that a separable strictly concave staircase program can be decomposed by means of prices alone.

The commodity flow model given in Chapter 8 is a very elementary example of the well known network flow model. For a good early reference on the subject, see L. Ford and D. Fulkerson [12].

The paper company model discussed in Chapter 9 is a network flow model with (non-network) side constraints. Similar kinds of constrained network models have appeared previously in the literature.

The original version of the warehouse model, the subject of Chapter 10, is due to A. Cahn [3] and appeared in 1948. Generalizations of the warehouse model by Charnes and Cooper appear in [5].

The capital budgeting models which appear in Chapter 11, were the subject of the Ph.D. thesis of Martin Weingartner, see [14]. He received a Ford Foundation Thesis prize for this work and his capital budgeting models appear in many current finance textbooks.

The personnel planning model which appears in Chapter 12 is a very simple version of the original one published in Abraham Charnes, William Cooper, and Richard Niehaus in [6]. Following the publication of that paper many hundreds of other papers on the same or similar subjects appeared by these and many other authors. Moreover, personnel models such as these have been applied successfully by personnel managers in various large industrial and military organizations.

References

1. Afriat, S. N., "Efficiency Estimation of Production Functions," *International Economic Review*, 13 (1972) 568–598.
2. Baumol, W. J., *Economic Theory and Operations Analysis*, Prentice–Hall, Englewood Cliffs, N.J., first ed. 1961, fourth ed. 1977.
3. Cahn, A. S., "The Warehouse Problem," (abstract), *Bulletin of the American Mathematical Society*, 54 (1948) 1073.
4. Charnes, A., R. W. Clower, and K. O. Kortanek, "Effective Control Through Coherent Decentralization with Preemptive Goals," *Econometrica*, 35 (1967) 294–320.
5. Charnes, A., and W. W. Cooper, "Generalizations of the Warehousing Model," *Operations Research Quarterly*, 6 (1955) 131–172.
6. Charnes, A., W. W. Cooper and R. J. Niehaus, "A Goal Programming Model for Manpower Planning," in J. Blood (ed.), *Management Science in Planning and Control*, Technical Association of the Pulp and Paper Industry, New York 1968.
7. Charnes, A., W. W. Cooper and E. Rhodes, "Measuring Efficiency of Decision Making Units," *European Journal of Operational Research*, 1 (1978) 429–444.
8. Dantzig, G., *Linear Programming and Extensions*, Princeton University Press, Princeton, N.J., 1963.
9. Dantzig, G., and P. Wolfe, "Decomposition Principle for Linear Programs," *Operations Research*, 1 (1960) 101–111.
10. Dorfman, R., P. A. Samuelson and R. M. Solow, *Linear Programming and Economic Analysis*, McGraw–Hill, New York, 1958.
11. Farrell, M. J., "The Measurement of Productive Efficiency," *Journal of the Royal Statistical Society*, CXX (1957) 253–290.

12. Ford Jr., L. R., and D. R. Fulkerson, *Flows in Networks*, Princeton University Press, Princeton, N. J., 1962.
13. Kantorovich, L., "Mathematical Methods of Organizing and Planning Production," Leningrad University, 1939 (in Russian). Translated into English and republished under the same title in *Management Science*, 6 (1960) 363–422.
14. Weingartner, H. M., *Mathematical Programming and the Analysis of Capital Budgeting Problems*, Prentice–Hall, Inc., Englewood Cliffs, N.J., 1963.

5

Limited Availability of Production Factors

Conventional production theory, as encountered in textbooks in economics is based on two postulates: (i) There exists a so-called *production function*, relating the quantity of outputs obtained to the quantity of inputs or *production factors* used; (ii) The producer is a *price-taker*, i.e., he faces given and fixed factor prices and output prices. Geometrically, both the demand curves for outputs and the supply curves for factors are horizontal. Using these assumptions it is possible to form the mathematical expression of total costs and total revenue, and then proceed to maximize net profit.

For many inputs, such as electricity and fuels, unskilled labor, lumber, steel, the assumption that prices are fixed may be quite realistic. But when it comes to providing the required inputs of skilled labor, machines, capital and land, a producer may often not be able to purchase in any quantity that he wishes: the availability of these inputs may be *restricted*, at least in the short run. A producer has on its payroll an existing stock of skilled labor; additional workers may be hired and trained, but it will take some time before they are able to add to the productive capacity. The producer will also have at his disposal some existing production facilities, such as machines, floor space, and other fixed equipment. Through investment, additional capital equipment may be acquired but, again, this will take time. In the short run, the producer must make do with the existing stocks. Geometrically, the supply curves for such factors are vertical.

The production theory that will be developed in the present chapter is based on these two postulates: (i) The production function, linking the quantities of inputs to the quantities of outputs, is linear. (ii) Some factors of production have a limited availability. The task of finding an optimal production plan then can be written as a problem of linear programming.

In the first instance, we shall simply assume that the production of each good is characterized by constant unit requirements of the various inputs (so-called *technical coefficients*). These requirements will be spelled out as the numbers of engineers, clerical

Figure 5.1

Illustration of the case of constant technical coefficients.

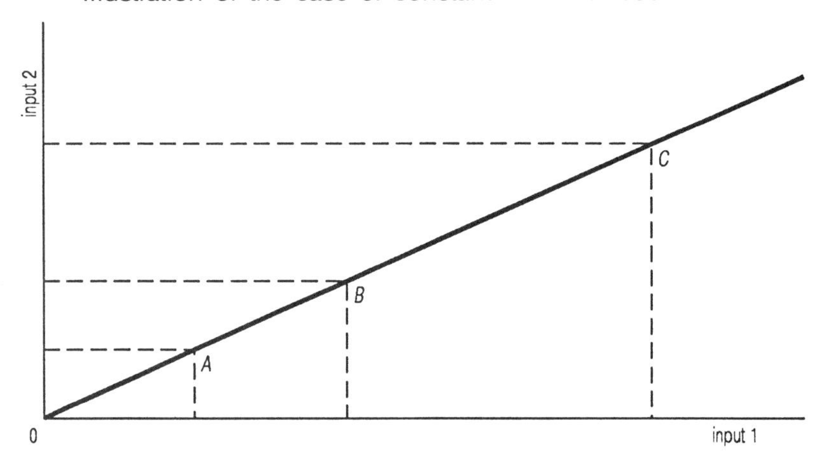

staff and other labor categories, the numbers of machine hours on various machines, and so on, needed to produce one unit of the good in question. In order to produce two units, twice as much of each input is needed. In other words, we assume *constant returns to scale*. See also Figure 5.1. The diagram shows the space of two inputs, input 1 and input 2. Point A indicates the requirements needed to produce one unit of the output in question. Point B which uses twice as much of each input, yields two units of output. As production is expanded further, the input point traces the ray $OABC$ through the origin.

In order to make these ideas specific, consider a producer who uses unskilled labor, raw materials and several different machines to produce several outputs. Unskilled labor and raw materials can be bought in the economic market-place as required, at fixed unit costs. But the existing supply of machines is limited.

We use the following notation:

m = number of machines.

n = number of goods.

x_j = number of units of good j to be produced.

a_{ij} = number of hours of machine i needed to produce one unit of good j.

$A = \|a_{ij}\|$ is the coefficient matrix.

p_j = unit sales price of good j.

c_j = raw materials cost for one unit of good j.

h_j = number of worker hours needed to produce one unit of good j.

r = wage rate ($/hr) for labor.

b_j = number of hours of machine i available.

u_i = the dual variable associated with constraint i whose interpretation is the *imputed value of an hour of machine* i.

The coefficients h_j, c_j and a_{ij} are the technical coefficients of unskilled labor, raw materials, and machine hours of machine i, respectively.

Let p be the row vector of sales prices, c be the row vector of raw material variable costs, and h be the row vector of worker hours needed. Then since rh is the row vector of variable wage costs, it follows that $\hat{p}$ defined as

$$\hat{p} = p - rh - c \tag{5.1}$$

is the net profit vector. Multiplying (5.1) on the right by the column output vector x we obtain

$$\hat{p}x = px - rhx - cx \tag{5.2}$$

which means that the net profit from an activity level x is the gross revenue, px, less the wage cost, rhx, less the raw materials cost cx.

What the owner of the factory wants to do is to choose an output vector x that does not exceed the machine availability and that maximizes net profit. The problem becomes the linear program stated in (5.3).

$$\begin{aligned} &\text{Maximize} \quad \hat{p}x \\ &\text{Subject to} \quad Ax \le b \\ &\qquad\qquad\quad\; x \ge 0 \end{aligned} \tag{5.3}$$

In words, the task of the producer is to maximize the net profit of his operations above labor and raw material costs, subject to the limited availability of machine hours on the machines. Outputs are required to be nonnegative. Problem (5.3) is called the *primal linear program.*

We now associate a dual variable u_i with each constraint of (5.3). We will shortly show that the (physical) dimensions of u_i are dollars/machine i hour, so that we can interpret *u_i as the imputed value of a machine i hour.*

If not all of the available machine i hours are used then the machine is idle part of the time, so that the value of still more time on machine i would be worthless; i.e., $u_i = 0$. On the other hand if all of the machine i hours are used up then the value of u_i for additional time on machine i is positive or at least nonnegative. Denoting optimal solution values by an asterisk, we conclude that the condition in (5.4) should hold.

$$u_i^*[b_i - (a_{i1}x_1^* + a_{i2}x_2^* + \cdots + a_{in}x_n^*)] = 0 \tag{5.4}$$

Stated in words this first *complementary slackness condition* is: (i) if $u_i^* > 0$, then the output vector x^* uses up all of the machine i hours exactly; and (ii) if some of machine i hours are not used by the output vector x^*, then u_i^*, the imputed value of additional machine i hours, must be zero.

The unit cost of producing good j is

$$rh_j + c_j + (u_1a_{1j} + u_2a_{2j} + \cdots + u_ma_{mj}) \tag{5.5}$$

where the first term in (5.5) is the unit labor cost, the second term the unit raw materials cost, and the summation in parentheses is the imputed machining cost, which is equal to its imputed value. The imputation scheme requires that the manufacture of any good can never yield a profit, i.e., the expression in (5.5) must be greater than or equal to the unit price of good j:

$$rh_j + c_j + (u_1 a_{1j} + u_2 a_{2j} + \cdots + u_m a_{mj}) \geq p_j \tag{5.6}$$

Rewriting (5.6) we obtain (5.7)

$$u_1 a_{1j} + u_2 a_{2j} + \cdots + u_m a_{mj} \geq p_j - rh_j - c_j = \hat{p}_j \tag{5.7}$$

The *dual linear program* associated with the primal problem (5.3) is to determine the dual variables u_i so that the total imputed value of all the machine hours is minimal, subject to constraints (5.7) and nonnegativity constraints:

$$\begin{aligned} &\text{Minimize} \quad ub \\ &\text{Subject to} \quad uA \geq \hat{p} \\ &\qquad\qquad\quad u \geq 0 \end{aligned} \tag{5.8}$$

If in the optimal solution there is any positive production x_j^* of product j its sales price must exactly equal the costs (real and imputed) of production, i.e., (5.6) and (5.7) must hold as equalities. Conversely, if the costs of production exceed the sales price, production of good j will be discontinued. This is expressed by (5.9), which is the second *complementary slackness condition*.

$$[(u_1^* a_{1j} + \cdots + u_m^* a_{mj}) - \hat{p}_j]x_j^* = 0 \tag{5.9}$$

If we combine the two complementary slackness conditions (5.4) and (5.9) it is easy to show that

$$\hat{p}_1 x_1^* + \cdots + \hat{p}_n x_n^* = u_1^* b_1 + \cdots + u_m^* b_m \tag{5.10}$$

From (5.10) it is clear that both objective functions are evaluated in dollars. From this it follows directly that the dimensions of the dual variable u_i are dollars/hour on machine i.

In vector form (5.10) is simply

$$\hat{p}x^* = u^* b \tag{5.11}$$

which means that at the optimum the objective functions of the maximizing primal and the minimizing dual problems are equal.

Relation (5.10) permits us to offer yet another interpretation of the dual variables u_i. Note that u_i^* is the marginal change of the objective function caused when b_i is increased by one unit. Hence, u_i^* can be interpreted as the net return (above labor costs) that the producer would be able to attain, were he to be offered an additional hour of time of ith machine. Hence, u_i^* is also *the highest price that a producer will be willing to pay for such an additional unit of machine capacity.*

Example 1. In order to illustrate numerically the above discussion, consider a factory that manufactures wooden dining room sets. Each dining set consists of one dining table and six upright chairs. The product line consists of three different brands, named Victorian, Bohemian, and Modern. The furniture market is highly competitive, and the wholesale prices received for the three brands are \$2,780, \$3,225, and \$2,450, respectively.

The manufacturing process requires that each product goes through three successive work shops: the saw shop, the carpenter shop, and the paint shop. Each of these work shops contains specialized machinery. The labor hours, raw materials cost and shop time requirements are shown below:

Resources Needed	*Victorian*	*Bohemian*	*Modern*	*Shop Hours Available*
Labor hours	16	20	10	
Raw materials cost	\$800	\$625	\$950	
Saw shop hours	2	3	2	400 hrs/wk
Carpenter shop hours	5	4	1.5	625 hrs/wk
Paint shop hours	1.5	1.25	0.75	200 hrs/wk

Labor is paid \$30/hour in each shop. The net profit from each brand is shown below:

	Victorian	*Bohemian*	*Modern*
Labor cost	480	600	300
Raw material cost	800	625	950
Total cost	1280	1225	1250
Selling price	2780	3225	2450
Net profit	1500	2000	1200

The above information can be used to formulate a linear program to determine the best weekly mix of the three brands to make. Let x_1, x_2, and x_3 denote the number of units of each brand to be made each week. The data box of the maximizing linear program then is:

Victorian x_1	*Bohemian* x_2	*Modern* x_3	
2	3	2	$\leq$ 400 saw shop hours
5	4	1.5	$\leq$ 625 carpenter shop hours
1.5	1.25	0.75	$\leq$ 200 paint shop hours
1500	2000	1200	

The optimal solution found by solving the GAMS program `FURNITURE` on page 307 is:

$$x_1^* = 39.29 \text{ units of Victorian per week}$$
$$x_2^* = 107.14 \text{ units of Bohemian per week}$$
$$x_3^* = 0 \text{ units of Modern per week}$$

(The fractional units represent partially finished dining sets at the end of the week.)

The solution printout also shows that there are 7.13 available hours not used in the paint shop. This implies that the dual variable of the third constraint must be 0. The complete optimal dual solution is

$$u_1^* = 571.43 \text{ \$/saw shop hour}$$
$$u_2^* = 71.43 \text{ \$/carpenter shop hour}$$
$$u_3^* = 0 \text{ \$/paint shop hour}$$

It is instructive to calculate the out of pocket and imputed costs of each brand of furniture as shown below:

Costs	*Victorian*	*Bohemian*	*Modern*
Labor (out of pocket)	480.00	600.00	300.00
Material (out of pocket)	800.00	625.00	950.00
Saw shop (imputed)	1142.86	1714.29	1142.86
Carpenter shop (imputed)	357.15	285.72	107.15
Paint shop (imputed)	0.00	0.00	0.00
Total	2780.01	3225.01	2500.01

The costs of the Victorian and Bohemian brands add up to exactly their market prices, as they should since these two are produced in positive amounts. However the total cost of the Modern brand *exceeds* its market price by $50, so that it is not produced.

We can also give a managerial interpretation of the dual solution by supposing that the factory manager asks, "What if we should expand one of the shops in order to increase our weekly output? Which shop would be the best to expand?" It is clear that the paint shop should not be enlarged because the imputed value of an additional hour in that shop is $0. It already has unused hours. As for the two other shops, an additional saw shop hour is about 8 times as valuable as an additional carpenter shop hour. The decision as to which of these two to expand depends on other factors such as the amount of investment needed for the expansion of each of these shops. It is clear that the values of the dual variables help in the evaluation of alternatives, but do not completely determine the answer to the expansion question.

Proportional Production

In the early part of the twentieth century it was common for workers to be paid *piecework wages*, that is, they would get a fixed amount for each unit they completed. This method of payment led workers to choose to make the parts they could finish most quickly and learn to produce them at a faster and faster rate. If the completed units could be sold as is, piecework wages offer a valuable incentive for maximum production. However, today most products require the production of various parts which are then assembled in certain proportions to make a completed product. An example is the dining room set considered previously which consists of one table and six chairs. In order not to have either finished chairs without a table or finished tables without chairs piling up in a warehouse, it is necessary to schedule the ongoing production of tables and chairs so that the one to six ratio of tables to chairs is maintained.

Example 2. In the dining room set considered in Example 1, assume that the times for the production of the Victorian model and the total shop hours of each type allocated to its production are as shown below:

	Chairs	*Tables*	
Saw shop	0.25 hrs/chair	0.5 hrs/table	80 hrs/wk allocated
Carpenter shop	0.6 hrs/chair	1.4 hrs/table	200 hrs/wk allocated
Paint shop	0.2 hrs/chair	0.3 hrs/table	60 hrs/wk allocated

In order to determine the optimal production quantities, the linear programming data box of the problem appears below:

	Chairs x	*Tables* y		
u_1	0.25	0.5	≤ 80	saw shop constraint
u_2	0.6	1.4	≤ 200	carpentry shop constraint
u_3	0.2	0.3	≤ 60	paint shop constraint
u_4	1	-6	$= 0$	proportionality constraint
	0	1		

Since each dining set contains one table, the objective function is to maximize y the number of tables which is the same as maximizing the number of dining sets. The first three constraints keep the production time requirements in the various shops within the stated limits. The last constraint is $x = 6y$, that is, exactly six times as many chairs as tables are to be produced.

The optimal solution can be found by solving the GAMS program PROPROD on page 308. The optimal primal solution is $x = 240$ and $y = 40$, so that 40 Victorian sets should be produced each week. The optimal dual solution is

$$u_1^* = 0, \qquad u_2^* = 0.2, \qquad u_3^* = 0, \qquad u_4^* = -0.12.$$

Notice that the last, equality, constraint has a negative dual variable, meaning that it is acting as a $\geq$ constraint. In other words, the optimizing solution would prefer to make *fewer* than six chairs per table. The reason is: the imputed cost of making one chair is $0.6u_2^* = 0.6 \times 0.2 = 0.12$, so that the imputed cost of making six chairs is $6 \times 0.12 = 0.72$; however, the imputed cost of making one table is only $1.4u_2^* = 1.4 \times 0.2 = 0.28$. It is obvious that whenever several different parts must be made to go into the same assembly, some will be easier to make and others more difficult. However, all must be completed in the required proportions in order to obtain the desired completed assemblies.

The Optimal Machine Loading Problem

There is a closely related production problem which also involves proportional production. That is the *machine loading* problem first formulated by the Russian mathematician

L. V. Kantorovich in the late 1930s. We formulate his machine loading problem next.

Consider a factory having m machines and producing n parts. Each part can be produced on each machine, but with varying degrees of efficiency. At the end of the day, the parts are assembled into final products; hence they must be produced in exact proportions so that, after the assembly of the final products, no parts are left over. The objective is to maximize the number of completed final products in order to meet (or exceed) the factory's production quota.

Example 3. As a numerical example, consider the problem (which first appeared in Kantorovich's paper) whose data is:

	Part 1 (parts/hr)	*Part 2 (parts/hr)*	*Machine availability*
Machine 1	10	20	9 hrs/day
Machine 2	20	30	9 hrs/day
Machine 3	30	80	3 hrs/day

There is also the additional condition that the total production of part 1 should be equal to the total production of part 2. In order to set up a linear program to solve this problem we define

$$x_{ij} = \text{the number of hours spent producing part } j \text{ on machine } i$$
$$z = \text{the number of units of each part produced.}$$

The data box for the problem appears below:

	x_{11}	x_{12}	x_{21}	x_{22}	x_{31}	x_{32}	z	
u_1	1	1						≤ 9
u_2			1	1				≤ 9
u_3					1	1		≤ 3
u_4	10		20		30		-1	$= 0$
u_5		20		30		80	-1	$= 0$
	0	0	0	0	0	0	1	

The optimal primal solution found by solving the GAMS program `KANTOROVICH` on page 309 was:

$$x_{11}^* = 8, \quad x_{12}^* = 1, \quad x_{21}^* = 9, \quad x_{32}^* = 3, \quad z = 260$$

All other x_{ij} were 0. Note that this production plan permits 260 of each part to be produced so that the number of completed products is also 260. The optimal dual solution is

$$u_1^* = 6.667, \quad u_2^* = 13.333, \quad u_3^* = 26.667, \quad u_4^* = -0.667, \quad u_5^* = -0.333$$

The first three dual variables give the imputed prices (or values) of the three kinds of machines. The dual variables u_4^* and u_5^* indicate the relative difficulty of making each of the parts. It is apparent that the imputed cost of producing part 1 is twice that of producing part 2.

Production Activities

We are assuming throughout that the production function—the relationship between inputs used and the output obtained—is linear. Up to now, this assumption has taken the following form: there is a single production method, and the technical coefficients which give the unit requirements of various inputs needed to sustain the production of one unit of that output are fixed.

If there are many alternative ways of organizing the production, the linear relationship between inputs and outputs may instead be formalized in the following manner. Let each production *activity* require a bundle of inputs and deliver a bundle of outputs. Use the letter x to denote the "level" or "intensity" of operation of the activity. If the activity is operated at twice the level, it will require twice the bundle of inputs and deliver twice the bundle of outputs. For instance, in milk production one Jersey cow maintained during one year may represent a unit level of operation. It requires fodder, capital and land. It delivers milk, calves and meat. Two Jersey cows require twice as much and deliver twice the output. The milk farmer may also own some Holstein cows, which are alternative production activities. Their unit requirements (the input requirements per unit of operation of the activity) and their unit outputs (the outputs resulting per unit of operation) may be different.

Consider a producer who operates two activities. Each activity represents an alternative method of manufacturing two goods. Use the following notation

x_1, x_2 = level of operation of the two activities

a_{ij} = quantity of input i needed to operate activity j at unit level, $i = 1, 2;\quad j = 1, 2$

b_{kj} = quantity of output k obtained when activity j is operated at unit level, $k = 1, 2;\quad j = 1, 2.$

The production relationships can be illustrated diagrammatically as in Figure 5.2. The diagram to the left shows the space of the two inputs. Each activity is represented by a ray through the origin. Point A indicates the unit level of activity 1. The unit input requirements are a_{11} and a_{21} respectively. Point C indicates the unit level of activity 2. The stippled ray through the origin illustrates the case of operating both activities at the same time, and at equal levels. Point B, which bisects the distance AC, indicates a situation where each activity is operated at the level 0.5.

The diagram to the right shows the space of the two outputs. Again, each activity is represented by a ray through the origin. Point D indicates the outputs obtained when activity 1 is operated at unit level. The outputs are b_{11} and b_{21} respectively. Point F indicates the outputs obtained when activity 2 is operated at unit level. Point E, which bisects the distance DF, shows the combination of outputs obtained when each activity is operated at the level 0.5.

Using the additional notation

W_1, W_2 = the availabilities of the two inputs

p_1, p_2 = market prices of outputs

one is then led to consider the linear program

Figure 5.2

Illustration of linear activities.
(a) The output space. (b) The input space.

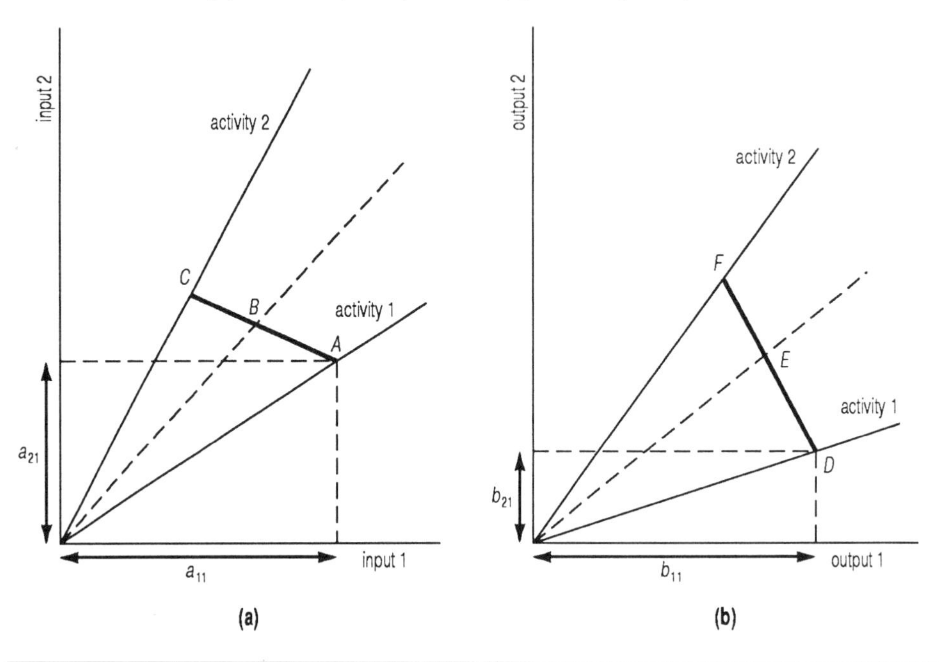

$$
\begin{aligned}
\text{Maximize} \quad & p_1(b_{11}x_1 + b_{12}x_2) + p_2(b_{21}x_1 + b_{22}x_2) \qquad (5.12)\\
\text{Subject to} \quad & a_{11}x_1 + a_{12}x_2 \leq W_1\\
& a_{21}x_1 + a_{22}x_2 \leq W_2\\
& x_1, x_2 \geq 0
\end{aligned}
$$

The reader is asked in Exercise 4 to write down the corresponding dual program, to write down all relations of complementary slackness, and to provide an economic interpretation of each of them.

Exercises

1. A factory manufactures steel card table sets consisting of one folding card table and four folding chairs. Three models are produced: Luxury, Standard, and Economy. The maximum demand for the Luxury model is 200 per week and its wholesale price is \$65, the maximum demand for the Standard model is 600 per week and its wholesale price is \$42, and the maximum demand for the Economy model is 850 per week and its wholesale price is \$26. There are four shops, forming, painting, assembly, and packing. The time requirements for each product in each shop, the

available shop hours, the labor hourly rates, and raw materials costs are given in the table below.

Shop	*Models*		
	Luxury	*Standard*	*Economy*
Forming	0.5	0.42	0.3
Paint	0.7	0.55	0.27
Assembly	0.45	0.32	0.2
Packing	0.15	0.12	0.1
Raw Materials Cost	\$25	\$9	\$16

Shop	*Available Labor Hours*	*Labor Pay rate*
Forming	700 hrs/wk	12 \$/hr
Paint	600 hrs/wk	15 \$/hr
Assembly	400 hrs/wk	14 \$/hr
Packing	250 hrs/wk	10 \$/hr

Find the optimal product mix and the optimal profit. Interpret each of the primal and dual variables.

2. In Exercise 1 the times required in each shop for the production of chairs and tables for the Standard model, and the total hours in each shop allocated to their production, are given as:

	Chairs (hrs/chair)	*Tables (hrs/table)*	
Forming Shop	0.075	0.12	252 hrs/wk
Paint Shop	0.1	0.15	330 hrs/wk
Assembly Shop	0.05	0.12	192 hrs/wk
Packing Shop	0.02	0.04	72 hrs/wk

Find the optimal production plan. Discuss the significance of the dual variables.

3. A machine shop contains three machines that run two 8-hour shifts a day five days a week making three different parts. The hourly output of each part when made on each machine is:

	Part 1 (parts/hr)	*Part 2 (parts/hr)*	*Part 3 (parts/hr)*
Machine 1	25	22	21
Machine 2	15	21	19
Machine 3	18	14	15

The parts must be made in equal numbers so that they can be assembled into final products with no parts inventory left over. Find the optimal weekly production schedule.

4. Write the dual problem for the primal problem in (5.12). Write and interpret the complementary slackness conditions.

6

The Production Frontier

Economists have devoted much effort on the development of a positive theory of rational behavior for economic *decision making units*, such as individuals, households, firms, banks, schools, government bureaucracies, etc. Such theories begin with the premise that, given a problem to be solved, a decision maker first collects all available information about every possible solution, performs all the calculations needed to evaluate and compare different alternatives, and then chooses a course of action that maximizes profit, or utility, or some other objective. This technique is embodied in the assumption of the existence of a "rational economic person," which is a customary assumption in economics.

Conventional economics has therefore had difficulty in explaining suboptimal behavior by decision makers, who for one reason or another, do not arrive at a rational solution that economists prescribe. One way to explain this behavior is by means of Herbert Simon's concept of "bounded rationality," which asserts that a decision making unit should include the costs of information gathering and computation as part of its objective function. For many the cost of determining optimal behavior is prohibitive so that they use a nonoptimal mode of behavior. The decision maker is then said to "satisfy" rather than to "optimize."

Even this concept can be violated by decision makers who do not seem to be able to arrive at rational solutions under any obvious definition. There are, at least in the short run, individuals who squander their money, managers who manage badly, engineers who make poor engineering designs, etc.

Frontier analysis is a recent development in economics which explicitly recognizes that some decision makers use suboptimal solutions. The purpose of frontier analysis is to distinguish the optimal (efficient) decision making units, which are said to be located at the *frontier*, from the suboptimal (inefficient) ones which are located away from the frontier. Since there may be several optimal decision making units located on the frontier, the multiple answers provided by frontier analysis indicate that an optimizing decision making unit may exist in several forms corresponding to different ways of organizing and managing the unit. However, firms that are not on the frontier do not make as efficient use of their inputs as some linear combination of other firms, indicating that their performance might be improved by changing some of their production or management procedures.

Data Envelopment Analysis is a linear programming technique for determining which decision making units (dmu's) lie on the frontier, which is the envelope of the input-output data points. The notation needed to describe this technique is:

$i = 1, \ldots, m$	index of the inputs of the dmu's
$j = 1, \ldots, n$	index of the dmu's
$k = 1, \ldots, r$	index of the outputs of the dmu's
$x_j = (x_{1j}, \ldots, x_{mj})$	(column) vector of inputs of dmu j
$y_j = (y_{1j}, \ldots, y_{rj})$	(column) vector of outputs of dmu j
$\lambda = (\lambda_1, \ldots, \lambda_n)$	(row) vector of weights
θ	a scalar "shrinking factor"

Our next task is to form weighted combinations of these inputs using the weights. The weighted combination of input vectors is:

$$x_1\lambda_1 + \cdots + x_n\lambda_n \tag{6.1}$$

The weighted combination of output vectors is:

$$y_1\lambda_1 + \cdots + y_n\lambda_n \tag{6.2}$$

where the weights are nonnegative:

$$\lambda_j \geq 0 \qquad \text{for } j = 1, \ldots, n \tag{6.3}$$

We assume, as in the concluding section of the previous chapter that each decision making unit exhibits constant returns to scale, i.e., if decision making unit j is operated at the scale factor λ_j then its outputs will be $y_j\lambda_j$ and its inputs will be $x_j\lambda_j$. Hence the composite decision making unit constructed by operating unit j with weight λ_j for $j = 1, \ldots, n$ will have outputs given by (6.1) and inputs given by (6.2). We denote this composite firm by (x^λ, y^λ).

If (x^0, y^0) is an actual dmu, say one of the dmu's (x_j, y_j) for $j = 1, \ldots, n$, we can compare its inputs and outputs with those of a composite firm (x^λ, y^λ). If we can find a nonnegative weight vector λ such that

$$y^\lambda \geq y^0 \tag{6.4}$$

$$x^\lambda < x^0 \tag{6.5}$$

then we say that dmu (x^0, y^0) is *dominated* or *inefficient* because there is a composite firm that requires fewer inputs (6.5) to produce the same or greater outputs (6.4). If no such weight vector λ exists, then we say that dmu (x^0, y^0) is *undominated* or *scale efficient* and is located on the *production frontier*.

We can restate (6.4) and (6.5) by making use of a scalar "shrinking factor" θ, as follows

$$y^{\lambda} \geq y^{0} \tag{6.6}$$

$$x^{\lambda} \leq \theta x^{0} \tag{6.7}$$

$$0 \leq \theta \leq 1 \tag{6.8}$$

Now we say that dmu (x^0, y^0) is *inefficient* if there exists a composite firm $(x^{\lambda}, y^{\lambda})$ such that conditions (6.6) through (6.8) are satisfied with $\theta < 1$. If $\theta \geq 1$ for all such composite firms then (x^0, y^0) is scale *efficient.*

Notice that θ is a multiplier that *shrinks* the inputs from x^0 to θx^0 in an equiproportional manner. We now assume that none of the real dmu's (x_j, y_j) for $j = 1, \ldots, n$ dominates any other real dmu.

Using the above formulation we can state the problem of finding the smallest value of θ as the following linear program:

$$\begin{aligned}
&\text{Minimize} \quad \theta \\
&\text{Subject to} \quad y_1\lambda_1 + \cdots + y_n\lambda_n \geq y^0 \\
&\qquad x^0\theta - (x_1\lambda_1 + \cdots + x_n\lambda_n) \geq 0 \\
&\qquad \lambda_1, \ldots, \lambda_n \geq 0 \\
&\qquad \theta \quad \text{unconstrained}
\end{aligned} \tag{6.9}$$

Since x^0, and $x_1, \ldots, x_n$ are all nonnegative, the second constraint forces θ to be nonnegative even though it is not explicitly constrained.

The condition $\theta \leq 1$ is not included in the constraint set of (6.9) because it will be fulfilled automatically. To see this, note that $\theta = 1$, $\lambda_j = 1$ for $j = 0$, and $\lambda_j = 0$ for $j \neq 0$ is always a feasible solution (i.e., it satisfies all of the constraints). Thus it is always possible drive θ down to 1.

If the optimal solution to (6.9) gives $\theta^* = 1$ then dmu (x^0, y^0) is scale efficient and if $\theta^* < 1$ then it is inefficient.

The literature on data envelopment analysis is rapidly expanding, with notable applications to elementary schools, hospitals, commercial banks, and electric utilities. Some of these dmu's can be represented as profit maximizers, but others cannot. In any case, some of the inputs and outputs of the dmu's may not be bought and sold in competitive markets and hence may not have a market price. DEA works just as well for a study of farming in a developing country in which most of the farm produce is consumed on the farm, as it does for United States farms in the wheat belt. It works just as well for a study of hospitals in Great Britain (which has a socialized health care system) as it does for profit maximizing hospitals in the United States. DEA is particularly well suited to deal with multi-attribute outputs, such as those in the semiconductor and computer industries. Note that some of the outputs could be performance indices, such as the memory size of semiconductors, rather than quantities of goods produced.

Example 1. An airline has 7 airplanes available to make a 300 mile flight carrying 200 passengers. Each airplane uses some fuel for the flight and also requires a certain number of service personnel, including pilots, stewards and stewardesses, baggage handlers, gate attendants, etc. The data requirements for each are:

	Service Personnel	*Fuel (gallons)*
A	29	2800
B	27	2000
C	23	2400
D	38	2500
E	22	3400
F	32	3500
G	25	2200

Each of the planes has an output of one trip, which exactly fulfills the requirements. We can now set up the data box for the linear programming problem in (6.9) to evaluate the efficiency of plane *A*:

	θ	λ_1	λ_2	λ_3	λ_4	λ_5	λ_6	λ_7	
Output	0	1	1	1	1	1	1	1	≥ 1
Inputs	29	−29	−27	−23	−38	−22	−32	−25	≥ 0
	2.8	−2.8	−2.0	−2.4	−2.5	−3.4	−3.5	−2.2	≥ 0
	1	0	0	0	0	0	0	0	

The solution to the linear program was found by solving the GAMS program `AIRPLANE` on page 310. It gave $\theta = 0.82$ meaning plane *A* is not efficient for this job. By changing the entries in rows 2 and 3 of column 1 of the data box above to 27 and 2.0 and solving we find that the new value of θ is $\theta = 1$ so that plane *B* is efficient. Similarly planes *C*, *E*, and *G* are efficient. For plane *D* the value is $\theta = 0.8$ so that it is not efficient. Also plane *F* has $\theta = 0.72$ so that it is inefficient.

In this example each of the planes has a single unit output consisting of just one trip. Hence the question of efficiency or domination depends solely on their inputs. The input vectors for each of the planes is plotted in Figure 6.1, and the set of all input vectors they dominate is shaded.

The efficiency frontier is the darkened line segments connecting points *B* and *C* and points *C* and *E*. Note that the efficiency frontier is the *lower envelope* of the data. The name *data envelopment analysis* arises from this fact.

Because of the assumption above that none of the real dmu's is dominated by any other, none of the points on the vertical line segment above *B* can be a real dmu, since such points are dominated by *B*. Similarly none of the points on the horizontal line beginning at *E* can be a real dmu since such points are dominated by *E*.

Notice that in Figure 6.1 point *G* is on the efficiency frontier exactly at the mid point of line segment *BC*. We now define a dmu to be *efficient* if it is an extreme point of the convex hull of all dmu's located on the efficiency frontier.

Figure 6.1

Plot of inputs needed for each plane to transport 200 passengers 300 miles. The darkened lines are on the frontier. Points *B*, *C*, and *E* are efficient while *A*, *D*, and *F* are inefficient. Point *G* is scale efficient but not efficient.

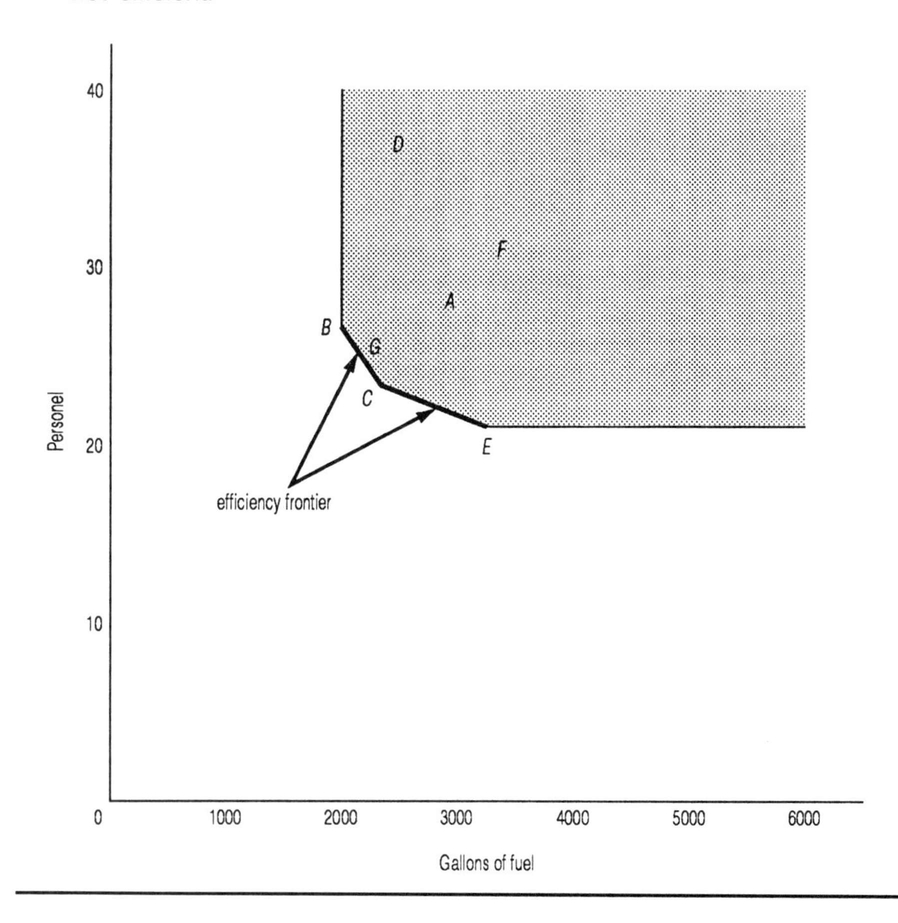

In Figure 6.1 the convex hull is the (solid) triangle BCE. From this definition it follows that points B, C, and E are efficient (and scale efficient) but point G is scale efficient only.

Example 2. As a second example we consider a chicken farmer who uses inputs of chickens, eggs and chicken feed to produce outputs of chickens and eggs. Observe that, in this case, two of the inputs are also outputs! In order for this process to work the production process must have an *expansion factor*, that is, the outputs of chickens and eggs at the end of one production period must be a multiple (> 1) of the inputs. Also part of the outputs of the first production period must be "fed back" as inputs of the next period. Part of the remainder can be consumed by the farmer and the rest sold. The inputs and outputs of several chicken farmers are given below:

	Inputs			*Outputs*	
Farmer	*Chickens*	*Eggs*	*Feed*	*Chickens*	*Eggs*
A	20	40	80	60	120
B	22	36	95	58	125
C	18	32	70	50	105
D	17	36	65	52	110
E	25	50	110	78	125
F	21	45	92	80	122

The variability of these numbers is due to various farming practices, different breeds of chickens, different kinds of feeds, etc.

In this case we cannot plot the data graphically, but fortunately we can still set up and solve the linear program of (6.9) to compare their efficiencies. The data box of the linear program, set up to test for the efficiency of farmer *A*, is shown below:

	θ	*A*	*B*	*C*	*D*	*E*	*F*	
Outputs	0	60	58	50	52	78	80	≥ 60
	0	120	125	105	110	125	122	≥ 120
Inputs	20	−20	−22	−18	−17	−25	−21	≥ 0
	40	−40	−36	−32	−36	−50	−45	≥ 0
	80	−80	−95	−70	−65	−110	−92	≥ 0
	1	0	0	0	0	0	0	

Solution of the problem by using the GAMS program CHICKEGG on page 311 gives $\theta = 0.975$, so that farmer *A* is not efficient.

By changing the right hand side of constraint 1 from 60 to 58, changing the right hand side of constraint 2 from 120 to 125, and changing the entries in rows 3, 4 and 5 of column 1 from 20 to 22, 40 to 36, and 80 to 95, respectively, we obtain the data box for evaluating farmer *B*. Its solution shows farmer *B* to be scale efficient. Similarly, one can show that farmers *C*, *D* and *F* are scale efficient, but farmer *E* is inefficient with $\theta = 0.889$.

If we let $u = [u_1, \ldots, u_r]$ and $v = [v_1, \ldots, v_m]$ be (row) vectors of dual variables corresponding to the first and second constraints of (6.9) we can derive the dual problem as

$$
\begin{aligned}
&\text{Maximize} \quad uy^0 \\
&\text{Subject to} \quad vx^0 = 1 \\
&\qquad -vx_j + uy_j \leq 0 \quad \text{for } j = 1, \ldots, n \\
&\qquad u, v \geq 0
\end{aligned}
\tag{6.12}
$$

The equality in the first constraint arises because the variable θ was unconstrained in (6.9). If we assume that $vx_j > 0$ for $j = 1, \ldots, n$, we can rewrite (6.12) as

$$\begin{aligned} &\text{Maximize} \quad \frac{uy^0}{vx^0} \\ &\text{Subject to} \quad \frac{uy_j}{vx_j} \leq 1 \qquad \text{for } j = 1, \ldots, n \\ &\qquad u \geq 0, \ v > 0 \end{aligned} \tag{6.13}$$

which is called a fractional programming problem. The condition $vx^0 = 1$ in (6.12) is simply a normalizaton factor which picks out one of infinitely many equivalent solutions, and can be imposed or not, as desired.

The following interpretation can be given to (6.13). Call the dual variables u_k and v_i *virtual multipliers*. The fractional program in (6.13) requires the calculation of the maximum ratio of weighted outputs to weighted inputs for dmu 0, which is called the *relative efficiency measure*, subject to the conditions that the similar ratios for each dmu should be less than or equal to 1.

It is easy to see that the optimal efficiency measure determined by (6.13) is equal to the optimal shrinking factor θ when $v^*x^0 = 1$ is imposed. This follows from the duality theorem which states that the optimal values of (6.9) and (6.12) are equal, i.e., $\theta^* = u^*y^0$. Since we chose to impose $v^*x^0 = 1$ we also obtain $\theta^* = u^*y^0/v^*x^0$.

Exercises

1. Verify the efficiency calculations for each plane in Example 1.

2. Show that if plane H, which requires 20 service personnel and 2500 gallons of fuel is added to the list of available planes in Example 1, then planes C, E, and G all become inefficient. What is the new frontier?

3. Find the efficiency frontier for the problem whose data is given in the following table.

Firm	y_j	x_{1j}	x_{2j}
1	2	10	10
2	2	20	5
3	2	30	4
4	2	27	9
5	2	14	8
6	2	5	20
7	2	4	20

   Plot the x points in the plane and indicate the efficiency frontier. Determine which points are efficient and which are not.

4. In a study of the productive efficiency of five electronic chip manufacturers, the following quantities of inputs and outputs were recorded:

		Firm Number				
		1	*2*	*3*	*4*	*5*
Inputs:	Labor Hours	1	2	6	6	4
	Capital Hours	3	3	8	9	5
	R & D	4	3	10	10	3
Outputs:	DRAM Chips	1	1.5	2	2	1.5
	RISC Chips	1	1	2	2	2

Construct a linear program that can be used to determine the efficiency of firm #2. Write down the data box. Define dual variables and formulate the corresponding dual program. State the dual theorem. Finally use the dual constraints and the dual theorem to prove that the optimal efficiency measure is a number in the interval $(0, 1)$.

5. Verify the efficiency calculations for the chicken and eggs example.

6. A company has eight salespeople who cover different regions of the country. It wishes to compare the efficiencies of the salespeople and has collected the following data:

		Salesperson							
		1	*2*	*3*	*4*	*5*	*6*	*7*	*8*
Inputs:	Years of sales experience	10	12	15	21	6	9	11	13
	Time spent, each customer	0.5	0.75	0.6	0.9	0.7	0.65	0.4	0.55
	Regional Economic Index	0.8	0.6	0.65	0.75	0.9	0.82	0.75	0.66
Outputs:	Net sales—old accounts	50	75	125	92	73	86	77	62
	Net sales—new accounts	65	60	95	87	59	72	69	71

Perform a DEA analysis of these salespeople.

7. Discuss how you might set up a data envelopment model for each of the following types of organizations by listing typical inputs and outputs. Also indicate how you would collect data for the calculations you would have to make.
   (a) The public schools in a given urban county.
   (b) A chain of fast food franchise outlets.
   (c) Carbonated beverage marketing.
   (d) Some other collection of related organizations with which you are familiar.

7

The Decentralization of Production

Production decisions made by modern corporations are often *decentralized* and made, in fact, by individual production *divisons*. Frequently there is a separate division for each product or group of products being manufactured. One may then visualize a *hierarchical* system of production planning: the corporate-wide problem which is solved by the corporate planning *center* responsible for coordinating the activities of the various divisions, and the individual production problems which are solved by the divisions. In this chapter the hierarchical system is modelled by means of a *stairstep* linear program.

If a division of the firm buys all of its inputs from the outside, and sells all of its goods to the outside, then it can be treated as a separate entity independently of the rest of the firm. If some factors of production controlled by the firm are in short supply, and if each division is allocated a fixed amount of these scarce resources, then each division may still be considered as a separate firm. But consider now the case in which the corporation as a whole faces a limited availability of one or several factors that are *shared* by several divisions. Examples might be: common capital resources of the firm, a common fleet of trucks, a common supply of raw materials, or a common supply of skilled labor. The various divisions must then compete for access to such scarce facilities. The problem arises of determining the optimal allocation of the scarce resources to the divisions.

Horizontal Integration

As an example consider a case of a corporation that has two divisions. (The extension to more than two divisions will be clear.) These divisions each make one or more products, which can be the same or different, which they sell to outside customers. Because each division carries out its own production independently, the firm is said to be integrated *horizontally.* However, they both make use of certain common corporate resources. Using the notation of Chapter 5, we can write the firm's optimization problem as in (7.1).

$$\begin{aligned} \text{Maximize} \quad & \hat{p}^{(1)}x^{(1)} + \hat{p}^{(2)}x^{(2)} \\ \text{Subject to} \quad & A^{(1)}x^{(1)} \le b^{(1)} \\ & A^{(2)}x^{(2)} \le b^{(2)} \\ & D^{(1)}x^{(1)} + D^{(2)}x^{(2)} \le d \\ & x^{(1)}, x^{(2)} \ge 0 \end{aligned} \tag{7.1}$$

The third set of constraints represent the k common resources, d (a k-component column vector), of the firm and the demands $D^{(1)}x^{(1)}$ and $D^{(2)}x^{(2)}$ that the two divisions impose on them. These constraints are sometimes called the *master* or *corporate* constraints.

The dual minimizing problem is given by (7.2)

$$\begin{aligned} \text{Minimize} \quad & u^{(1)}b^{(1)} + u^{(2)}b^{(2)} + vd \\ \text{Subject to} \quad & u^{(1)}A^{(1)} + vD^{(1)} \ge \hat{p}^{(1)} \\ & u^{(2)}A^{(2)} + vD^{(2)} \ge \hat{p}^{(2)} \\ & u^{(1)}, u^{(2)}, v \ge 0 \end{aligned} \tag{7.2}$$

The two problems (7.1) and (7.2) are said to have a *staircase structure*, for obvious reasons. If the master resource constraints (involving $D^{(1)}$, $D^{(2)}$, and d) are absent then the problem is said to be *completely decomposable*.

Suppose now that the master resource constraints exist and that the dual linear programs (7.1) and (7.2) have been solved by the corporation. Let v^* be considered to be a vector of transfer prices charged by the center to the divisions for the use of the common shared resources. Substituting v^* in (7.2) and rearranging terms gives

$$\begin{aligned} \text{Minimize} \quad & u^{(1)}b^{(1)} + u^{(2)}b^{(2)} + \text{constant} \\ \text{Subject to} \quad & u^{(1)}A^{(1)} \ge \hat{p}^{(1)} - v^*D^{(1)} = p^{\#(1)} \\ & u^{(2)}A^{(2)} \ge \hat{p}^{(2)} - v^*D^{(2)} = p^{\#(2)} \\ & u^{(1)}, u^{(2)} \ge 0 \end{aligned} \tag{7.3}$$

where $p^{\#(1)}$ and $p^{\#(2)}$, which can be called *corrected prices*, are defined on the right hand sides of the constraints.

The dual of (7.3) is given by (7.4)

$$\begin{aligned} \text{Maximize} \quad & p^{\#(2)}x^{(1)} + p^{\#(2)}x^{(2)} \\ \text{Subject to} \quad & A^{(1)}x^{(1)} \le b^{(1)} \\ & A^{(2)}x^{(2)} \le b^{(2)} \\ & x^{(1)}, x^{(2)} \ge 0 \end{aligned} \tag{7.4}$$

Note that (7.3) and (7.4) are completely decomposable linear programs, and can be solved separately. Hence we define divisional problems (7.5) for division 1 and (7.6) for division 2.

$$\begin{aligned} &\text{Maximize} \quad p^{\#(1)}x^{(1)} \\ &\text{Subject to} \quad A^{(1)}x^{(1)} \leq b^{(1)} \\ &\qquad\qquad\quad x^{(1)} \geq 0 \end{aligned} \tag{7.5}$$

$$\begin{aligned} &\text{Maximize} \quad p^{\#(2)}x^{(2)} \\ &\text{Subject to} \quad A^{(2)}x^{(2)} \leq b^{(2)} \\ &\qquad\qquad\quad x^{(2)} \geq 0 \end{aligned} \tag{7.6}$$

Thus the use of transfer prices has, at least formally, enabled us to decompose the company problem (7.1) into two divisional problems (7.5) and (7.6). It is easy to see that any global solution $x^{*(1)}$ and $x^{*(2)}$ to (7.1) will also be feasible for each of the divisional problems, i.e., $x^{*(1)}$ will satisfy the constraints of (7.5) and $x^{*(2)}$ will satisfy the constraints of (7.6). Moreover, by tracing through the steps used to derive (7.5) and (7.6), it is easy to show that optimal solutions to (7.1) are also optimal for these subdivision problems.

The result now obtained can be explained in plain English as follows. Let the center calculate the vector of dual variables of the master constraints, v^*. The center sends the corrected prices to the divisions which are now instructed to solve their own divisional programs (7.5) and (7.6). We then know that any optimal solution to the center's problem, which of course it will wish to implement, will constitute an optimal solution to the divisional problems.

We now ask: is there also so called *coherent decentralization:* that is, does the totality of the optimal solutions to the (corrected) divisional programs constitute an optimal solution to the global problem of the center? In other words, can the center after having computed and communicated the dual variables of the master constraints, let the divisions make their own decisions and yet be sure that an overall optimum for the firm is reached? Unfortunately, the answer to this question is a no. The reason is mathematical complications that arise when a linear programming problem has more than one optimal solution (the optimum point falling no longer at a corner of the region of feasible solutions but rather on one of its facets). If the divisional programs (7.5) and (7.6) both have unique optimal solutions, there will indeed be coherent decentralization. But if one or both of the divisional programs have many optimal solutions (lying on the facet of the set of the set of feasible divisional solutions), the center must give to the divisions some rule telling them precisely which of their possible optimal solutions they are to choose. See the numerical examples.

Note that the decentralization process as outlined above does not alleviate the burden of information gathering and computation carried by the administrative center. The center needs complete information about all division decision problems, about the master constraints *and* it needs to solve the entire center problem (7.1) in order to be able to compute the dual variables of the master constraints and the corrected prices.

The so called "decomposition algorithm," developed by G. Dantzig and P. Wolfe, provides a mechanism for finding in a decentralized way the optimal solution of the master program. The scenario of the decomposition algorithm may be visualized as a hypothetical dialogue between the center and the divisions, where at each stage some tentative transfer prices are announced by the center, then corrected prices are determined by the divisions, who then compute their ensuing optimal solutions and thereupon send back to the center their *proposals* for their individual use of the shared resources. The center collects these proposals, compares them with the overall availability and computes *new transfer prices* which are delegated back to the divisions. This dialogue continues until the master constraints are satisfied exactly.

The decomposition algorithm is attractive because the center needs neither to know the structures of the divisional problems, nor to solve them. Instead, the center needs only to keep track of the master constraints and to solve for revised transfer prices on the basis of comparing divisional proposals with the quantities available of the shared resources.

The Dantzig-Wolfe decomposition algorithm is said to be *price-directive*, in the sense that the center computes tentative corrected prices and sends them to the divisions. Other decentralization algorithms (which we shall not discuss) have been suggested that are instead *resource directive*, i.e., the center allocates maximal amounts that each division may use of the shared resources.

Example 1. A chain of service facilities (such as automobile repair shops) has locations in three cities: A, B and C. Each facility sells two products, 1 and 2. The demand per week at each location is displayed in the table below.

	A	B	C
Product 1	200	100	100
Product 2	300	180	90

These figures give the maximum demand at each location. It is perfectly possible for the firm to sell less than the maximum if it can't supply potential customers who will then buy from a local competing firm instead.

Product 1 nets $21.50 per unit and product 2 nets $7.25 per unit. These figures are calculated net of the cost of unskilled labor (which is hired locally as required) and net of the costs of incidentals such as tools, equipment, and various other inputs.

Output at each service facility is limited by the number of work stations available. The numbers of work stations at each location are

A	6 work stations
B	4 work stations
C	4 work stations

Each work station can be utilized at most 40 hours per week. Product 1 requires 0.75 workstation hours per unit for completion; product 2 requires 0.50 workstation hours per unit.

The operation of the chain further relies on the presence of technical management consultants. These management consultants travel between locations. There are available a total of 250 management consultant hours per week for the entire chain. Product 1 requires 0.5 management consultant hours per unit for completion; product 2 requires 0.2 management hours per unit. Management is not paid a fixed wage; instead, it is paid a commission based on the joint returns of the entire chain.

Use notation as follows:

$$x_{jA} = \text{sales of product } j \text{ at city } A$$
$$x_{jB} = \text{sales of product } j \text{ at city } B$$
$$x_{jC} = \text{sales of product } j \text{ at city } C$$

and the information supplied in the problem text may then be drawn upon to formulate the linear programming problem represented by the data box below:

	x_{1A}	x_{2A}	x_{1B}	x_{2B}	x_{1C}	x_{2C}	
u_{1A}	1	0					≤ 200
u_{2A}	0	1					≤ 300
u_{3A}	0.75	0.5					≤ 240
u_{1B}			1	0			≤ 100
u_{2B}			0	1			≤ 180
u_{3B}			0.75	0.5			≤ 160
u_{1C}					1	0	≤ 100
u_{2C}					0	1	≤ 90
u_{3C}					0.75	0.5	≤ 160
v	0.5	0.2	0.5	0.2	0.5	0.2	≤ 250
	21.5	7.25	21.5	7.25	21.5	7.25	

We recognize immediately the characteristic stairstep format. There are three *divisional constraints* at each location, spelling out the restrictions imposed upon operations by local demand and by the availability of work station hours. There is also a *master constraint*, which involves all three locations, and requires the total usage of management consultant hours of the entire chain to be at most 250 hours.

The dual variables are indicated in the left hand side of the data box. The optimal u_{1A}^* may be interpreted as the imputed unit value of the demand for product 1 at city A. It is also the highest price that the chain would be willing to pay to have the demand at location A increased up by one unit, because it predicts the corresponding change in the objective function. When it is positive, all of the local demand is being met. The optimal u_{2A}^* is the imputed unit value of the demand for product 2 at location A. The optimal u_{3A}^* is the imputed unit cost of the availability of workstation hours; when it is positive, all work stations at city A are busy 40 hours per week.

Dual variables for cities B and C are introduced in an analogous manner.

There is also a dual variable associated with the master constraint, denoted by v. The optimal value v^* may be interpreted as the imputed price of the availability of management consultant hours. When it is positive, all available consultant hours are used.

The data in the above data box appears in the GAMS program MASTER (page 311). Numerical solution gives the following result:

$$x^*_{1A} = 200 \qquad x^*_{1B} = 100 \qquad x^*_{1C} = 100$$
$$x^*_{2A} = 10 \qquad x^*_{2B} = 170 \qquad x^*_{2C} = 90$$

The optimal values of the duals are given as:

$$u^*_{1A} = 3.375 \qquad u^*_{1B} = 3.375 \qquad u^*_{1C} = 3.375$$
$$u^*_{2A} = 0 \qquad u^*_{2B} = 0 \qquad u^*_{2C} = 0$$
$$u^*_{3A} = 0 \qquad u^*_{3B} = 0 \qquad u^*_{3C} = 0$$

and the optimal value of the dual of the master constraint is

$$v^* = 36.25.$$

An additional demand of one unit of any location for one unit of product 1 would bring in a net surplus of 3 dollars and 38 cents. The rest of the dual variables are zero, giving the following interpretations. The maximum demand for product 2 is not limiting net profit at any location, and additional demand will not increase it. Nor is the availability of work station hours at the various locations a scarce factor. An increased number of work stations would not result in higher net returns since there is a surplus of unused work station hours at each location.

The optimal value of the dual of the master constraint is $36.25. This is the imputed cost or value of one management consultant hour. It is also the highest price that the chain would be willing to pay for an additional management hour per week. The large price indicates that the availability of management consultants is really the bottleneck in the entire operation of the chain.

We now calculate the *corrected prices* of the two products according to the formula given in the dual program (7.3) above. The correction term of each price is obtained as the product of the coefficient of the master constraint and the dual of that constraint, giving:

$$\begin{aligned} \text{corrected price of product 1 at any location} &= 21.5 - 0.5 \times 36.25 \\ &= 3.375 \\ \text{corrected price of product 2 at any location} &= 7.25 - 0.2 \times 36.25 \\ &= 0. \end{aligned}$$

The correction formula has an obvious economic interpretation. The correction term 0.5×36.25 equals the imputed cost of management consultants *per unit of product 1.* The corrected price $21.5 - 0.5 \times 36.25 = 3.375$ is the net return per unit of product 1 calculated over and above the cost of unskilled labor, incidental expenses, equipment, etc. *and* the imputed cost of management consultants.

The corrected primal program (7.4) above is given by the data box below.

x_{1A}	x_{2A}	x_{1B}	x_{2B}	x_{1C}	x_{2C}	
1	0					$\leq$ 200
0	1					$\leq$ 300
0.75	0.5					$\leq$ 240
		1	0			$\leq$ 100
		0	1			$\leq$ 180
		0.75	0.5			$\leq$ 160
				1	0	$\leq$ 100
				0	1	$\leq$ 90
				0.75	0.5	$\leq$ 160
3.375	0	3.375	0	3.375	0	

The master constraint has been removed, and the problem actually breaks up into three separate linear programming problems, one for each division. Each such corrected divisional problem asks for the maximization of the divisional return at each city (corrected for the imputed cost of the division's use of global resource), subject to its own divisional constraints. The GAMS program for the problem is DECOMP which appears on page 312.

In order to compare the optimal solution to the master problem (data box on page 101) with the three decentralized problems illustrated in the data box above, we now provide a geometrical illustration of the two solutions given in Figure 7.1. There are three diagrams in Figure 7.1, one for each city. Each diagram shows the set of feasible solutions at each location. The set of feasible solutions to the divisional constraints at each city has been shaded in the diagrams. The black dot in each diagram indicates the location of the optimal solution to the master problem.

In accordance with the decentralization result given above, the part of the optimal solution to the center's master problem relating to a division is also an optimal solution to the corrected divisional problem. But note that the converse is not necessarily true. Each corrected divisional problem has an interval of alternative optima indicated by a darkened line segment in the interval. But only a single point on the darkened line segment is part of the master optimal solution.

The conclusion is that it is not enough simply to give to each division the imputed price of the master constraint and let it solve its own corrected problem, because each subproblem has an interval of optimal solutions which includes but is not restricted to the global solution of the original problem. The center could send information to each division as to which of its optimal divisional solutions to use, but this amounts to simply sending it the optimal solution to the original problem. We conclude that price information alone is not sufficient for the linear model we are considering.

Figure 7.1

Illustration of constraint regions and optimal solutions to the multi-location problem. For each division the set of its feasible solutions is shaded; the set of its optimal solutions is the darkened line segment; the black dot is the divisional solution given by the solution to the master problem.

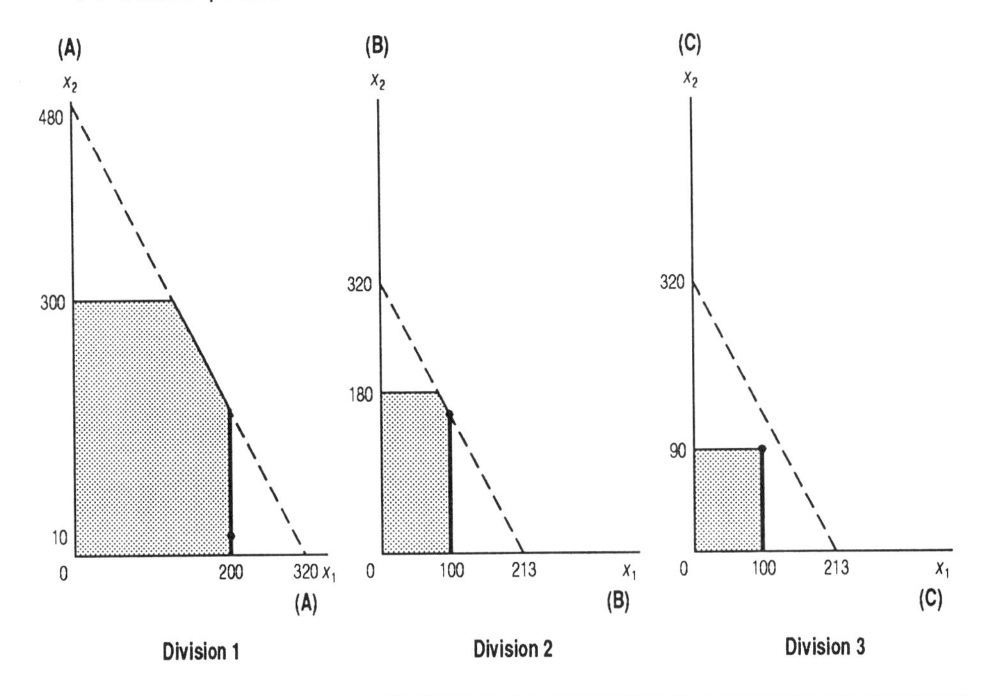

Decentralization in a Nonlinear World: Coherent Decentralization by Prices Alone

As we have just seen, it is in general not possible to effect coherent decentralization in a linear model by giving price information alone. It is easy to see that these difficulties somehow have to do with the assumption of linearity. Once the duals of the master constraints have been computed, and corrected prices have been sent from the center to each division, the difficulty is that there is no guarantee that the optimal solutions computed by each division are unique.

We now propose to replace the assumption of a linear objective function for the master program by a separable and strictly concave *nonlinear* objective function instead. What this means is that the master objective function is still the sum of divisional objective functions, but each divisional objective function is now required to be strictly concave rather than linear. We will then see that coherent decentralization can indeed be carried out by sending price information alone.

In order to see what is involved, let us return to the master program (7.1). Remember that the prices $\hat{p}^{(1)}$ and $\hat{p}^{(2)}$ appearing in the maximand were calculated as unit net profits after the deduction of costs of labor and raw materials from the price. [Equation (5.1) in Chapter 5 defines $\hat{p} = p - rh - c$ where rh are labor costs and c is the raw matrial cost per unit.] Changing the underlying assumptions slightly, assume now instead that *marginal labor costs* and *raw material costs* increase linearly with output:

$$\begin{aligned}\hat{p}_j^{(1)} &= p_j^{(1)} - \gamma_j^{(1)} - \delta_j^{(1)} x_j^{(1)} \\ \hat{p}_j^{(2)} &= p_j^{(2)} - \gamma_j^{(2)} - \delta_j^{(2)} x_j^{(2)} \qquad \text{for } j = 1, \ldots, n\end{aligned} \tag{7.7}$$

The return $\hat{p}_j^{(1)}$ is now the net profit on the *last* unit of commodity j produced by division 1, calculated net of labor costs and raw material costs. The return $\hat{p}_j^{(2)}$ is the net profit on the last unit of commodity j produced by division 2. The parameters γ and δ are known positive numbers.

The master program (7.2) must then be amended to read

$$\begin{aligned}\text{Maximize} \quad & \sum_{j=1}^{n} \{p_j^{(1)} x_j^{(1)} - [\gamma_j^{(1)} x_j^{(1)} + 0.5\delta_j^{(1)} (x_j^{(1)})^2]\} \\ & + \sum_{j=1}^{n} \{p_j^{(2)} x_j^{(2)} - [\gamma_j^{(2)} x_j^{(2)} + 0.5\delta_j^{(2)} (x_j^{(2)})^2]\} \\ \text{Subject to} \quad & A^{(1)} x^{(1)} \leq b^{(1)} \\ & A^{(2)} x^{(2)} \leq b^{(2)} \\ & D^{(1)} x^{(1)} + D^{(2)} x^{(2)} \leq d \\ & x^{(1)}, x^{(2)} \geq 0\end{aligned} \tag{7.8}$$

The objective function is written as the sum of two terms, one term for each division, and the objective function is *separable*. The expression for each division is the total net return of that division, the unit price less the total labor costs and raw material costs. The reader may want to check the calculation by differentiating the expression for the total net return with respect to each output variable and show that the result gives the marginal net profits given in (7.7).

Assuming that the parameters $\delta_j^{(1)}$ and $\delta_j^{(2)}$ are *positive* (meaning strictly increasing marginal costs), it follows that the objective function in program (7.8) is *strictly concave*. The constraints are linear so that the optimal solution may fall entirely inside the feasible constraint set, or it may fall on some facet of the constraint set. The important thing is that the optimum will be *unique*.

Reasoning as before and forming the corrected prices

$$\begin{aligned}&\hat{p}^{(1)} - v^* D^{(1)} \\ &\hat{p}^{(2)} - v^* D^{(2)},\end{aligned}$$

one is led to form the two *decentralized problems*, the division 1 problem

$$\begin{aligned}\text{Maximize} \quad & (p^{(1)} - v^* D^{(1)}) x^{(1)} - \sum_{j=1}^{n} [\gamma_j^{(1)} x_j^{(1)} + 0.5\delta_j^{(1)} (x_j^{(1)})^2] \\ \text{Subject to} \quad & A^{(1)} x^{(1)} \leq b^{(1)} \\ & x^{(1)} \leq 0\end{aligned} \tag{7.9}$$

and the division 2 problem

$$\text{Maximize} \quad (p^{(2)} - v^*D^{(2)})x^{(2)} - \sum_{j=1}^{n} [\gamma_j^{(2)} x_j^{(2)} + 0.5\delta_j^{(2)}(x_j^{(2)})^2] \tag{7.10}$$

$$\text{Subject to} \quad A^{(2)}x^{(2)} \leq b^{(2)}$$

$$x^{(2)} \geq 0$$

This time, there is no ambiguity because of the possible presence of alternative optima. Let the (unique) optimal solution to the master program be $x^{(1)*}$, $x^{(2)*}$. Then $x^{(1)*}$ is the (unique) optimal solution to the decentralized problem (7.9), and $x^{(2)*}$ is the (unique) optimal solution to the decentralized problem (7.10). The corrected prices therefore effect coherent decentralization.

Example 2. Returning to the chain of service facilities discussed in Example 1, we now modify the assumptions regarding the value of the net return of each product. Earlier we assumed that the net returns are $\hat{p}_1 = \$21.50$ per unit for the first product and $\hat{p}_1 = \$7.25$ per unit for the second product.

This time we assume that the marginal costs of unskilled labor, and the costs of incidentals, tools, equipment and various inputs are an increasing function of output. The marginal net return of each product is taken to be

marginal net profits of product 1 = 27 − 0.12 × (sales of product 1)

marginal net profits of product 2 = 7.5 − 0.02 × (sales of product 2).

These marginal net profits are assumed to be calculated by the same formula at all three locations.

The linear programming formulation in the original data box will then be replaced by a nonlinear version as exhibited below:

	x_{1A}	x_{2A}	x_{1B}	x_{2B}	x_{1C}	x_{2C}	
u_{1A}	1	0					≤ 200
u_{2A}	0	1					≤ 300
u_{3A}	0.75	0.5					≤ 240
u_{1B}			1	0			≤ 100
u_{2B}			0	1			≤ 180
u_{3B}			0.75	0.5			≤ 160
u_{1C}					1	0	≤ 100
u_{2C}					0	1	≤ 90
u_{3C}					0.75	0.5	≤ 160
v	0.5	0.2	0.5	0.2	0.5	0.2	≤ 250
	$\geq$	$\geq$	$\geq$	$\geq$	$\geq$	$\geq$	
	$27 - 0.12x_{1A}$	$7.5 - 0.02x_{2A}$	$27 - 0.12x_{1B}$	$7.5 - 0.02x_{2B}$	$27 - 0.12x_{1C}$	$7.5 - 0.02x_{2C}$	

The GAMS program for this problem is MASTER1 which appears on page 313. The computer will print the following optimal primal solution to the master problem:

$$x^*_{1A} = 137.76 \qquad x^*_{1B} = 100.0 \qquad x^*_{1C} = 100.0$$
$$x^*_{2A} = 165.61 \qquad x^*_{2B} = 150.0 \qquad x^*_{2C} = 90.0$$

The optimal values of the dual variables are

$$u^*_{1A} = 0 \qquad u^*_{1B} = 4.53 \qquad u^*_{1C} = 4.53$$
$$u^*_{2A} = 0 \qquad u^*_{2B} = 0.31 \qquad u^*_{2C} = 1.51$$
$$u^*_{3A} = 0 \qquad u^*_{3B} = 0 \qquad u^*_{3C} = 0$$

and the optimal value of the dual of the master constraint is $v^* = 20.94$.

The corrected prices can then be obtained as follows:

$$\begin{pmatrix}\text{corrected marginal net profit}\\ \text{of product 1 at any location}\end{pmatrix} = 27 - 0.5 \times \$20.94 - 0.12\,(\text{sales of product 1})$$
$$= 16.53 - 0.12\,(\text{sales of product 1})$$

$$\begin{pmatrix}\text{corrected marginal net profit}\\ \text{of product 2 at any location}\end{pmatrix} = 7.5 - 0.2 \times \$20.94 - 0.02\,(\text{sales of product 2})$$
$$= 3.312 - 0.02\,(\text{sales of product 2})$$

The three corrected decentralized problems are exhibited in the following data box.

x_{1A}	x_{2A}	x_{1B}	x_{2B}	x_{1C}	x_{2C}	
1	0					≤ 200
0	1					≤ 300
0.75	0.5					≤ 240
		1	0			≤ 100
		0	1			≤ 180
		0.75	0.5			≤ 160
				1	0	≤ 100
				0	1	≤ 90
				0.75	0.5	≤ 160
$\geq$	$\geq$	$\geq$	$\geq$	$\geq$	$\geq$	
$16.53 - 0.12x_{1A}$	$3.312 - 0.02x_{2A}$	$16.53 - 0.12x_{1B}$	$3.312 - 0.02x_{2B}$	$16.53 - 0.12x_{1C}$	$3.312 - 0.02x_{2C}$	

The three independent divisional problems can be solved individually and the optimal solutions now *coincide* with the optimal solutions to the master problem. The optimal solutions are also indicated in the three divisional diagrams in Figure 7.2.

The optimal solution is obtained by solving DECOMP1 which appears on page 314. The solution for the first division is at an *interior* point in its constraint set as shown in Figure 7.2. The optimal solutions to the second and third division are the indicated corner points of their respective constraint sets. Both

Figure 7.2

Illustration of the divisional constraint regions and the optimal solutions to the separable concave decentralization problem. In each case, the set of its feasible solutions is shaded, and its optimal solution is a black dot. The solution to the master problem coincides with those of the divisional problems.

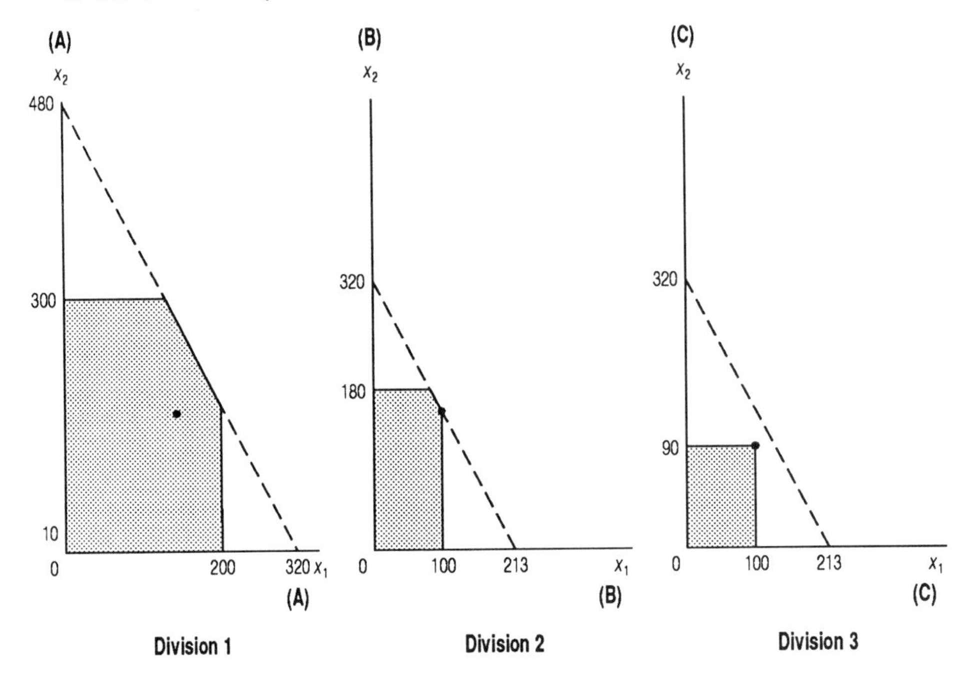

demand constraints for division three are binding, and its workstation constraint is slack.

Vertical Integration

When a corporation manufactures component parts or other *intermediate* goods which it uses up later in the production chain, the company is said to have *vertical integration*. An example is an integrated oil company that pumps its own oil, refines it, distributes it and markets it under its own brand name. On a smaller scale, vertical integration occurs when a brewery operates its own mountain water intake, or when a publishing company owns its own paper mill, or when a computer manufacturer makes its own computer chips, etc. Virtual integration has historically been common in paper companies, automobile companies, steel companies, etc. See Chapter 9 for a paper company model.

Using the notation of Chapter 5, we can write the linear programming model of a vertically integrated company as in (7.11)

$$\text{Maximize} \quad -\hat{c}^{(1)}x^{(1)} + \hat{p}^{(2)}x^{(2)}$$

$$\text{Subject to} \quad \begin{aligned} A^{(1)}x^{(1)} &\leq b^{(1)} \\ -x^{(1)} + T^{(2)}x^{(2)} &\leq 0 \\ A^{(2)}x^{(2)} &\leq b^{(2)} \\ x^{(1)}, x^{(2)} &\geq 0 \end{aligned} \tag{7.11}$$

where $\hat{c}^{(1)} = rh^{(1)} + c^{(1)}$ is the variable cost vector for division 1, $\hat{p}^{(2)} = p - rh^{(2)} - c^{(2)}$ is the net profit vector for division 2, and $T^{(2)}$ is the transfer matrix giving the quantities of intermediate goods needed by the second division. Vector $x^{(1)}$ gives the quantities of the intermediate goods that are manufactured by division 1 and then used in the production of the final products in quantities $x^{(2)}$ which are sold to the outside world.

Again, problem (7.11) is a *global* problem that is formulated for the totality of operations of the entire corporation. The maximand represents the total profit from all operations. It is formed by adding the gross revenue from total sales to the outside world $px^{(2)}$ and deducting all variable costs and wages paid in both divisions.

We shall refer to the first two constraints in problem (7.11) as *pipeline constraints* or *pass-on constraints* and to variables $x^{(1)}$ as *pass-on variables*. They define the flow of each intermediate good and transmit it (through a pipeline, as it were) from division 1 to division 2.

Following the procedure for the previous example, we write the dual problem to (7.11) as

$$\text{Minimize} \quad u^{(1)}b^{(1)} + u^{(3)}b^{(2)}$$

$$\text{Subject to} \quad \begin{aligned} u^{(1)}A^{(1)} - u^{(2)} &\geq -\hat{c}^{(1)} \\ u^{(2)}T^{(2)} + u^{(3)}A^{(2)} &\geq \hat{p}^{(2)} \\ u^{(1)}, u^{(2)}, u^{(3)} &\geq 0 \end{aligned} \tag{7.12}$$

Assume now that we have solved this pair of dual problems and know the optimal value $u^{*(2)}$ of the second dual variable vector. As before, we use these as transfer prices which division 1 charges division 2 for its outputs $x^{(1)}$. As in the previous example we rewrite (7.12) as

$$\text{Minimize} \quad u^{(1)}b^{(1)} + u^{(3)}b^{(2)}$$

$$\text{Subject to} \quad \begin{aligned} & u^{(1)}A^{(1)} \geq -\hat{c}^{(1)} + u^{*(2)} = p^{(1)} \\ & u^{(3)}A^{(2)} \geq \hat{p}^{(2)} - u^{*(2)}T^{(2)} = p^{(2)} \\ & u^{(1)}, u^{(2)} \geq 0 \end{aligned} \tag{7.13}$$

The dual to this problem is

$$\text{Maximize} \quad p^{(1)}x^{(1)} + p^{(2)}x^{(2)}$$

$$\text{Subject to} \quad \begin{aligned} A^{(1)}x^{(1)} &\leq b^{(1)} \\ A^{(3)}x^{(2)} &\leq b^{(2)} \\ x^{(1)}, x^{(2)} &\geq 0 \end{aligned} \tag{7.14}$$

Again the problems in (7.13) and (7.14) are completely decomposable, and divisional problems similar to (7.9) and (7.10) can easily be derived. Further results on this model are given in the exercises.

Program (7.11) offers an example of so-called *multi-stage programming*. In the present example there are just two stages, but the reader can easily visualize larger applications with many stages, the output of divisions located on an earlier stage being fed into divisions on later stages by means of pipeline constraints.

Make or Buy

A production manager sometimes faces the question whether to manufacture some given component parts in-house or to buy them in the marketplace. Continuing our discussion of program (7.11), assume this time that the corporation may also buy the required intermediate goods in the marketplace at prices $q^{(3)}$. There are then two ways of securing the required amounts: buying a quantity y of them in the market or manufacturing $x^{(1)}$ of them in-house. Form the program

$$\begin{aligned} \text{Maximize} \quad & \hat{p}^{(1)}x^{(1)} + \hat{p}^{(2)}x^{(2)} - q^{(3)}y \\ \text{Subject to} \quad & A^{(1)}x^{(1)} \leq b^{(1)} \\ & -x^{(1)} + T^{(2)}x^{(2)} - y = 0 \\ & A^{(2)}x^{(2)} \leq b^{(2)} \\ & y \leq Y \\ & x^{(1)}, x^{(2)}, y \geq 0 \end{aligned} \tag{7.15}$$

Here the vector Y gives the maximum amount of the intermediate goods that can be bought in the outside market.

An optimal solution to program (7.15) will typically involve some mixture $x^{*(1)} + y^*$ which indicates the optimal way to procure intermediate goods. Some part $x^{*(1)}$ of the requirements will be manufactured in-house, and another part y^* will be bought in the market.

In Exercise 3 you will be asked to derive the dual problem to (7.15) and to derive constraint (7.16) on the dual variables:

$$u^{(2)} \leq q^{(3)} + u^{(4)}. \tag{7.16}$$

The economic interpretation of this constraint is the following: the internal transfer price $u^{(2)}$ of an intermediate good is at most equal to the outside price $q^{(3)}$ of the good plus the scarcity premium $u^{(4)}$ on the outside availability of that good.

Reasoning and expanding the programming format in the fashion illustrated above, it is easy to deal with other similar extensions such as cases where the corporation may alternatively manufacture the finished goods $x^{(2)}$ or buy them in the market from wholesale traders in order to ship them on to the ultimate consumers.

Note that while the programming format rapidly expands as the model is expanded to include additional production possibilities, the coefficient matrix on the left hand side is typically quite *sparse*, which still allows for rapid numerical solution on a computer.

Exercises

1. Rework the linear decentralized firm model for the case in which the divisions get the following different prices in their respective cities due to local competition:

Product	Price in City		
	A	*B*	*C*
1	$23.00	$22.00	$21.00
2	9.50	10.00	9.00

2. Rework the nonlinear decentralized firm model with the following price functions:

Location	Marginal Net Profit	
	Product 1	*Product 2*
A	$30 - 0.15x_{1A}$	$11 - 0.03x_{2A}$
B	$28 - 0.14x_{1B}$	$12 - 0.02x_{2B}$
C	$27 - 0.12x_{1C}$	$10.5 - 0.025x_{2C}$

3. Write the dual program for the primal linear program in (7.15). Show that the last dual constraint can be rewritten as (7.16).

4. There are two plants (origins) the supplies of which are denoted x and y respectively. The supply price functions are

$$-10 + 2x$$
$$-8 + 3y.$$

Both plants sell their products in one and the same market (destination). The unit transportation costs from plants to the market are 0.5 and 1.0, respectively. The total demand at the market is 10.

The transportation capacities from plants to the market are limited. The maximum quantity that can be shipped from the first plant is 7 and the maximum from the second plant is 4.

(a) Construct a nonlinear programming model that determines the optimal production and optimal shipments at each plant. (Hint: The supply price function can be interpreted as marginal costs. Minimize total manufacturing costs and transportation costs subject to the relevant constraints.) Write down the data box. Define Lagrange multipliers and provide an economic interpretation of them. Write down all Kuhn-Tucker conditions and interpret them.

(b) The optimal solution is $x^* = 6.50$ and $y^* = 3.50$. The Lagrange multipliers of the capacity constraints are zero; the multiplier of the market constraint is 3.50. Check that complementary slackness conditions hold.

(c) Show that the data box has the form of a decentralization problem. Which are the divisional constraints? Which are the master constraints? Form the corrected divisional problem. Show that the optimal master solution satisfies the Kuhn-Tucker conditions of each corrected divisional problem. Hence, show that master solution solves the corrected divisional problems and there is coherent decentralization.

8

Commodity Flows in Networks: Oil Production

The term *production* is used by economists to denote the creation of goods and services that have economic value. To the economist then, production encompasses design, fabrication, transportation, warehousing, sales and marketing, in fact the entire *logistics system* that transforms raw materials and primary resources into final consumer goods.

As an example of such a logistics system, consider the oil industry. Crude oil is pumped from various oil fields; each field may contain several distinct reservoirs yielding crude oil having different chemical compositions. The crude oil is transported through pipelines, which sometimes extend over vast distances, to gas-oil separator plants from which the oil goes to refineries and the gas stream is piped to gas plants. The gas plants extract methane, sulphur and natural gas liquids. The entire network from reservoirs to ultimate consumers may span half the globe.

In order to model the characteristic features of such networks of distribution, we may turn to a stylized case of a *pure network* (Figure 8.1). A single homogeneous commodity is transported via the network, which consists of *nodes* and directed *arcs* connecting pairs of nodes. Each node can be a net *supply node*, a net *demand node*, or a neutral *transshipment node* of the commodity. Thus in Figure 8.1 nodes 1 and 2 are supply nodes, 3 and 4 are transshipment nodes and 5 and 6 are demand nodes. Also in Figure 8.1 there are eight arcs: $(1,3)$, $(1,4)$, $(2,3)$, $(2,4)$, $(3,5)$, $(3,6)$, $(4,5)$, and $(4,6)$. We will associate flow variables x_{ij} with these arcs.

There are also four *half arcs:* (b_1) and (b_2) representing supplies of the commodity entering the system at nodes 1 and 2, and (b_5), and (b_6) representing demands of the commodity leaving the system from nodes 5 and 6. We will associate constant supplies and demands with these half arcs.

Figure 8.1

Commodity network flow model.

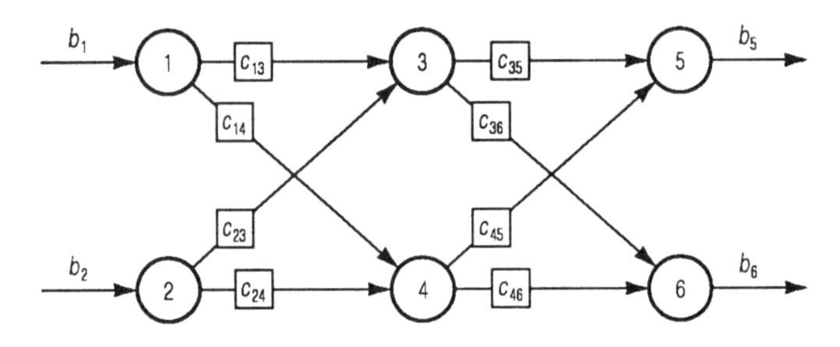

In order to set up the maximal flow problem as a linear program we define the *node arc incidence matrix* M as follows:

	Arcs							
Nodes	(1, 3)	(1, 4)	(2, 3)	(2, 4)	(3, 5)	(3, 6)	(4, 5)	(4, 6)
1	−1	−1	0	0	0	0	0	0
2	0	0	−1	−1	0	0	0	0
M = 3	1	0	1	0	−1	−1	0	0
4	0	1	0	1	0	0	−1	−1
5	0	0	0	0	1	0	1	0
6	0	0	0	0	0	1	0	1

Note that each arc corresponds to a column of M, and there is exactly two nonzero entries in each column: -1 in the row of the "from node" of the arc and $+1$ in the row of the "to node" of the arc. For example, in the first column labelled arc $(1, 3)$ there is a -1 in row 1 and a $+1$ in row 3; all other entries in the column are 0. If we look in the matrix at row 3 of M corresponding to node 3, we see that there are $+1$'s in row 3 corresponding to arcs pointing into node 3 and -1's corresponding to arcs pointing out from node 3.

We also define a six component column vector of supplies and demands as in (8.1). The components

$$(-b_1, -b_2, 0, 0, b_5, b_6) \tag{8.1}$$

of b correspond to the six nodes in Figure 8.1, supplies are denoted by negative numbers and demands as positive quantities. We let x_{ij} be the amount shipped through arc (i,j), and let x be the column vector of such x's shown in (8.2).

$$x = (x_{13}, x_{14}, x_{23}, x_{24}, x_{35}, x_{36}, x_{45}, x_{46}) \tag{8.2}$$

It is then possible to write the *conservation of flow condition* as in (8.3).

$$Mx = b \tag{8.3}$$

If these equations are written out (see Exercise 1) it is easy to see that there is one equation for each node, and the equation simply states that the sum of all flows into the node equals the sum of all flows out of that node. Let e be an n component row vector of all 1's, where n is the number of nodes. It is easy to see that $eM = 0$ since each column of M has exactly one $+1$ and one -1 and all the rest of its components are 0's. Hence if we multiply (8.3) by e on the left we get

$$eMx = 0 = eb = -b_1 - b_2 + b_5 + b_6 \tag{8.4}$$

Thus a necessary condition that a feasible flow exists is

$$b_1 + b_2 = b_5 + b_6 \tag{8.5}$$

i.e., total supplies are equal to or greater than total demands. Recall that a similar necessary condition held for the transportation problem treated in Chapter 1.

Now let c_{ij} be the cost of shipping a unit of flow on arc (i,j). Define the row vector

$$c = (c_{13}, c_{14}, c_{23}, c_{24}, c_{35}, c_{36}, c_{45}, c_{46}). \tag{8.6}$$

Consider the minimum cost flow linear program

$$\begin{aligned} \text{Minimize} \quad & cx \\ \text{Subject to} \quad & Mx = b \\ & x \geq 0 \end{aligned} \tag{8.7}$$

The data box for this program in component form in which we have chosen specific values for the b_i's and c_{ij}'s is shown below.

	x_{13}	x_{14}	x_{23}	x_{24}	x_{35}	x_{36}	x_{45}	x_{46}		
u_1	-1	-1	0	0	0	0	0	0	$= -150$	b_i's
u_2	0	0	-1	-1	0	0	0	0	$= -200$	
u_3	1	0	1	0	-1	-1	0	0	$= 0$	
u_4	0	1	0	1	0	0	-1	-1	$= 0$	
u_5	0	0	0	0	1	0	1	0	$= 175$	
u_6	0	0	0	0	0	1	0	1	$= 175$	
c_{ij}'s	8	6	9	11	21	18	22	15		

Note that the dual variables are marked on the left in the figure. We can state the dual problem to (8.7) as in (8.8).

$$\begin{aligned} \text{Maximize} \quad & ub \\ \text{Subject to} \quad & uM \geq c \\ & u \text{ unconstrained in sign} \end{aligned} \tag{8.8}$$

The reason that the dual variables are unconstrained is that the primal constraints in (8.7) are equalities.

Since each column of M has exactly one $+1$ and one -1 entry with the rest being zero it is easy to see that the constraint corresponding to arc (i,j) is of the form $-u_i + u_j \leq c_{ij}$. It follows that if u_i^* is an optimal dual solution, then so is $u_i^* + k$, where k is *any* real number, because

$$-(u_i^* + k) + (u_j^* + k) = -u_i^* + u_j^* \leq c_{ij}$$

(the k's cancel out).

The optimal value of u_i^* of the dual variable at node i can be interpreted as the imputed value of the commodity at node i. Spelling out the dual constraints in program (8.8), and also remembering complementary slackness, we must have, at the point of optimum:

$$\begin{aligned}
-u_1^* + u_3^* &\leq 8, & x_{13}^*(8 + u_1^* - u_3^*) &= 0 \\
-u_1^* + u_4^* &\leq 6, & x_{14}^*(6 + u_1^* - u_4^*) &= 0 \\
-u_2^* + u_3^* &\leq 9, & x_{23}^*(9 + u_2^* - u_3^*) &= 0 \\
-u_2^* + u_4^* &\leq 11, & x_{24}^*(11 + u_2^* - u_4^*) &= 0 \\
-u_3^* + u_5^* &\leq 21, & x_{35}^*(21 + u_3^* - u_5^*) &= 0 \\
-u_3^* + u_6^* &\leq 18, & x_{36}^*(18 + u_3^* - u_6^*) &= 0 \\
-u_4^* + u_5^* &\leq 22, & x_{45}^*(22 + u_4^* - u_5^*) &= 0 \\
-u_4^* + u_6^* &\leq 15, & x_{46}^*(15 + u_4^* - u_6^*) &= 0
\end{aligned}$$

In words, the imputed appreciation of value along arc (i,j) can never exceed the unit cost c_{ij}. If a positive flow is transmitted along the link, the imputed appreciation equals c_{ij}.

In order to solve the problem we solve the GAMS program PUMPOIL on page 315. The answers it prints out are shown below

The minimum solution is:

Arc	*Flow*
(1,3)	0
(1,4)	150
(2,3)	175
(2,4)	25
(3,5)	175
(3,6)	0
(4,5)	0
(4,6)	175

The maximum solution is:

Node	*Value*
1	$5 + k$
2	k
3	$9 + k$
4	$11 + k$
5	$30 + k$
6	$26 + k$

The value is 9050.

The easiest way to see what the solution means is to display it graphically, as in Figure 8.2, where we have chosen $k = 0$. Note that there are five positive flows. It can be shown that for an n node problem there will be at most $n - 1$ positive flows in the optimal solution. Also note that there are three paths of positive flow from a source node to a demand node. A breakdown of the flows on these paths and their costs is shown in the table below.

Path	*Capacity*	*Cost*	$u_{\text{final}} - u_{\text{initial}}$	*Cost per path*
1→4→6	150	21	$26 - 5 = 21$	3150
2→3→5	175	30	$30 - 0 = 30$	5250
2→4→6	25	26	$26 - 0 = 26$	650
			Total Cost	9050

Figure 8.2

Optimal network flows and dual variables.

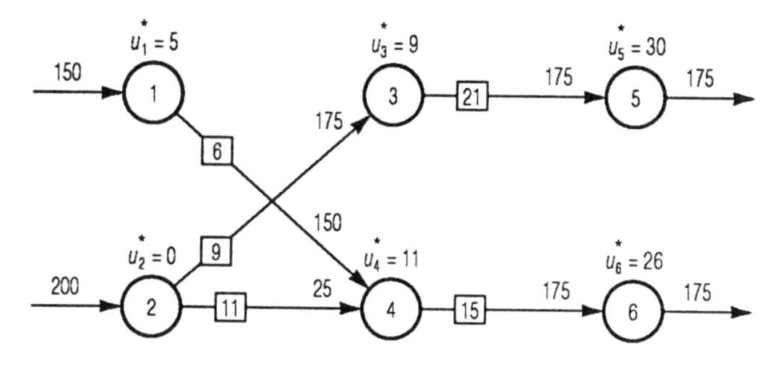

Note that in every case the difference between the dual variable at the final node minus the dual variable at the initial node is always equal to the cost. This is a necessary (but not sufficient) condition that a path be used to send positive flow in an optimal solution. The unit costs vary widely from 21 to 30 over the paths, but overall this is the lowest cost way to transport the goods to meet final demands. Note that the sum of the costs per path add up to the total cost of 9,050 which also appears in the GAMS solution table.

Production and Distribution

Frequently there are arcs that have an upper bound to their carrying capacity. This is particularly common for arcs that represent production of the commodity under consideration. The next example illustrates this concept.

An oil distributor pumps oil at two locations 1 and 2, then ships it through a distribution network similar to that in Figure 8.1 to refineries at locations 5 and 6. The graph of oil flows is given in Figure 8.3. The arrows going into nodes 1 and 2 represent pumping activities which have their own costs and upper bounds as marked. The final demands are the amounts b_5 and b_6 marked on arrows going out of nodes 5 and 6, respectively.

The data box for this problem is shown below. Note that the upper bounds on pumping activities appear as constraints 7 and 8.

	x_1	x_2	x_{13}	x_{14}	x_{23}	x_{24}	x_{35}	x_{36}	x_{45}	x_{46}	
1	1		−1	−1							$= 0$
2		1			−1	−1					$= 0$
3			1		1		−1	−1			$= 0$
4				1		1			−1	−1	$= 0$
5							1		1		$= b_5$
6								1		1	$= b_6$
7	1										$\leq X_1$
8		1									$\leq X_2$
	c_1	c_2	c_{13}	c_{14}	c_{23}	c_{24}	c_{35}	c_{36}	c_{45}	c_{46}	

Figure 8.3

Upper bounded oil pumping example.

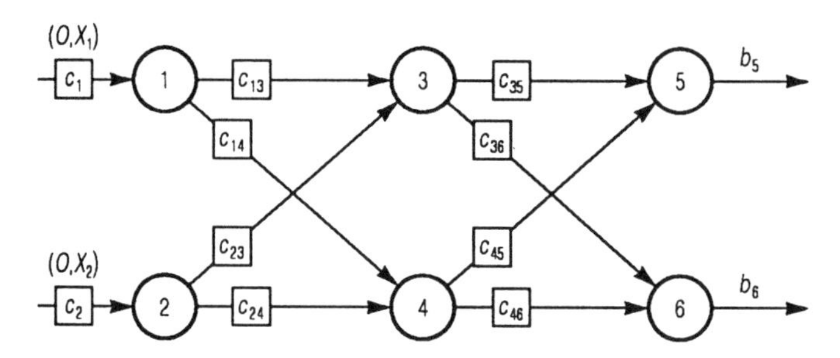

In Exercise 2 you are asked to solve this problem for specific values of costs and prices.

The aim of the linear program above is to minimize both production costs and transportation costs. The dual variables have been entered in the left hand margin. There is a dual variable u_i corresponding to each node i in the network. There are also dual variables v_1 and v_2 corresponding to the production capacities at the two pumping sites 1 and 2. As before, the optimal u_i^* at each node i can be interpreted as the imputed value of the commodity at node i. Note that $v_1, v_2 \leq 0$ (the capacity constraints are "wrong way" in a minimization problem). The optimal v_1^* and v_2^* are imputed surcharges to be applied when production at pumping sites 1 and 2 hit their capacity levels.

There are dual relations along each link of the network as before, spelling out the condition that the imputed appreciation of value along a link can never exceed the cost incurred along the link. There is also a new set of dual constraints

$$u_1 + v_1 \leq c_1$$
$$u_2 + v_2 \leq c_2$$

The corresponding relations of complementary slackness are

$$u_1^* + v_1^* \leq c_1, \qquad x_1^*(c_1 - u_1^* - v_1^*) = 0, \qquad x_1^* \geq 0$$
$$u_2^* + v_2^* \leq c_2, \qquad x_2^*(c_2 - u_2^* - v_2^*) = 0, \qquad x_2^* \geq 0$$

The imputed value of oil at a pumping site cannot exceed the unit production cost plus the possible capacity surcharge. If a positive amount of oil is pumped, the imputed value equals the sum of the unit production cost and the possible capacity charge. But if the same unit cost total falls short of the imputed value, no oil is pumped at that site.

Note that the program above takes the form of multi-stage programming (see Chapter 7). Using the theory of decentralization in vertically integrated systems, we realize that it would be possible to design a system of decentralization in which the integrated oil company is split into two divisions: a production division involving the pumping of oil from the oil fields and a transportation division encompassing the distribution of pumped oil via the network in Figure 8.3, finally to reach the refineries.

Exercises

1. Let $b_1 = 150$, $b_2 = 200$, $b_5 = 175$, $b_6 = 175$; then write the equations corresponding to (8.3). Show that each equation states that the sum of the amounts flowing into each node equals the sum of the amounts flowing out of the node.

2. Solve the oil pumping problem in the data box on page 117 with the same data as in the data box on page 115 plus $c_1 = 48$, $c_2 = 52$, $X_1 = 150$, and $X_2 = 225$. Discuss in detail the optimal primal and dual solutions. Make small changes in some of the data and use the dual solution to predict the changed solution. Then make additional runs to verify these predictions.

3. For the oil pumping example in the data box on page 115, add the upper bounds on arc flows of the form $x_{ij} \leq X_{ij}$ given by

i,j	13	14	23	24	35	36	45	46
X_{ij}	75	100	135	100	150	100	125	125

Re-solve the problem and interpret the solution.

4. Consider a so-called transshipment problem with three origins A, B, and C. The supplies at the origins are 70, 100, and 30 units, respectively. Goods are shipped from origins to three final destinations G, H, and I, via three transit points D, E, and F. The demands at the destinations are 70, 90, and 40 units, respectively.

   A transit point can be reached from any origin, and has direct communication to any final destination. The unit transportation costs from origins to transit points, and from transit points to destinations are (in dollars):

From \ To	D	E	F
A	5	3	5
B	15	6	10
C	2	11	12

From \ To	G	H	I
D	4	8	10
E	8	2	4
F	3	4	2

No transit point can handle more than 88 units of total arrivals.

(a) Construct a linear programming model that solves the transshipment problem. Define dual variables and write down the dual problem. Interpret the dual variables and the dual contraints.

(b) Solution on a computer produces the optimal solution,

$$X^*_{AF} = 70, \quad X^*_{BE} = 88, \quad X^*_{BF} = 12, \quad X^*_{CD} = 30, \quad X^*_{DG} = 30$$

$$X^*_{EH} = 88, \quad X^*_{FG} = 40, \quad X^*_{FH} = 40, \quad X^*_{FI} = 40$$

and shipments along all other links equal to zero. Also, it turns out that the imputed prices at the three origins, A, B, and C, are \$5, \$0, and \$7, respectively. Starting out from these three values, explain how the dual constraints can be employed to deduce recursively the imputed prices at all transit points and all destinations. Calculate by hand the optimal values of the remaining dual variables.

9

Production in a Vertically Integrated Company

It is common that firms in some industries such as paper, steel, petroleum, and to a certain extent automobiles, are organized in a vertical manner. That is, such a firm owns most or all of the productive facilities along the entire path of production of their goods, from the extraction of raw materials through production of various intermediate products, the production of the final products, and even, unless prevented by law, the sales outlets for final products. Such a firm may change from being a completely vertical organization to one that is only partially vertical, or the reverse, from time to time depending on the current business climate. Also events such as leveraged buyouts may make it profitable for the new owners to sell off parts of a vertically organized firm. In this chapter we will not discuss the advantages and disadvantages of vertical integration, but merely discuss some of the problems peculiar to that kind of a business structure.

A vertically organized firm is necessarily spread over a fairly large geographic area. For example, the firm may own forests, mines, or agricultural areas located in various parts of a given country or even throughout the world. The products of these primary activities may be partially refined or processed near the actual production site; then they are sent to one or more stages for further processing; and finally they end up as finished products at the loading dock of a factory. From there they go to warehouses or even retail outlets where they are sold either to intermediate sales organizations or to the final consumer.

One way of looking at this kind of activity is that a vertically integrated firm is involved in and must compete in a number of different businesses. The output of each stage of production can be regarded as an intermediate product which can be bought or sold as it is, or it may be passed on to a later manufacturing stage. It is clear that the company must have a wide range of managerial talent to cover each of these different businesses. The company must continuously evaluate whether at any given stage, it is better to be a producer, a buyer, or a seller of the intermediate product at that stage. As we shall see the dual variables of the production constraints at each stage will give valuable information which will help in answering such questions.

A Vertically Integrated Paper Company

As our principal example we shall consider a paper company which owns large acreages of forests, log grinding and chipping machines, pulping and paper mills. It sells three final products which are kraft paper, a heavy brown paper used in making cardboard boxes and milk cartons, and which is sold to companies making these products; newsprint which is sold in bulk to various newspapers; and finally book paper which is sold to book publishers.

Trees of the proper kinds and sizes are cut in the company's forests, cut into four foot lengths, and floated down nearby rivers to the company plant that contains grinding and chipping machines. After the logs are peeled, they are processed into ground wood and wood chips. Those products are loaded onto freight cars and transported to the company's pulping mills. There a proper mixture of ground wood and chips is put into a large vat, mixed with various chemicals and heated for a suitable period of time until it becomes wood pulp. The finished pulp is pumped into railroad freight tanker cars, and transported to large paper mills that make the various finished products.

Besides cutting its own logs it is possible for the paper company to buy logs from local tree farmers near to the company forests. Pulp may also be bought from or sold to other paper companies. Even the finished products such as kraft paper, newsprint, and book paper can be bought from or sold to other paper companies. It may be advantageous to buy or sell such intermediate or final products this way depending upon the relative costs of production and warehousing of each company and the transportation costs between the companies. Other factors such as capacity shortages, forest fires, amount of consumer demand, etc., may influence these decisions.

Figure 9.1 shows the materials flow diagram of the paper company. The nodes of the diagram represent factories or storage locations for the outputs of various stages of the process. Nodes 1 and 2 represent sources of logs. Node 0 (not shown in the diagram) is a dummy node representing the outside. Arrows represent transportation activities of the outputs from one node to another. Each arrow has a flow variable associated with it which measures the amount of flow leaving the previous node. The flags on these arrows give the per unit transportation cost on the arrow. Triangles on arrows, such as those going from node 3 to nodes 4 and 5, contain a loss factor which in this case is due to the fact that the logs have their bark peeled. The absence of a triangle indicates that there is no loss on the transportation step. The outside sales variables, $x_{10,0}$, $x_{11,0}$, and $x_{12,0}$ have upper and lower bounds represented by a pair (l, u) beside their costs.

At five of the nodes in the diagram, namely nodes 6, 7, 10, 11, and 12, there are ovals surrounding the arrows entering the node. Each oval contains a pair of fractions that add up to one. Each of the ovals represents a *ratio constraint* which forces the variables on the two arrows entering to be blended together in that proportion to produce the product that comes out of the node. For instance, at node 6 we see that pulp 1 consists of 60% ground wood and 40% wood chips, while at node 7 we see that pulp 2, which is a better grade than pulp 1, consists of 30% ground wood and 70% wood chips. Similarly, note that the three products kraft paper, newsprint, and book paper are made

Figure 9.1

Flow diagram of the paper company.

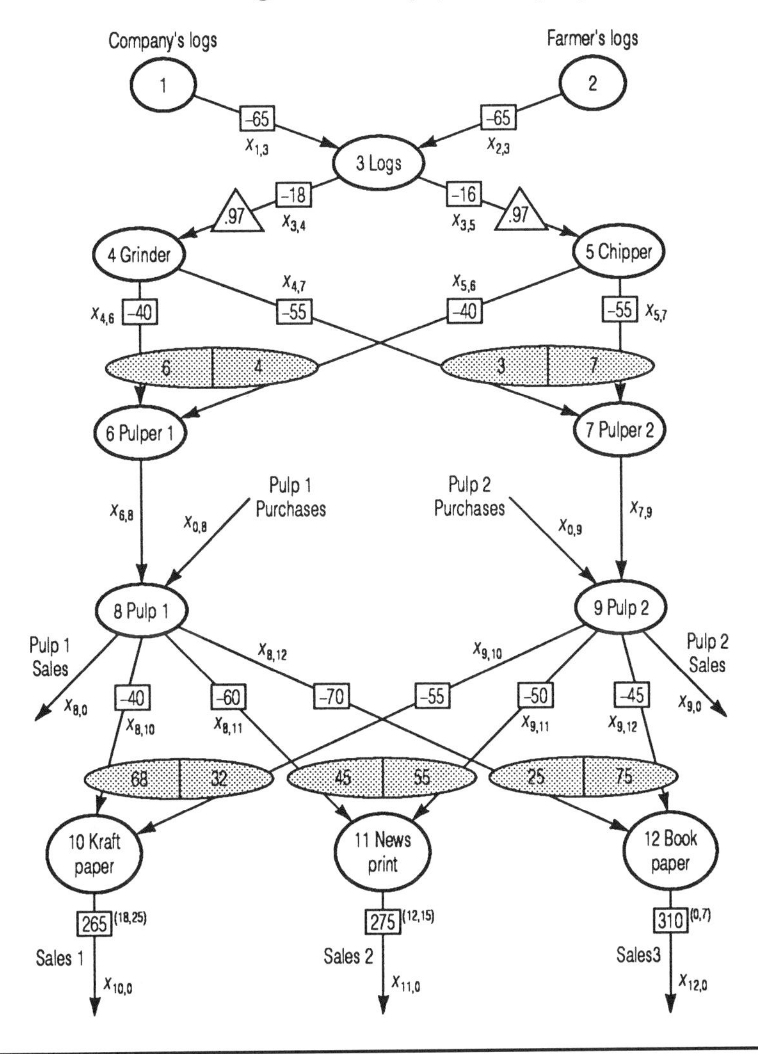

by blending the two kinds of pulp together in different proportions. These constraints are not network constraints, but will be imposed by the linear programming solution software.

Let us derive the ratio constraint corresponding to the 0.6 to 0.4 mixture of ground wood and wood chips entering node 6. The conservation of flow constraint at node 6 is just

$$x_{4,6} + x_{5,6} = x_{6,8} \tag{9.1}$$

But we also know that

$$0.6x_{6,8} = x_{4,6} \tag{9.2}$$

If we solve (9.2) for $x_{6,8}$ and substitute into (9.1), it is easy to show that

$$0.4x_{4,6} = 0.6x_{5,6}$$

which can be rewritten with all variables to the left as

$$0.4x_{4,6} - 0.6x_{5,6} = 0 \tag{9.3}$$

and is the form in which it should be entered into the software program.

The general rule for ratio constraints is: if variable x_i consists of a fraction a of variable x_j plus a fraction $(1 - a)$ of variable x_k the ratio constraint needed to enforce this is:

$$(1 - a)x_j - ax_k = 0 \tag{9.4}$$

Ratio constraints are also called recipe constraints, since they define the composition of the output flow variable as a fractional part of one input flow variable with the remainder being the other flow variable.

As previously mentioned there are three final goods in the model: kraft paper, newspaper, and book paper. They fetch market prices of $265, $275, and $310, respectively, per ton. Also the company can enter the market (see nodes 8 and 9) for pulp, either as a buyer or as a seller. It may even buy pulp of one grade and sell pulp of the other grade. The market price of pulp 1 is $120 per ton, and the price of pulp 2 is $140 per ton.

In Figure 9.1 there are 23 flow variables marked on the arrows of the figure. Names for these variables can be inferred from that figure, or by referring ahead to the names for them given on page 126.

We now derive the constraints that must be obeyed by those variables. Nodes 1 and 2 do not have constraints. There are 10 nodal constraints corresponding to the nodes 3, 4, . . . , 12 in Figure 9.1, as follows:

node 3	$-x_{1,3} - x_{2,3} + x_{3,4} + x_{3,5} = 0$	(9.5)
node 4	$-0.97x_{3,4} + x_{4,6} + x_{4,7} = 0$	(9.6)
node 5	$-0.97x_{3,4} + x_{5,6} + x_{5,7} = 0$	(9.7)
node 6	$-x_{4,6} + x_{5,6} + x_{6,8} = 0$	(9.8)
node 7	$-x_{4,7} + x_{5,7} + x_{7,9} = 0$	(9.9)
node 8	$-x_{6,8} - x_{0,8} + x_{8,0} + x_{8,10} + x_{8,11} + x_{8,12} = 0$	(9.10)
node 9	$-x_{7,9} - x_{0,9} + x_{9,0} + x_{9,10} + x_{9,11} + x_{9,12} = 0$	(9.11)
node 10	$-x_{8,10} - x_{9,10} + x_{10,0} = 0$	(9.12)
node 11	$-x_{8,11} - x_{9,11} + x_{11,0} = 0$	(9.13)
node 12	$-x_{8,12} - x_{9,12} + x_{12,0} = 0$	(9.14)

Next we have five ratio constraints:

node 6	$0.4x_{4,6} - 0.6x_{5,6} = 0$	(9.15)
node 7	$0.7x_{4,7} - 0.3x_{5,7} = 0$	(9.16)
node 10	$0.32x_{8,10} - 0.68x_{9,10} = 0$	(9.17)

node 11	$0.55x_{8,11} - 0.45x_{9,11} = 0$	(9.18)
node 12	$0.75x_{8,12} - 0.25x_{9,12} = 0$	(9.19)

The remaining nine are upper or lower bound constraints:

kraft paper upper bound	$x_{10,0} \leq 25$	(9.20)
kraft paper lower bound	$x_{10,0} \geq 18$	(9.21)
newspaper upper bound	$x_{11,0} \leq 15$	(9.22)
newspaper lower bound	$x_{11,0} \geq 12$	(9.23)
book paper upper bound	$x_{12,0} \leq 7$	(9.24)
pulp 1 purchase upper bound	$x_{0,8} \leq 0$	(9.25)
pulp 1 sales upper bound	$x_{8,0} \leq 0$	(9.26)
pulp 2 purchase upper bound	$x_{0,9} \leq 0$	(9.27)
pulp 2 sales upper bound	$x_{9,0} \leq 0$	(9.28)

Finally, the objective function to be maximized is:

$$\begin{aligned} z = & - 65x_{1,3} - 65x_{2,3} - 18x_{3,4} - 16x_{3,5} - 40x_{4,6} - 55x_{4,7} \\ & - 40x_{5,6} - 55x_{5,7} - 40x_{8,10} - 60x_{8,11} - 70x_{8,12} \\ & - 55x_{9,10} - 50x_{9,11} - 45x_{9,12} + 265x_{10,0} + 275x_{11,0} \\ & + 310x_{12,0} - 120x_{0,8} + 120x_{8,0} - 140x_{0,9} + 140x_{9,0} \end{aligned} \qquad (9.29)$$

The data box for this problem is a matrix with 24 rows and 23 columns. Of the 552 entries in this matrix only 56 or 10.1% are nonzero. In other words the matrix is *sparse*. For larger models of industrial processes, the sparsity of such data boxes is much less, averaging only one or two percent. For this reason it is better to enter the model algebraically as stated in (9.5) through (9.29) using an algebraic modelling language. Refer to the software program PAPERCO on page 316 to see how this can be done.

The primal solution to the problem is shown in the table below in the column labeled Scenario 1. This corresponds to the current operating procedure in effect in the company. However the paper company is contemplating entering the wholesale pulp business, so that it has proposed two other scenarios which are shown in the table below.

	Scenario 1	*Scenario 2*	*Scenario 3*
Maximum sales of Pulp 1	0	3	6
Maximum purchases of Pulp 1	0	5	6
Maximum sales of Pulp 2	0	3	10
Maximum purchases of Pulp 2	0	5	10
Price of Pulp 1	120	120	120
Price of Pulp 2	140	140	150

Scenario 2 corresponds to small sales and purchases of Pulp 1 and Pulp 2 both at the current prices, while Scenario 3 corresponds to somewhat larger sales and purchases as well as an increase in the price of Pulp 2 from 140 to 150 dollars per ton. Note that these figures require changing only the right hand sides of constraints (9.25) through (9.28) and the coefficient of x_{23} in (9.29).

The primal solutions for each of these scenarios are shown in the next table. Clearly the small increase of 0.42% in net profit for Scenario 2 would not warrant the entry into the pulp markets if that is an accurate prediction of the state of that market. Scenario 3, however, gives 3.08% profit improvement and just might be attractive enough to enter the market. In the exercises you will be asked to solve two more scenarios that are still more optimistic.

Arc	*Name*	*Scenario 1*	*Scenario 2*	*Scenario 3*
1, 3	tons company logs used	48.454	50.515	52.577
2, 3	tons farmer's logs used	0.000	0.000	0.000
3, 4	logs sent to grinder	22.423	22.113	21.804
3, 5	logs sent to chipper	26.031	28.402	30.773
4, 6	ground wood to pulper 1	15.300	13.500	11.700
4, 7	ground wood to pulper 2	6.450	7.950	9.450
5, 6	chips sent to pulper 1	10.200	9.000	7.800
5, 7	chips sent to pulper 2	15.050	18.550	22.050
6, 8	pulp 1 sent to storage	25.500	22.500	19.500
7, 9	pulp 2 sent to storage	21.500	26.500	31.500
8, 10	pulp 1 sent to kraft mill	17.000	17.000	17.000
8, 11	pulp 1 sent to newsprint mill	6.750	6.750	6.750
8, 12	pulp 1 sent to book paper mill	1.750	1.750	1.750
9, 10	pulp 2 sent to kraft mill	8.000	8.000	8.000
9, 11	pulp 2 sent to newsprint mill	8.250	8.250	8.250
9, 12	pulp 2 sent to book paper mill	5.250	5.250	5.250
10, 0	kraft paper sent to sales 1	25.000	25.000	25.000
11, 0	newsprint sent to sales 2	15.000	15.000	15.000
12, 0	book paper sent to sales 3	7.000	7.000	7.000
0, 8	pulp 1 purchases received	0.000	3.000	6.000
8, 0	pulp 1 sales delivered	0.000	0.000	0.000
0, 9	pulp 2 purchases received	0.000	0.000	0.000
9, 0	pulp 2 sales delivered	0.000	5.000	10.000
	Objective value	4451.660	4470.271	4588.880
	Improvement	0.0%	0.42%	3.08%

All quantities are measured in tons. Refer to Figure 9.1 for the flow diagram on which the flow variables are marked. The conditions for the three cases are stated in the table at the bottom of page 125.

The dual solution to all three scenarios is shown with interpretations in the table on page 127. Note that there is a dual variable for each of the constraints (9.5) through (9.28). Exactly the same dual solution is valid for all three cases, except for the value of the last dual variable which should be 10.88 in Scenario 3. In Exercise 2 you are asked to discuss the meaning of each of these dual variables.

Constraint	*Name of dual variable*	*Values in Dollars per ton*
(9.5)	imputed value of logs	65.00
(9.6)	imputed value of ground wood	85.57
(9.7)	imputed value of wood chips	83.51
(9.8)	imputed value of output of pulper 1	124.74
(9.9)	imputed value of output of pulper 2	139.12
(9.10)	imputed value of pulp 1	124.74
(9.11)	imputed value of pulp 2	139.12
(9.12)	imputed value of kraft paper	174.14
(9.13)	imputed value of newsprint	187.15
(9.14)	imputed value of book paper	186.78
(9.15)	imputed cost of pulp 1 ratio constraint	−2.70
(9.16)	imputed cost of pulp 2 ratio constraint	−2.10
(9.17)	imputed cost of kraft paper ratio constraint	29.38
(9.18)	imputed cost of newsprint ratio constraint	4.38
(9.19)	imputed cost of book paper ratio constraint	−10.62
(9.20)	imputed value of relaxing kraft upper bound	90.86
(9.21)	imputed value of relaxing kraft lower bound	0.00
(9.22)	imputed value of relaxing newsprint upper bound	87.85
(9.23)	imputed value of relaxing newsprint lower bound	0.00
(9.24)	imputed value of relaxing book paper upper bound	123.20
(9.25)	imputed value of relaxing pulp 1 sales upper bound	0.00
(9.26)	imputed value of relaxing pulp 1 sales lower bound	4.74
(9.27)	imputed value of relaxing pulp 2 sales upper bound	0.00
(9.28)	imputed value of relaxing pulp 2 sales lower bound	0.88

Besides using this linear programming model to answer the question as to whether or not to enter the pulp market, it can also be used to answer questions such as: should we build a new pulp mill, and if so, where should it be located; should we build other kraft mills or newsprint plants, and where should they be located; etc. In evaluating such proposals it is necessary to add additional nodes corresponding to the new facilities, to calculate or estimate their operating and transportation costs, and their production capacities, and to re-solve the model. If the addition of such facilities makes a sufficient decrease in production costs it may then be possible to reduce sales prices of some of the final products and thereby expand demand. Changes in demand can be estimated by a linear, or even a nonlinear function and included in the model.

Without going any further in the development of uses for the model it is clear that it is a valuable tool for making managerial decisions. For this reason it is very common for large companies to have constructed very large and detailed models of the operations of their company. Sometimes these models are constructed by employees of the company, and sometimes by a management consultant firm. But the almost universal acceptance of this kind of modelling technique by large firms indicates their importance to such firms.

Exercises

1. Consider the following two scenarios:

	Scenario 4	*Scenario 5*
Maximum sales of Pulp 1	10	15
Maximum purchases of Pulp 1	12	17
Maximum sales of Pulp 2	15	18
Maximum purchases of Pulp 2	9	15
Price of Pulp 1	130	135
Price of Pulp 2	155	160

   (a) Solve the linear program for Scenario 4.

   (b) Solve the linear program for Scenario 5.

   (c) Compare and evaluate Scenarios 1–5, and write a report to management concerning the desirability of entering the wholesale pulp market in each of these cases.

2. Discuss in detail the managerial meanings of each of the dual variables in the table on page 127. Illustrate your discussion with the solutions to the five scenarios found above.

3. Assume the cost of logs supplied by farmers has dropped to $58/ton, and that they can supply up to 27 tons at that price. Find and discuss the new solution to the model.

4. Refer to the original model in Figure 9.1 and answer the following question. Due to recent results of company research a new process for making book paper has been developed that requires only 71% of pulp 2 instead of 75%. What is the impact of this discovery on the company's net profits?

10

Inventory Management: Warehousing

Business firms frequently hold inventories (i.e., stocks) of finished goods, of raw materials, or of intermediate products that they buy from other firms for further processing. In terms of national accounting, the buildup of such inventory is a case of investment, and the holding of an inventory represents capital. In the early part of this century economists used to call inventory "revolving capital," to distinguish it from fixed capital such as buildings, machines or land. Inventories "revolve" because they will eventually be used up in the production process or sold. Just as the owner of a supermarket wants his goods on the shelves to "move" as fast as possible, the owner of a firm wants his inventory of intermediate goods and raw materials to be used up during the production cycle. Indeed, the main problem of *inventory management* is to design a system of ordering inventory at the right times in the right amounts.

Using terms that were originally suggested by Keynes for the study of the demand for money, we may distinguish the following three motives for holding inventory:

1. A "Transactions Motive" arising because the time path of the demand for a product may not be synchronized with the time path of the supply of the product; the role of inventory is to bridge the gap between supply and demand.
2. A "Speculation Motive" by which it may actually be advantageous for the firm to use or sell the commodity later rather than now, if prices are expected to appreciate over time. The inventory then serves as a device of "smoothing" the time path of production or of sales. In the case of outputs, the time path of production can then be divorced from the time path of sales. Effectively, then, the firm engages in "time arbitrage," making a profit by buying or producing the good at one point of time and selling it at a higher price at a later point in time.

3. A "Precautionary Motive," arising because the timing of demands and the sales prices may be uncertain; also, the timing of supplies and the supply prices to be paid may also be uncertain. Thus inventory serves as a buffer against such stochastic variability.

In the literature of operations research, considerable efforts have been spent on the development of mathematical techniques for finding the optimal way of holding inventory in the face of stochastic demand (the precautionary motive). Typically, these formulas aim at an optimal mix of two kinds of costs associated with inventories: on the one hand *holding costs*, calculated per unit of inventory, such as the costs of owning or leasing and operating sufficient warehouse capacity, and for operating these facilities; on the other hand *stockout costs*, which are penalties that the business firm supposedly has to pay if it fails to meet demand. Clearly, if the inventory of a given good is large, holding costs are considerable but expected stockout costs are low. Conversely, if the inventory is small, holding costs are also small, but the expected stockout costs are high. Thus there exists a trade off between these two types of costs, and balancing them defines an optimal level of inventory. Many companies today use automated inventory control systems where a computer monitors all movements of inventories, calculates optimal *reordering points* at which replenishment of purchased inputs is made, and may even trigger automatic purchase orders.

In most industries, the sizes of inventories fluctuate in a typical fashion over the business cycle. In the automobile industry, for instance, inventories of finished cars are low during the upturn and during the boom, due to brisk sales. But as total demand tapers off when the end of the boom period is reached, inventories build up beyond normal levels. At this time of the cycle, credit costs are typically high and the automobile manufacturers take steps to reduce excess inventory, in the first instance perhaps by creating incentives to move inventory at a faster pace to dealers, but eventually by curtailing production. The downturn of the business cycle is characterized by cutbacks in production; but if demand drops even faster the net result will be a continued buildup of excess inventories. These inventories will act as a drag on the economy, and production must continue on a reduced scale until the excess inventory has been depleted.

Why does an automobile manufacturer end up accumulating inventory in the face of a weakening demand? The transactions motive and the precautionary motive presumably act equally strongly during all phases of the business cycle. If the manufacturer believes that the weakening of demand is only temporary in nature, the speculation motive calls for defering some sales until prices have firmed, rather than accepting lower prices now. But there is also another mechanism at work here: the manufacturer is willing, at least in the short run, to build up inventories rather than to lay off labor, which is also costly. The smoothing problem includes the task of solving for an optimal time path of labor (see Chapter 12).

In this chapter we will discuss a warehousing inventory model with deterministic demands. Thus we illustrate the transactions and speculation motives for inventory control.

The Inventory Model

Consider a firm that owns a raw materials warehouse; it buys a commodity which it can either (a) use for productive purposes, (b) store for later use or sale, or (c) sell for a profit. We use the following notation:

T = total number of time periods.

t = time period, where $t = 1, 2, \ldots, T$.

x_t^+ = the quantity bought in period t.

x_t^- = the quantity sold in period t.

α = the unit transactions cost which has to be paid each time a purchase or sale is made.

p_t = the market price at time t; a seller gets $p_t - \alpha$; a buyer pays $p_t + \alpha$.

d_t = the demand of the firm for the commodity at time t.

I_0 = the initial stock of the commodity.

I_t = the stock of inventory held at time t.

I_T = the required final inventory of the commodity.

$\bar{I}$ = the fixed warehouse capacity.

h = the unit holding cost for inventory.

Figure 10.1

Three period inventory network flow model. I_0 is the initial and I_3 the final inventory.

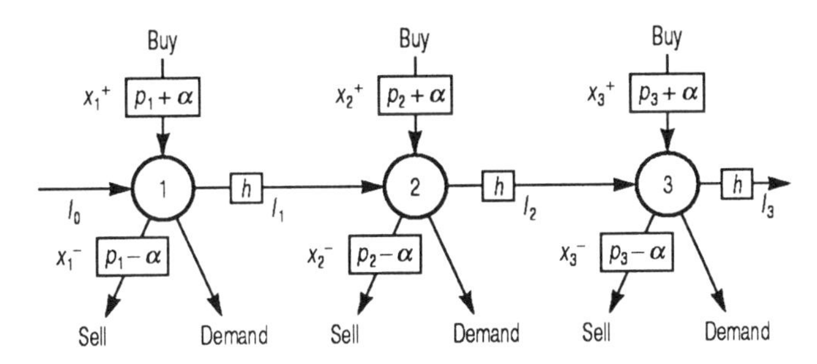

In Figure 10.1 a pure network inventory model of the process is shown. Note that at each time period the firm can buy, sell, deliver, or store the commodity. To buy or sell, the firm enters a national commodity market where a fixed price p_t is quoted in period t. The agents in this market are all speculators (dealers). The demand curve in this market is horizontal. To deliver (i.e., cover demand), the firm turns to local users of the commodity who use it as an input into a production process. Their demand curve is vertical, with demand d_t. If the demands are all zero then we have a purely *speculative model* and if selling is prohibited then we have a pure *demand model*. The objective of the firm is to procure the required amounts of the commodity in such a way as to minimize the difference between profits from speculation and the costs of obtaining the commodity for productive purposes.

Using the above notation the problem can be stated as the following linear programming problem:

$$\text{Maximize} \quad \sum_{t=1}^{T} [(p_t - \alpha)x^- - (p_t + \alpha)x_t^+ - hI_t] \tag{10.1}$$

$$\text{Subject to} \quad x_t^- - x_t^+ + I_t - I_{t-1} = -d_t \tag{10.2}$$

$$I_t \le \bar{I} \tag{10.3}$$

$$x_t^-, x_t^+, I_t \ge 0 \tag{10.4}$$

In (10.2) there is a constraint for each node. Note that the signs of the coefficients of variables corresponding to arcs *coming into* the node are negative, while the signs of variables *going out of* the node are positive.

A Pure Speculation Example

Let us consider an example in which $T = 5$, $h = 1$, $\alpha = 2$, $I_0 = I_5 = 300$, $\bar{I} = 500$ and the prices and demands are given in the table below (Figure 10.2 gives the network model of this example).

t	1	2	3	4	5
p_t	75	65	89	77	80
d_t	0	0	0	0	0

From the network model of Figure 10.2 we can easily derive the data box of the corresponding linear program which is shown below. The data box has dimensions 9×14. The first five constraints are the nodal constraints and the last four constraints are upper bounds on the inventory variables. (Note that $I_0 = 300$ and $I_5 = 300$ and so need not be included as variables.)

x_1^+	x_2^+	x_3^+	x_4^+	x_5^+	I_1	I_2	I_3	I_4	x_1^-	x_2^-	x_3^-	x_4^-	x_5^-	
−1	0	0	0	0	1	0	0	0	1	0	0	0	0	$= 300 = I_0$
0	−1	0	0	0	−1	1	0	0	0	1	0	0	0	$= 0$
0	0	−1	0	0	0	−1	1	0	0	0	1	0	0	$= 0$
0	0	0	−1	0	0	0	−1	1	0	0	0	1	0	$= 0$
0	0	0	0	−1	0	0	0	−1	0	0	0	0	1	$= -300 = -I_5$
0	0	0	0	0	1	0	0	0	0	0	0	0	0	≤ 500
0	0	0	0	0	0	1	0	0	0	0	0	0	0	≤ 500
0	0	0	0	0	0	0	1	0	0	0	0	0	0	≤ 500
0	0	0	0	0	0	0	0	1	0	0	0	0	0	≤ 500
−77	−67	−91	−79	−82	−1	−1	−1	−1	73	63	87	75	78	

The problem above was solved by solving the GAMS program `PURINVEN` on page 318. The following primal variables were nonzero: $x_2^+ = 500$, $x_4^+ = 300$, $I_2 = 500$, $I_4 = 300$, $x_1^- = 300$, $x_3^- = 500$. The best way to interpret this solution is by representing it in the graph shown in Figure 10.3. There the zero variables are indicated by dotted arcs and the nonzero variables by solid arcs.

The objective value for the problem was 7400. This can easily be calculated from the nonzero variables, marked in Figure 10.3, as follows:

$$300 \cdot 73 + 500 \cdot 87 - 500 \cdot 67 - 300 \cdot 79 - 500 - 300 = 7400.$$

Figure 10.2

Network flow model for the pure speculation model.

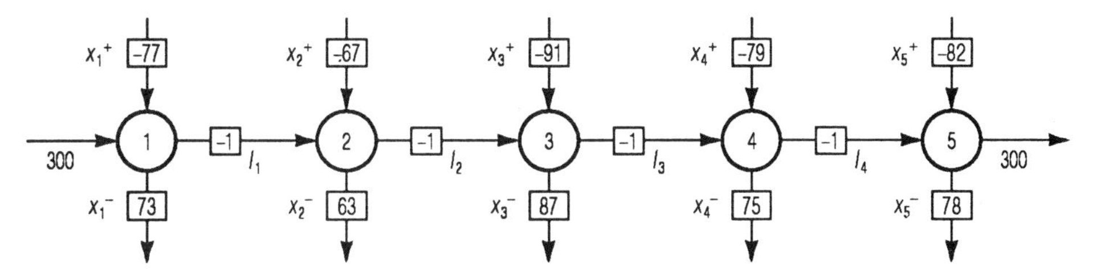

Note in Figure 10.3 that, if we ignore the dotted arcs, the solution breaks up into three separate parts because two solid arcs never enter the same node. In fact for the optimal solution to the pure speculation model the following rules can be proved to hold:

1. Never buy and sell at the same time (because this causes a per unit loss of 2α).
2. When selling, sell to empty the warehouse, or sell down to meet the final inventory demand.
3. When buying, buy to fill the warehouse, or buy to fulfill a final inventory demand.

The dual solution is also interesting and is shown below.

t	*1*	*2*	*3*	*4*	*5*	*6*	*7*	*8*	*9*
u_t	73	67	87	79	80	0	19	0	0

The values of the first five dual variables are easy to interpret: they are the net unit prices of the commodity at each node. This price includes storage costs, when appropriate. For instance the price of 80 at node 5 is 79, the cost at node 4, plus 1, the cost of holding for one period. The interpretation of $u_7 = 19$ is also clear: it is the imputed value of having a larger warehouse in the second period (which is the only time at which the

Figure 10.3

Primal solution for the pure speculation example.

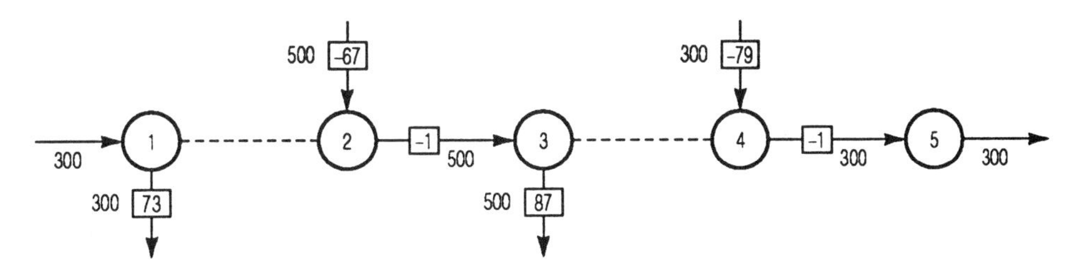

Figure 10.4

Network flow model for inventory demand example.

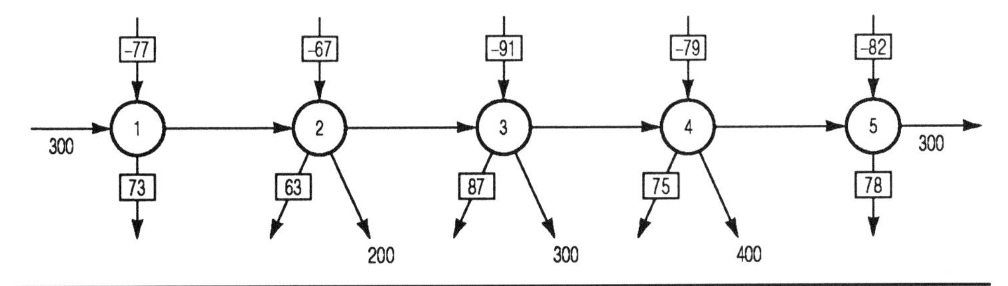

An Inventory Problem with Demand

We modify the preceding example by adding demands as shown below. The graph of the new problem is shown in Figure 10.4.

t	*1*	*2*	*3*	*4*	*5*
d_t	0	200	300	400	0

If we look at the node equations (10.2) it is easy to see how the data box on page 132 should be modified for the current example. All that has to be done is to change the right hand sides of constraints 2, 3, and 4 to −200, −300, and −400, respectively.

The linear programming software found the solution by solving INVENDEM on page 319 to be as indicated in the network diagram of Figure 10.5. As before, zero shipments are represented by dotted arcs and nonzero shipments by solid arcs. The objective function value is −63,700 which can be calculated as follows:

$$300 \cdot 73 + 200 \cdot 87 - 700 \cdot 67 - 700 \cdot 79 - 500 - 300 = -63{,}700$$

The result of the speculative buying and selling of the firm, calculated net of holding costs, is a large negative number. That is only natural considering that the total volume of speculative buying exceeds the total volume of speculative selling.

The dual solution to the inventory example is exactly the same as that shown in the middle of page 133.

Figure 10.5

Solution to inventory with demand example.

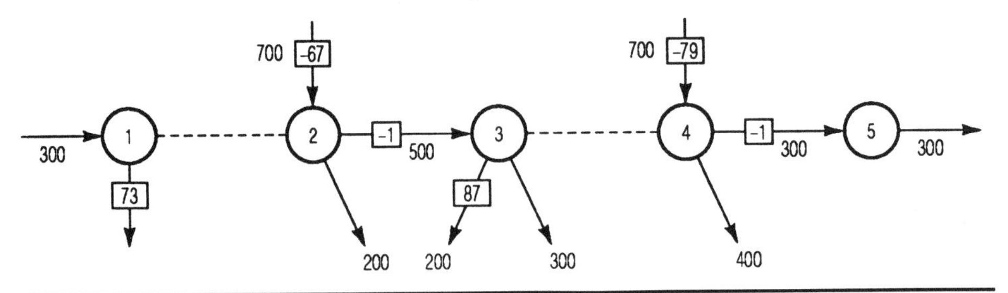

Inventories Dampen Price Swings

Inventories serve as buffers not just to individual producers, wholesalers, and consumers but also to the economy at large. Inventories smooth prices over time. An expected future shortage and expected price rises create incentives for operators of warehouses to increase storage in the expectation of capital gains. As the warehouses eventually unload their holdings the shortage will be alleviated, and prices will not rise as much as they would otherwise have done. Conversely, an expected future glut and expectations of falling prices induce operators of warehouses to plan to buy when prices are low. Their demands will support the market and prices will not fall as much as they would otherwise have done.

Thus the "speculative" behavior of the operators of the warehouses (their pursuit of capital gains on their inventory holdings) actually benefits the market. It redirects supply from periods of glut to periods of shortage. In this sense the speculators perform an important stabilizing function.

In order to illustrate, consider a simple variation on the inventory model, this time relating to *all* warehouses in the market. Further, assume that all shipments from producers are first routed to the warehouses, and that all deliveries to consumers are made from warehouses. In other words, the operator of a warehouse is a "middleman" in the market.

Let both demand and supply be price sensitive. A numerical example is provided below, listing the demand price function and the supply price function in each time period:

period t	*demand price*	*supply price*
1	$40 - 0.75d_1$	$-30 + 2x_1$
2	$42 - 0.75d_2$	$-25 + 2x_2$
3	$44 - 0.75d_3$	$-20 + 2x_3$
4	$46 - 0.75d_4$	$-15 + 2x_4$
5	$48 - 0.75d_5$	$-10 + 2x_5$

where d_t is consumer demand in period t and x_t is producer supply in period t added to inventory (x_t thus corresponds to the earlier notation x_t^+).

The demand curves are slowly being shifted upwards over time. The supply curves are also shifting upwards, but somewhat faster. Without storage and without inventories, prices would therefore rise. Indeed, without storage and inventories, prices and quantities would be as shown in the table below:

period t	*demand d_t = supply x_t*	*price*
1	25.45	20.91
2	24.36	23.72
3	23.27	26.54
4	22.18	29.36
5	21.09	32.18

In order to calculate the numbers in the table above, we set demand = supply and demand price = supply price in each time period and solve.

With storage, the story is different. Assume that the storage cost is $h = 0.8$, that initial and terminal inventory equals I_0 equals 300, that desired inventory at the planning horizon I_5 is also 300, and that the capacity of the warehouse is $\bar{I} = 310$.

To solve for optimal inventories, consider the nonlinear programming problem

$$\begin{aligned}
\text{Maximize} \quad & (40d_1 - 0.375d_1^2) + (42d_2 - 0.375d_2^2) + (44d_3 - 0.375d_3^2) \\
& + (46d_4 - 0.375d_4^2) + (48d_5 - 0.375d_5^2) + (-30x_1 + x_1^2) \\
& + (-25x_2 + x_2^2) + (-20x_3 + x_3^2) + (-15x_4 + x_4^2) \\
& + (-10x_5 + x_5^2) - 0.8(I_1 + I_2 + I_3 + I_4)
\end{aligned}$$

$$\begin{aligned}
\text{Subject to} \quad d_1 - x_1 + I_1 &= 300 \qquad (10.5) \\
d_2 - x_2 - I_1 + I_2 &= 0 \\
d_3 - x_3 - I_2 + I_3 &= 0 \\
d_4 - x_4 - I_3 + I_4 &= 0 \\
d_5 - x_5 - I_4 &= -300 \\
I_1 &\le 310 \\
I_2 &\le 310 \\
I_3 &\le 310 \\
I_4 &\le 310 \\
d_t, x_t, I_t &\ge 0
\end{aligned}$$

Numerical solution of the GAMS program INVENDAMP on page 320 gives:

period t	*demand* d_t^*	*supply* x_t^*	*inventories* I_t^*	*price*
1	20.47	27.32	306.85	24.65
2	22.07	25.22	310.00	25.45
3	23.27	23.27	310.00	26.55
4	24.47	21.32	306.85	27.65
5	26.07	19.22	300.00	28.45

(The price in each period is the Lagrange multiplier of the market balance constraint. Since both demand and supply is positive in each time period, complementary slackness ensures that the Lagrange multiplier equals both the demand price and the supply price.)

So, prices are still rising over time, but at a much slower pace. The shortage in later periods has been alleviated because the warehouse operator added to his inventory in periods 1 and 2, and released his inventory in periods 4 and 5.

Exercises

1. (a) Solve the pure speculation example using the following data: $T = 6$, $h = 2$, $\alpha = 5$, $I_0 = 1000$, $I_7 = 1200$, $\bar{I} = 1500$ and prices

t	1	2	3	4	5	6
p_t	190	175	169	182	196	185

Write detailed interpretations of the numerical solutions you find.

(b) Redo part (a) but with the following demands

t	1	2	3	4	5	6
d_t	0	1600	1200	1000	900	0

2. Solve the following inventory problem: $T = 6$, $h = 2$, $\alpha = 1$, $I_0 = 800$, $I_7 = 500$, $\bar{I} = 1500$ and

t	1	2	3	4	5	6
p_t	180	183	186	189	192	195
d_t	0	0	0	0	0	700

Explain your answer.

3. Construct numerical examples, such as the one in Exercise 2, to illustrate the following rules:
   (a) Speculation is profitable during a given time interval only if the average rate of price increase is greater than the unit storage cost.
   (b) If speculation is profitable during a given time interval then the difference between the buying and selling prices is greater than the total holding cost plus the total transaction cost.

4. Solve the speculation with demand model using the following data: $T = 7$, $h = 2$, $\alpha = 3$, $I_0 = 800$, $I_8 = 1{,}000$, $\bar{I} = 1{,}500$ and prices and demands given by

t	1	2	3	4	5	6	7
p_t	75	80	82	79	85	87	83
d_t	500	1200	1100	900	1300	1000	1100

5. Show that another way of calculating the demands and prices shown in the table in the middle of 136 is to remove all of the inventory variables in (10.5) and to solve the resulting nonlinear programming model.

11

Capital Budgeting

Capital budgeting by a firm involves decisions concerning investments of the firm's financial resources in long term projects such as purchases of land, buildings, equipment, other firms, new factories, etc. Each such investment usually requires periodic payments, and yields periodic receipts over several time periods. Such future payments and receipts are frequently not known exactly, but must be forecasted or estimated. Also, future payments and receipts for each project must be discounted, using an appropriate rate of interest, to get its *net present value* (NPV), so that different projects can be compared using current dollars.

As we shall see, just comparing the NPV of two or more projects is usually not enough, since each involves different streams of payments and receipts occurring at different time periods. Hence it is necessary to calculate period by period total net cash flows from a set of projects under consideration so that it is possible to see whether accepting some or all of the projects in the set would create a cash flow problem during some future period. We shall illustrate this procedure in the examples and exercises to be covered in this chapter.

The capital budgeting process is one of the most important activities of a firm since it involves questions of whether to enter a new business or to leave an old one, to market a new product or to drop an old one, to expand an existing factory or to build a new one, etc. Thus the most basic questions that will determine the long term viability of the firm are under consideration. The process of analyzing all the possible projects and answering such questions is called *strategic planning*. The purpose of this chapter is to give an introduction into this important area.

Net Present Value

If you invest \$100 now in an account that pays 10%, then one year from now it will be worth $\$110 = 100 \times 1.1$; two years from now it will be worth $\$121 = 100 \times (1.1)^2$; three years from now it will be worth $\$131.1 = 100 \times (1.1)^3$, etc. Conversely, if you know that you will need \$100 in one year, you need deposit only \$90.91 = 100/(1.1) now in the account, and next year it will be worth \$100. If you know that you will need \$100 two years from now, then you must deposit only \$82.64 = $100/(1.1)^2$ now in order that the account will be worth \$100 two years from now. And so on. (Use your calculator!)

In the same way, in order to evaluate money that will be received or paid in the future can be calculated using the interest rate r, which is usually stated as $100r$ percent, as follows:

the present value of \$$a$ received or paid today is \$$a$;

the present value of \$$a$ received or paid in one year is \$$a/(1 + r)$;

the present value of \$$a$ received or paid in two years is \$$a/(1 + r)^2$;

etc.

We summarize this in a formula:

$$\text{the present value of } \$a \text{ received or paid in } t \text{ years} = \$a/(1 + r)^t \qquad (11.1)$$

It is clear that this method of evaluating future payments or receipts tends to make them smaller (in absolute value). Commonly this is known as *discounting*. The future value is also termed *net present value* (NPV).

In the same way one can calculate the net present value (NPV) of a future stream of payments and receipts, $p(0), p(1), p(2), \ldots, p(n)$ discounted at interest rate r as:

$$\text{NPV} = p(0) + p(1)/(1 + r) + p(2)/(1 + r)^2 + \cdots + p(n)/(1 + r)^n \qquad (11.2)$$

Example 1. As an example consider the payment stream (in thousands of dollars) through four periods at a discount rate of $r = 0.10$ shown in the table below. To get the NPV of the whole project we just calculate the NPV of each payment or receipt using the formula in (11.1) and add the results together. This is exactly the same thing as using formula (11.2).

t	$p(t)$	NPV$[p(t)]$
0	−200	−200
1	125	113.64
2	125	103.31
3	125	93.91

NPV = 110.9

Suppose we consider the same four period project as the one in the table above but which starts at the beginning of period 1 and ends at the end of period 4. Since each term in the sum would be divided by one more factor of $(1 + r)$ the whole NPV is decreased by that amount. Hence the NPV of the new project is 110.9/1.1 = 100.8. By a similar analysis the same project started at the beginning of period 2 and running to the end of period 5 would have an NPV of 100.8/1.1 = 91.6.

Example 2. Suppose now that we have three projects A, B, and C, each of which can start now or one time period from now. Projects starting now will have a subscript 1 and those starting one period later will have subscript 2. The stream of cash flows generated by each of the projects, again using a discount rate of $r = 0.1$, is tabulated in below.

	A_1	A_2	B_1	B_2	C_1	C_2
	−200	0	−300	0	−250	0
	125	−200	175	−300	150	−250
	125	125	175	175	150	150
	125	125	175	175	150	150
	0	125	0	175	0	150
NPV	110.9	100.8	135.2	122.9	123	111.8

The last figure in each column is the net present value of the project in that column. Note that each project requires a payment in the first period, and then produces a positive return for exactly three years. From this it is clear that the projects, if accepted, will be in danger of producing a negative cash flow only during the first two years.

Example 3. Suppose now that the firm has budget constraints (in thousands of dollars) of 300 and 375 for years 1 and 2, and it wants to know which of the six projects above it can accept without exceeding its budgets in the first two years. It defines the following binary decision variables:

x_1 = accept project A_1

x_2 = accept project A_2

x_3 = accept project B_1

x_4 = accept project B_2

x_5 = accept project C_1

x_6 = accept project C_2

Since these variables can take on only values 0 and 1, the interpretations of their values is that the corresponding statement is true when the value of the variable is 1 and false if it is zero. Using this, we can set up the following integer programming model of the firm's decision problem:

$$\text{Maximize} \quad 110.9x_1 + 100.8x_2 + 135.2x_3 + 122.9x_4 + 123x_5 + 111.8x_6$$

$$\text{Subject to} \quad 200x_1 + 300x_3 + 250x_5 \leq 300 \qquad (11.3)$$

$$-125x_1 + 200x_2 - 175x_3 + 300x_4 - 150x_5 + 250x_6 \leq 375$$

where x_1 through x_6 are binary variables.

Notice that the coefficients of the projects have had their signs changed in problem (11.3) from what they were in the previous example. That is because the first period payment appears on the left hand side of the first constraint so that if the corresponding project is accepted, its cost is subtracted from the first period budget of 300. On the other hand the second period receipts appear with negative signs on the left hand side of the second constraint so that if the corresponding project is accepted its second period receipt is added to the second period budget of 375. In this way such receipts can be immediately reinvested in the second period.

If you solve the GAMS program CAPBUD on page 321 you will find the optimal integer solution, which is $x_3 = x_4 = x_6 = 1$ (and all other x_j's $= 0$). The optimal objective value is equal to 369.9. In other words the optimal solution is to accept projects B_1, B_2, and C_2. By substituting this answer into the constraints and objective function of (11.3) you will be able to check that it is feasible and yields the stated objective value.

In many cases projects are interrelated because they may require the same physical or managerial resources of the firm, they may mutually aid each other, they may mutually interfere with each other, etc. For this reason it is desirable to state these interrelationships as logical constraints in the binary integer programming problem so that they will be enforced as part of the solution to that problem. Recall that in Chapter 4 we showed simple examples of such logical constraints. The next example illustrates their application to capital budgeting problems.

Example 4. Consider the same projects as are listed in table on page 141, and assume that the management of the firm has set up the following project interrelationship constraints:

(a) If A_1 is accepted, then A_2 must also be accepted.

(b) If C_2 is accepted, then C_1 must also be accepted.

(c) If either A_2 or B_2 is accepted, then C_1 must also be accepted.

It is easy to see that these conditions can be translated into the following logical constraints:

$$\begin{aligned} &(a) \quad x_1 - x_2 \le 0 \\ &(b) \quad -x_5 + x_6 \le 0 \\ &(c) \quad x_2 + x_4 - 2x_5 \le 0 \end{aligned}$$

If we add these constraints to the binary integer programming problem of (11.3) we get the following problem:

$$\begin{aligned} \text{Maximize} \quad & 110.9x_1 + 100.8x_2 + 135.2x_3 + 122.9x_4 + 123x_5 + 111.8x_6 \\ \text{Subject to} \quad & 200x_1 + 300x_3 + 250x_5 \le 300 \qquad (11.4) \\ & -125x_1 + 200x_2 - 175x_3 + 300x_4 - 150x_5 + 250x_6 \le 375 \\ & x_1 - x_2 \le 0 \\ & -x_5 + x_6 \le 0 \\ & x_2 + x_4 - 2x_5 \le 0 \end{aligned}$$

where x_1 through x_6 are binary variables.

The computer software gives the following solution to the revised program called CAPBUD1, as $x_2 = x_4 = x_5 = 1$ with objective value of 346.7. In other words, the optimal capital budgeting decision is to accept projects A_2, B_2 and C_1. You should check that all of the logical constraints, as well as the budget constraints of the problem in (11.4) are satisfied, and that the optimal objective value is as stated.

Note that the optimal objective value went down because of the added logical constraints. This illustrates the general rule: if constraints are added to a maximizing linear program, then the objective value of the new (more constrained) problem will be less than or equal to that of the original problem.

Example 5. As a final example, consider the addition of project D to the previous problem, with D_1 and D_2 representing the project starting immediately and after one time period, respectively. Assume also that D requires the immediate investment of \$350 and will return \$225 per period for each of the next three periods. We define new variables

$$x_7 = \text{accept project } D_1$$
$$x_8 = \text{accept project } D_2.$$

We also assume the following logical constraints:

(a) At most 2 of the projects A_1, B_1, C_1, and D_1 can be accepted.

(b) At most 3 of the projects A_2, B_2, C_2, and D_2, can be accepted.

(c) If B_1 is accepted, then B_2 must also be accepted.

(d) If D_2 is accepted, then D_1 must also be accepted.

(e) If either B_1 or C_1 is accepted, then D_1 must also be accepted.

The data box of the problem is shown below.

x_1	x_2	x_3	x_4	x_5	x_6	x_7	x_8	
200	0	300	0	250	0	350	0	≤ 750
−125	200	−175	300	−150	250	−225	350	≤ 650
1	0	1	0	1	0	1	0	≤ 2
0	1	0	1	0	1	0	1	≤ 3
0	0	1	−1	0	0	0	0	≤ 0
0	0	0	0	0	0	−1	1	≤ 0
0	0	1	0	1	1	−2	0	≤ 0
110.9	110.8	135.2	122.9	123.0	111.8	157.3	143.0	

The software program gave the following solution: the optimal objective value is 760.2 and optimal primal solution is $x_3 = x_4 = x_6 = x_7 = x_8 = 1$. In other words, the best thing to do is to accept projects B_1, B_2, C_2, D_1, and D_2.

Notice that conditions (a) and (e) together imply that all three of projects B_1, C_1, and D_1 cannot be accepted. In fact, either B_1 or D_1 can be accepted, but not both. The binary programming solution technique takes care of all such logical implications automatically.

Exercises

1. Show that the NPV calculations for each of the six projects in the table on page 141 are correct.

2. Rework Example 4 with the following logical constraints in place of (a), (b) and (c):

   (a′) Exactly one of A_1 or A_2 must be accepted.

   (b′) At most one of C_1 or C_2 can be accepted.

   (c′) If B_1 is not accepted then B_2 must be accepted.

3. Change the righthand sides of the first two constraints in the data box on page 143 to 850 and 900, respectively and re-solve the problem. Explain the differences between the new and old solutions.

4. Consider the three projects in the table on page 141. Assume that each of them can be carried out immediately or delayed either one or two periods. Set up the corresponding problem, which will have nine variables and three constraints. Assume that budget constraints of 1200, 1100, and 900 are available for each of the three years corresponding to investing immediately, waiting one year, or waiting two years to invest in each of the projects. Solve the resulting problem.

5. Add three logical constraints to the problem in Exercise 4 that prevent the same project being started at more than two of the three start dates. Add three more logical constraints that prevent starting more than two out of three of the projects at any one start date. Now solve the resulting problem. Compare the new answers to those in Exercise 4.

12

Personnel Planning

In Chapter 10 a pure network flow model was devised for inventory management. The principal characteristic of such a pure network model is that the sizes of the commodity flows on each arc are preserved; i.e., the amount of material entering an arc equals the amount leaving it.

In contrast, *a network flow with a gains model* includes arcs for which the amounts of flows can change. Examples are: money flows which increase or decrease due to interest received or paid; perishable goods flows which decrease due to spoilage; and crops which increase due to growth over time.

Labor

In order to carry out its business, a firm needs the services of men and women to fill positions for marketing, production, purchasing, and other specialized functions. Each such position is called a "job," and for each job we can write down a list of desirable characteristics that the worker preferably should possess. The particular person who at any given point in time fills the job will typically fit these job descriptions more or less perfectly. There is a *matching problem* to match existing jobs and existing workers in an optimal way.

When a worker is first employed by a firm, the management may have some definite expectations about what this person is capable of doing and what kind of potential he or she has for acquiring additional abilities through on-the-job learning. Some abilities are innate, some have been acquired through basic specialized education, and some have been acquired through practice and experience. As the worker climbs the promotional ladder, the employer can shift the worker from a given job to a more demanding one. The employer can also try to facilitate this trend by providing formal training programs and by screening employees for promotion within the corporation.

The "human capital" embodied in a young person entering his or her first job, is defined to be the discounted value of that person's expected income stream. As this person continues, partly as a result of effort and hard work, or perhaps as a result of additional formal training programs, the value of his or her human capital increases. The employer may engage in a diversity of programs designed to promote such enhancement, and may allocate funds on a routine basis for such furtherance. Education and training can be characterized as *investment in human capital*.

If we look at the "life cycle" of a worker's relationship with one particular firm, then, the cycle starts with the original act of *hiring*. The worker may match the designated job more or less perfectly, and eventually a number of adjustments can occur as the worker acquires on-the-job experience, is shifted to other tasks, enters voluntary training programs, and climbs the career and seniority ladder inside the firm. Some workers will leave the firm voluntarily; this is called *attrition*. As time passes, the firm may face both structural and cyclical changes in its demand for labor. In the case of adverse developments, the firm may need to reduce its workforce. To the extent that the required reduction of manpower cannot be attained through attrition, management may decide to discontinue some jobs so that some workers must be laid off.

A Personnel Planning Model

In this chapter a network flow with a gains model of personnel planning in a large organization will be discussed. In this model the number of workers at the beginning and the number at the end of an arc representing a time period can be different due to deaths, retirements, resignations, dismissals, etc., of employees.

Consider a simplified situation, where a firm employs just one category of workers. The number of workers needed in each time period t is denoted r_t. The task is to design a policy of hiring and firing over some time span $t = 1, 2, \ldots, T$ so that this demand is met at all times while keeping total personnel costs at a minimum.

Let the number of workers on board at time t be N_t; clearly we require $N_t \geq r_t$. One possible policy is to hire and fire workers in each time period so that $N_t = r_t$ always. If there are some fluctuations in r_t over time, however, such a policy may lead to considerable hiring and firing costs, and it may be more advantageous to the firm to look for a policy of *smoothing* the workforce over time and to accept the presence of some excess labor $N_t > r_t$ in the face of a temporary decline in r_t.

The complete notation to be used is listed below:

T = number of time periods.
N_t = number of workers on board at time t for $t = 1, \ldots, T - 1$.
w_t = wage rate paid per period.
H_t = number of workers hired at time t.
h = hiring costs per worker.
F_t = numbers of workers fired at time t.
f = firing costs per worker.
r_t = number of workers needed at time t.
a_t = the survival rate at time t where $0 < a_t \leq 1$, and $1 - a_t$ is the attrition rate.
N_0 = initial work force on board.
N_T = target workforce at end of planning horizon.

Figure 12.1

Arc with cost w and gain factor a, indicating the flow of employees from time t to time $t + 1$.

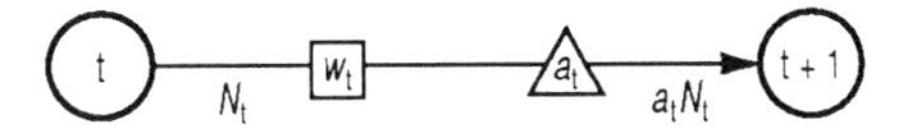

We can write a workforce balance equation for each time period as follows:

$$N_t = a_{t-1}N_{t-1} + H_t - F_t \tag{12.1}$$

This equation states that the new workforce, N_t is equal to the number of workers from the previous period, $a_{t-1}N_{t-1}$, who remain as employees, plus those newly hired less those fired.

Since the employer wants to minimize the costs of personnel we can write the following linear program for the problem.

$$\text{Minimize} \quad \sum_{t=1}^{T} (hH_t + fF_t + w_tN_t) \tag{12.2}$$

$$\text{Subject to} \quad -H_t + F_t + N_t - a_{t-1}N_{t-1} = 0 \quad \text{for } t = 1, \ldots, T \tag{12.3}$$

$$N_t \geq r_t \quad \text{for } t = 1, \ldots, T \tag{12.4}$$

$$H_t, F_t, N_t \geq 0 \tag{12.5}$$

Equation (12.3) is the balance constraint for each node, while (12.4) is the lower bound requirements constraint for each node. (Note: we always set $a_0 = 1$.)

In order to represent the problem graphically we use the conventions for an arc with a gain factor shown in Figure 12.1. Note that the cost of the arc is w_t. If N_t employees are on board at time t only a_tN_t remain as employees at time $t + 1$; the remainder, $(1 - a_t)N_t$, having died, or retired from, or voluntarily quit their jobs.

Using these conventions, the network with a gains flow model is shown in Figure 12.2. The required levels of personnel, r_t, are noted beside each node, corresponding to the lower bound constraints (12.4).

Figure 12.2

Network flow with gains model for personnel planning.

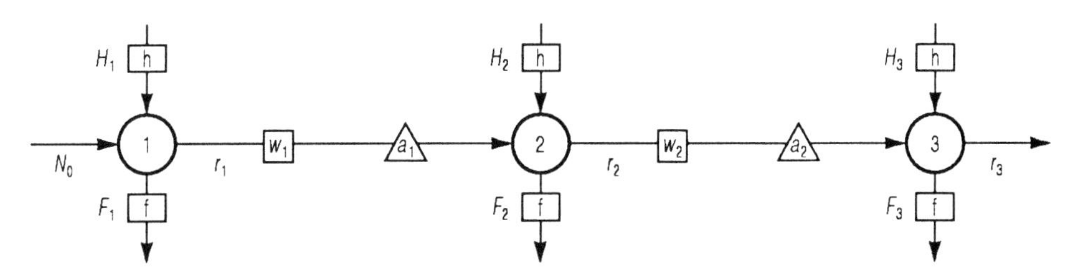

Figure 12.3

Graph of network flow solution for Example 1.

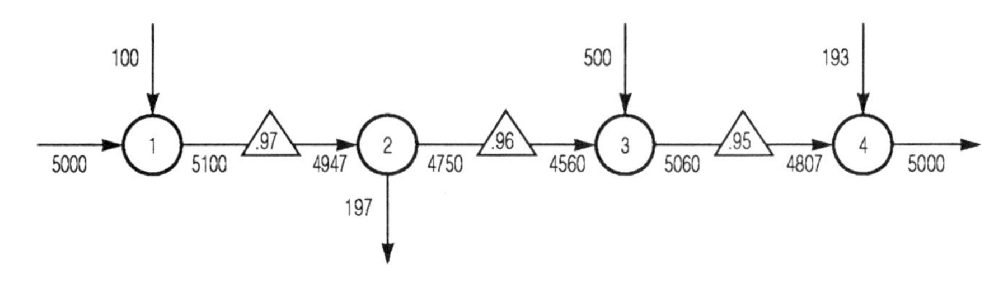

Example 1. Let us work an example with $T = 4$, $h = 0.2$, $f = 0.4$, $w_t = 5$, $a_1 = 0.97$, $a_2 = 0.96$, $a_3 = 0.95$, $N_0 = N_4 = 5000$. We also assume that the requirements are as shown below:

t	1	2	3	4
r_t	5100	4750	5060	5000

From the data just given, the network flow graph of Figure 12.2 and equations (12.2) through (12.5), it is easy to derive the data box for the example shown below. Note that N_0 and N_4 are not included as variables since they are known quantities.

H_1	H_2	H_3	H_4	N_1	N_2	N_3	F_1	F_2	F_3	F_4	
−1	0	0	0	1	0	0	1	0	0	0	$= 5000 = N_0$
0	−1	0	0	−0.97	1	0	0	1	0	0	$= 0$
0	0	−1	0	0	−0.96	1	0	0	1	0	$= 0$
0	0	0	−1	0	0	−0.95	0	0	0	1	$= -5000 = -N_4$
0	0	0	0	1	0	0	0	0	0	0	≥ 5100
0	0	0	0	0	1	0	0	0	0	0	≥ 4750
0	0	0	0	0	0	1	0	0	0	0	≥ 5060
0.2	0.2	0.2	0.2	5	5	5	0.4	0.4	0.4	0.4	

The problem in the data box above was solved using the GAMS program PERSONNEL on page 323. The primal solution is given below:

t	*1*	*2*	*3*	*4*
H_t	100	0	500	193
F_t	0	197	0	0
N_t	5100	4750	5060	5000

The best way to interpret the solution is to display it graphically as shown in Figure 12.3. In that figure the arcs having gain factors show the numbers of personnel entering and leaving the arc.

Figure 12.4

Graph of network flow solution for Example 2.

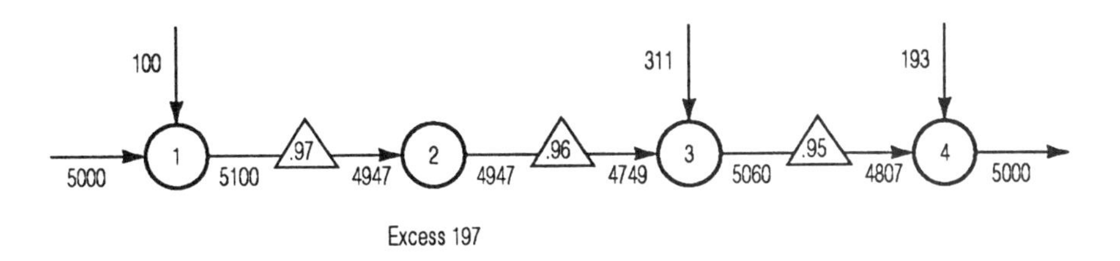

The dual solution to the problem is shown below. The first four dual variables correspond to the nodal constraints.

1	0.20	*Nodal constraints*
2	−0.40	
3	0.20	
4	0.20	
5	−5.59	*Requirements constraints*
6	−4.41	
7	−5.01	
8	−5.20	

Note that if there is hiring at a node then the corresponding dual variable is the hiring cost, but if there is firing, the dual variable at the node is the negative of the firing cost. The last four dual variables correspond to the lower bound requirements at each node. They are all negative and can be interpreted as the imputed cost at each time period of increasing the personnel requirement by one. In Exercise 1 you will be asked to solve the model with differing personnel requirements and show that (within limits) the dual variables predict the changes in the objective function that are caused by changes in these requirements.

Example 2. In Example 1 the wage rates w_t were chosen to represent the yearly wage and fringe benefits costs in tens of thousands of dollars as were the hiring and firing costs h and f. It was found that it paid to fire a surplus of 197 workers at node 2 when the model indicated that they would not be needed for a whole year. But then the model indicated hiring 500 workers at node 3 when the needs for workers increased. Some of those rehired may well have been among the 197 fired at node 2.

Now let us reconsider the problem over a shorter time period, such as a month, and reduce the wage costs w_t from 5 to 0.5. The solution of the new problem is shown graphically in Figure 12.4. Notice that there still is an excess of workers at node 2, but instead of firing them the model finds it cheaper to retain them for the month from node 2 to node 3 at a cost of 0.5 instead of incurring a firing cost of 0.2 and hiring cost of 0.4 for a total of 0.6. This also reduces the hiring requirement at node 3 from 500 to 311. The rest of the solution is the same as that in Figure 12.3.

Example 3. In classical economics, which relies on equilibrium concepts, the assumption is made that when jobs are available, the wages for such jobs will be increased until exactly enough workers will appear to take those jobs. They may be attracted from jobs paying lower wages, or from parts of the country where jobs are not available. This may well be true "in the long run," but in the short run world of a personnel manager, only workers who are located in the immediate region of the firm can be counted on to fill the current job openings and those to be available in the near future. Thus the manager may have to "stockpile" workers in times of excess availability in order to have them on hand when they are needed later. This is especially true for skilled workers in areas where there are shortages.

In order to model this situation we impose hiring limits of 100 on each time period of the personnel model in Example 1. However just adding such constraints will simply make the new problem infeasible because not all of the personnel requirements shown in the table in Example 1 can be achieved when such hiring constraints are imposed. Therefore we must add goal shortage variables that permit the linear programming model to fail to satisfy some constraints.

The data box of the new model is shown below. Notice that four new constraints have been added at the bottom of the tableau that impose upper bounds on the hiring variables H_1, H_2, H_3, and H_4. Also four new goal variables have been added, G_1, G_2, G_3, and G_4, that permit the model not to satisfy some lower bound constraints at a penalty P.

H_1	H_2	H_3	H_4	N_1	N_2	N_3	F_1	F_2	F_3	F_4	G_1	G_2	G_3	G_4	
−1	0	0	0	1	0	0	1	0	0	0	0	0	0	0	$= 5000$
0	−1	0	0	−0.97	1	0	0	1	0	0	0	0	0	0	$= 0$
0	0	−1	0	0	−0.96	1	0	0	1	0	0	0	0	0	$= 0$
0	0	0	−1	0	0	−0.95	0	0	0	1	0	0	0	−1	$= -5000$
0	0	0	0	1	0	0	0	0	0	0	1	0	0	0	≥ 5100
0	0	0	0	0	1	0	0	0	0	0	0	1	0	0	≥ 4750
0	0	0	0	0	0	1	0	0	0	0	0	0	1	0	≥ 5060
1	0	0	0	0	0	0	0	0	0	0	0	0	0	0	≤ 100
0	1	0	0	0	0	0	0	0	0	0	0	0	0	0	≤ 100
0	0	1	0	0	0	0	0	0	0	0	0	0	0	0	≤ 100
0	0	0	1	0	0	0	0	0	0	0	0	0	0	0	≤ 100
0.2	0.2	0.2	0.2	5	5	5	0.4	0.4	0.4	0.4	P	P	P	P	

Specifically, G_1 was added to permit the number of workers at node 1 to be less than 5100; G_2 permits the number of workers at node 2 to be less than

Figure 12.5

Graph of network flow solution for Example 3.

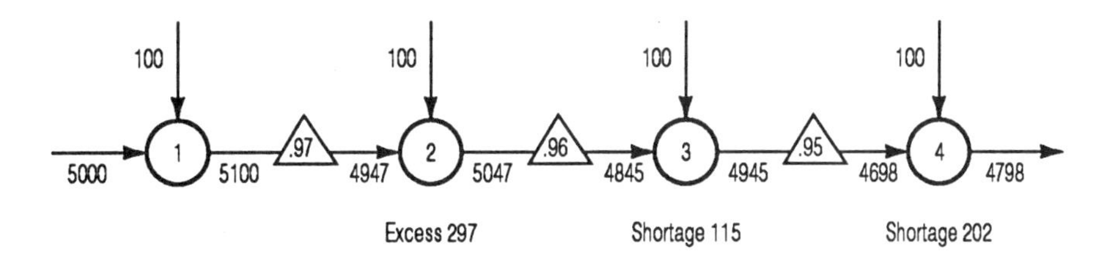

4750; G_3 permits the number of workers at node 3 to be less than 5060; and G_4 permits the number of workers at node 4 to be less than 5000. The penalty for violating each of these constraints is $P = 500$ per worker. No penalties were imposed for having excess workers at any node.

The solution of the linear program whose data box is shown on the previous page is shown graphically in Figure 12.5. Notice that the goal of 5100 workers at node 1 was met exactly. However there was an excess of 297 workers at node 2 for which the model did not impose a penalty. There were, however, shortages of 115 workers at node 3 and 202 workers at node 4. We see that the personnel model is able to make a partial but not complete match between personnel needs and actual employees hired.

Example 4. As another variant of Example 3, let us assume that the hiring bounds are changed from 100 for each node to bounds of 200, 150, 100, and 100 for nodes 1, 2, 3, and 4. The new solution is shown in Figure 12.6. Note that the solution now gives excess personnel numbers of 100, 344, and 26 at nodes 1, 2, and 3. The shortage at node 4 has been reduced from 202 to 68. Thus the match between personnel needs and personnel on hand has been improved considerably.

Figure 12.6

Graph of network flow solution for Example 4.

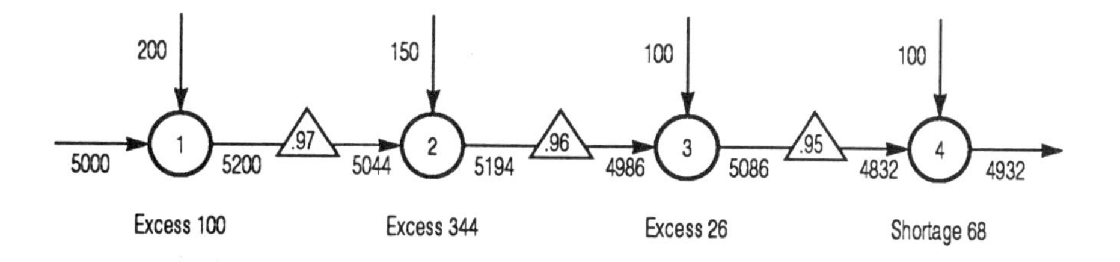

Exercises

1. Make the following changes to the personnel model in Example 1 and show that the dual variables predict correctly the change in the objective function.

   (a) Change N_2 to 4760.

   (b) Change N_3 to 5000.

   (c) Change N_4 to 5010.

2. Solve the personnel planning model given in (12.2) through (12.5) with the following data: $T = 5$, $h = 0.3$, $f = 0.5$, $N_0 = 8000$, $N_5 = 8100$ and:

t	*1*	*2*	*3*	*4*
v_t	8200	8500	8300	8100
a_t	0.96	0.98	0.99	0.97
w_t	4.0	4.2	4.3	4.1

   Give detailed interpretations for the values of each of the primal and dual variables.

3. Solve the personnel problem in Example 3 with hiring bounds of 100, 150, 200 and 100 in periods 1, 2, 3, and 4.

4. Solve the personnel problem in the data box on page 150 with penalty costs of 250, 750, and 1000. Discuss the effect on the solution of changing these penalty costs.

PART

Industry Modeling, Spatial Networks, Activity Analysis, & Input-Output Economics

INTRODUCTION

Interdependent Systems

Introductory economic analysis is conveniently organized under two headings, micro economics and macro economics. Micro economics deals with the behavior of single economic agents, such as a consumer or a producer. The economic behavior of a financial institution, or even of a government bureaucrat, is also micro theory. The entire treatment in Part II is micro theory.

Macro economics was born as part of the Keynesian revolution of economic thought that occurred in the 1930s and 1940s. It deals with national economic aggregates, such as gross national product, national income, total savings, total consumption, the general price level, and the relationships between such aggregates.

An "interdependent system" represents yet a third approach to the study of economics. An interdependent system is an assembly of microeconomic building blocks that are joined together via markets. It is a representation of an industry or even of the entire economy that proceeds from the bottom up, a construct that mimics the constituent parts of a real economy and their interactions via markets.

The term "interdependent system" is employed by economists perhaps most commonly in relation to a model of general equilibrium such as the Walras model, involving representations of all consumers and all producers, and a market for every commodity or service. The interdependent systems that we shall be concerned with here are of a more limited nature: they are *partial* systems relating only to some particular industry manufacturing some particular array of consumer goods, and the demand for those goods. Consumer income and the prices of all other goods outside the current modeling effort are supposed to be given and fixed.

Economic model building has both an analytic and a synthetic aspect. Through analysis of real life phenomena, the economist gains an understanding of causal structures and the richness of empirical detail. Building on such understanding and such insight, the economist can proceed to a subsequent process of synthesis, developing theoretical models of the firm, of the market, and of the supply of productive resources. Joining these elementary concepts together into larger structures, it is possible to create representations of many firms and many resource owners and many consumers interacting via markets. It is to this process of synthesis that we now turn.

Using the tools of mathematical programming and software representations of mathematical programs, we shall be able to lend considerable realism to an interdependent model. Different micro agents, such as resource owners, producers, shippers, and wholesalers, may be modeled in considerable detail, spelling out the various scheduling, transportation and marketing problems that they each face. In the mathematical program, and in the software representation of that program, these various units may be joined together by interacting in markets for consumer goods, in markets for intermediate goods, in markets for energy, markets for natural resources, and markets for labor. The resulting constructs may seem unwieldy. But, as we shall see, the electronic computer can do what a human may find mindboggling: to keep track of a very great number of individual agents and individual markets, each having its individual characteristics, and interacting with each other in their own individual fashions.

The "Invisible Hand"

In famous passages in his book *The Wealth of Nations* (1776), Adam Smith argued that the fundamental problems of production and distribution in a competitive economy are solved through the operation of an "invisible hand." Although the behavior of each individual is driven by the desire for self betterment, there will arise an orderliness in the pricing of individual commodities. Producers will find it compatible with their self-interest to supply to markets the quantities of goods that consumers want to buy. The mutual competition of the economic actors causes labor and capital to be moved from less to more profitable occupations or areas, thus constantly readjusting to changing conditions. Collectively, economic actors and markets operate as a self-correcting mechanism.

Through the representation of an interdependent system it is possible to translate these early intuitive notions into specific theoretical results, and to provide an exact account of the achievements (and limitations) of the invisible hand. Even accepting Adam Smith's propositions, it is by no means evident that it is possible to construct in a laboratory setting an artificial economy that functions the way he envisaged it. Thus, the great virtue of the model of an interdependent system is that it demonstrates that the competitive economy of the invisible hand is indeed viable and that it does provide solutions to the fundamental problems of production and distribution.

The model representation of an interdependent system must be of a mathematical nature; in the chapters of Part III the reader will meet various such representations. At this point, a simple diagrammatical illustration may be invoked to explain the fundamental ideas.

Consider an industry using two inputs to produce two outputs. The industry could, for instance, be agriculture, with the inputs being capital and labor, and the outputs being grain and meat.

It is assumed that the industry is "small" compared to the markets for resources at large, so that the prices of the two inputs can be regarded as known and given, unaffected by the resource use of the industry itself.

There are many individual producers (farmers). Each producer employs some mix of the two inputs to produce the two outputs. In the Introduction to Part II, we have characterized what it means for each producer to be optimally adjusted. In the space of the two inputs, the producer will move to a point at which the tangent to the isoquant curve has a slope that equals (the negative of) the ratio between the input prices. (See

Figure III-1

Industry isocost map.

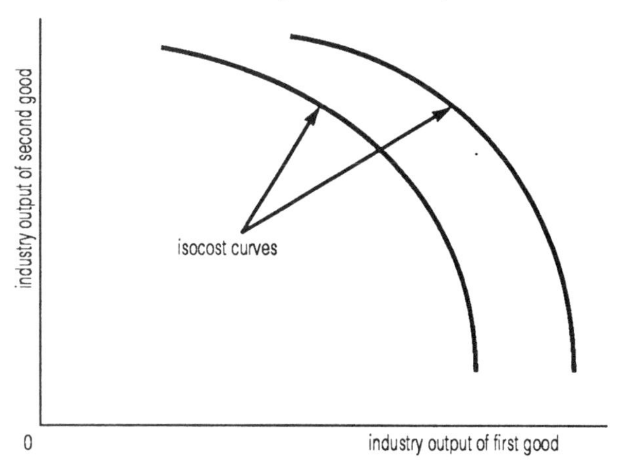

Figure II-5.) In the space of the two outputs, the producer will adjust to a point at which the tangent to an isocost has a slope that equals (the negative of) the ratio between the two output prices. (See Figure II-6.)

Next, turn to the space of industry outputs illustrated in Figure III-1 above. Along all points of a given isocost curve, the total industry input bill, calculated as (price of first input) × (industry use of the first input) + (price of second input) × (industry use of second input), remains fixed and constant. Remember that any individual isocost curve must be located in its entirety beneath its tangent. The same property holds for the industry isocost curve. The industry isocost curve illustrates that, for a given bill of industry costs, there exist possibilities of substitution between the two outputs.

For the purpose of the interdependent system to be demonstrated now, the simplifying assumption will be made that consumer demand is fixed and known. That is, the system to be developed will focus on the production decisions in the industry, but the demand side of the industry is treated less explicitly, simply assuming a given list of demands. In Figure III-2, the demand point is point *C*. Industry demand for the first output equals *OA* and industry demand for the second output is *OB*.

This interdependent system can be solved diagrammatically in the following fashion:

(i) Locate the lowest industry isocost curve that passes through point *C*. This isocost is indeed the minimal cost at which it is possible to produce the outputs *OA* and *OB*.

(ii) The slope of any straight line in the output space defines a price ratio between the two outputs. Now draw the tangent to the isocost curve through point *C*. Along this tangent, in the vicinity of *C*, the rate of substitution that is possible at the margin, replacing one output by the other, equals the output price ratio. The price ratio is the solution that we are looking for. It is the price ratio that will actually be established as a result of the competitive mechanism.

Figure III-2

Illustration of industry equilibrium.

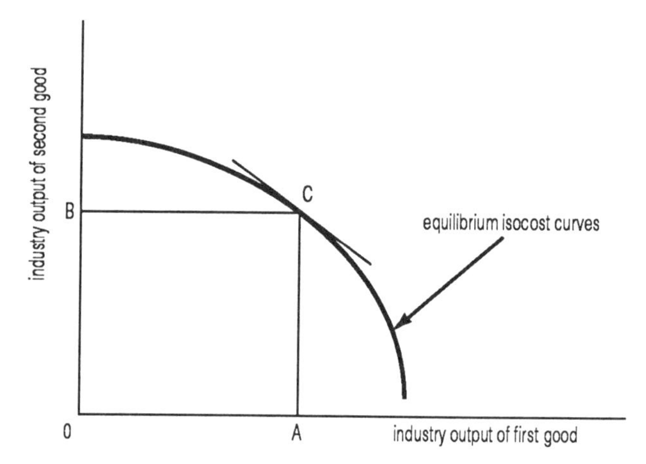

To see why, remember that each individual producer will adjust along his individual isocost curve to a point where his marginal rate of substitution equals the ratio between the two output prices (see Figure II-5). Thus, establishing the solution price ratio of Figure III-2, each single producer will be induced to make input and output decisions which are precisely those that underlie the construction of the solution industry isocost curve in Figure III-2. In other words, this price ratio will call forth precisely the industry output totals *OA* and *OB*. All producers are adjusted. All markets are competitive.

(Small interdependent models can be constructed in many ways. The reader may be familiar with another variant, involving a so-called production possibility curve, showing all combinations of total inputs that can be reached with given and fixed endowments of all resources. Through the competitive mechanism, the particular point on the production possibility curve will be established at which the tangent to the curve also touches the map of consumer indifference curves as a tangent. See the detailed discussion in Chapter 17 on activity analysis.)

Capitalism Versus State Socialism

In the United States and in Western Europe, economies are organized with free enterprise and private ownership and control of capital. Adam Smith's concepts of free market formation and the invisible hand are still the guiding principles of production and distribution. But the detailed workings of the system are tempered by fiscal policy (such as a social safety net), environmental policy, etc.

An entirely different approach to the basic problems of production and distribution was proposed by Karl Marx and later translated into a system of state socialism as practiced in the Soviet Union. Rather than relying on free markets, state socialism is a command economy. All means of production are owned by the state. A central planning agency develops annual production targets. All prices are set by decree.

It should be noted that the theory of interdependent systems, such as the small diagrammatical prototype illustrated in Figure III-2, is accepted by market economists and Marxists alike. This theory is noncontroversial. What is controversial is the question how one should actually, in a real economy, establish the solution point. It can be established in a free market economy, by the invisible hand. Alternatively, the Marxist solution is for the central planning agency to compute the optimal point, to announce the optimal prices (which presumably will render all markets in equilibrium), and to set mandatory production targets equal to the optimal output of each good.

This is not to say that the difference between capitalism and state socialism is just political, and that the two kinds of economic order are economically equivalent. What it means is that on this level of simplified theory, the economics of the two systems cannot be distinguished from each other.

However, there is a consensus among economists that a state socialist economy is plagued by inherent shortcomings in terms of weak incentives and little ability to adapt to change. The market economy can respond rapidly to changing consumer preferences and to new technology. A planned economy is rigid. Increasingly, in a market economy, the rising standard of living takes the form of new and better consumer products and services, not the least in the fields of electronics and health care. A planned economy can produce only standardized products, manufactured to meet centrally formulated specifications. Such differences between the two systems are not captured by simple economic models which are static.

An Overview of the Chapters in Part III

There are three types of questions that will be answered in this part of the book. The first question is: How are decisions made about the organization of the processes for producing inputs and outputs in the industry? Obviously, the aggregate of these decisions equals the sum total of the indivdual micro decisions already studied in Part II. The second question is: How are market prices determined for both outputs and inputs needed by the industry? The third question is: What incomes will the factors of production earn? Consider factors such as labor and capital equipment employed in the industry. The factor income is obtained as the quantity of the factor employed times its market price. The third question refers to the distribution of factor incomes among factors (the so-called horizontal income distribution).

A basic industry model is presented in Chapter 13.

Since different parts of the same firm or different segments of the same market may be distributed over several geographic locations, it is necessary to model both the production and the transportation of goods from production to distribution locations. This is done in Chapter 14. The transportation costs along the distribution paths must be added to the original production costs to arrive at imputed values (or prices) at the points of sale.

In recent years the general public has become aware of the environmental costs of many production activities. Factors produce economic goods that are desired by consumers, but they also utilize scarce resources, some of which are nonrenewable. Some also produce economic bads such as industrial refuse, toxic chemicals, and polluted land, water, and air. In order to control the production of such bads, governments may impose taxes, limit production quantities, require the safe disposal of toxic waste, etc. This is the subject of Chapter 15.

The World Bank has pioneered the use of mathematical programming methods for industry planning in many countries in Latin America, Asia, and Africa. The time frame for such plans may be three or five years, sometimes even longer. Chapter 16 explains the methods of investment planning employed by the World Bank. These methods build upon the techniques of capital budgeting explained in Part II, and involve mixed integer programming (linear programming with some or all 0–1 variables).

The following chapters extend the process of aggregation even further, progressing from simple industry models to entire sectors of the economy. Chapter 17 sets the stage, explaining the concept of activity analysis due to Koopmans. It deals with the entire production logistics chain in the economy, all the way from the use of primary goods, via intermediate goods, to final consumer goods. Chapter 18 provides a first application: energy economics and the conversion of scarce energy resources to electricity.

So-called neoclassical economics deals with systems of markets that are all in equilibrium (all markets clear). But the real world does not always satisfy the neat mathematical postulates of equilibrium theory. There is unemployment. There are institutional rigidities and market imperfections. In order to deal with such "over-constrained" economics, Chapter 19 outlines some considerations of economic disequilibrium.

Chapter 20 provides an introduction to input-output economics, due to Wassily Leontief.

Notes on Literature Relevant to Part III

Agricultural economists were among the first to apply linear programming at an industry level, see the standard works by Heady [10] and Takayama and Judge [22]. The nonlinear spatial formulation (in Chapter 14) is due to Takayama and Judge [21].

At an early point, researchers associated with the World Bank took an interest in industry modeling. A work in this direction which was to have considerable influence, was H. Chenery's study [5]. Later, in the 1970s, the World Bank organized a collection of industry studies in Mexico (Goreux and Manne [9]) and in other developing countries.

The environmental problems discussed in Chapter 15 have been around for a long time. The concept of external economies goes back to A. C. Pigou [20] who pointed out that the satisfaction of a consumer may be affected not only by his own consumption but also by other people's consumption, and by negative external economies of production. He discussed the possibility of correcting the price system for the presence of such distortions, using excise taxes and subsidies.

Goal programming was developed by Charnes, Cooper and Ferguson [3]. A comprehensive survey is Charnes and Cooper [2]. For the technique of goal-focusing, see reference [4].

Chapter 16, dealing with the planning of industrial investment programs, follows Kendrick and Stoutjesdijk [11].

The treatment of activity analysis in Chapter 17 is standard. See Koopmans [12] and [13]. The numerical experiments recorded in Figure 5.6 draw on the "spiral method" by Charnes and Cooper [1].

Since the days of the Arab oil embargo of 1973, there have appeared literally hundreds of analyses of U.S. and international energy prospects based on linear programming. A leading researcher in the field is A. Manne, see e.g., reference [16]. The first simple model in Chapter 18 draws on Weyant [26].

The disequilibrium approach has recently experienced a renaissance in economics (for a classic early work see Lindahl [15]). But whereas the interest in the present text is partial economics and sector economics, the so-called "fixed-price models" of Drèze [7] and others deal with disequilibrium in an entire interdependent system of markets or in a macro-economic model. Here, we are only concerned with the initial possible occurrence of *ex ante* market gaps (excess supplies or excess demands). How these gaps are eventually resolved *ex post*, with the economic agents modifying their market behavior in the light of perceived quantity constraints ("rationing") is not dealt with here.

The mathematical programming formulation of price disequilibrium outlined in Chapter 19 was pioneered by Morgenstern and Thompson, see [17] and, [18] and their subsequent book [19], Chapter 12. See also Thompson and Thore [23]. Our text builds on Faxén and Thore [8] (disequilibrium in retraining networks) and Thore and Isser [25] (disequilibrium in the market for crude oil).

The classical reference for input-output economics (Chapter 20) is Wassily Leontief [14] who was the 1973 Nobel Laureate in Economics. The linear programming formulation of the input-output model was first presented in Dorfman, Samuelson and Solow [6].

For additional nonlinear numerical examples for Part III, see Thore [24].

References

1. Charnes, A. and W. W. Cooper, *Management Models and Industrial Applications of Linear Programming*, Volumes I–II, John Wiley, New York, 1961.
2. Charnes, A. and W. W. Cooper, "Goal Programming and Multiple Objective Optimizations," *European Journal of Operational Research*, 1 (1977) 39–54.
3. Charnes, A., W. W. Cooper and R. O. Ferguson, "Optimal Estimation of Executive Compensation by Linear Programming," *Management Science*, 2 (1955) 138–151.
4. Charnes, A., W. W. Cooper, J. J. Rousseau and A. Schinnar, "A Goal Focusing Approach to Analysis of Intergenerational Transfers of Income," in *International Journal of Systems Sciences*, 17 (1986) 433–436.
5. Chenery, H. B., "The Interdependence of Investment Decisions," in *The Allocation of Economic Resources*, editor M. Abramovitz, Stanford University Press, Stanford, California, 1959.
6. Dorfman, R., P. A. Samuelson and R. M. Solow, *Linear Programming and Economic Analysis*, McGraw-Hill, New York 1958.
7. Drèze, J., "Existence of an Exchange Equilibrium under Price Rigidities," *International Economic Review*, 16 (1975) 301–320.
8. Faxén, K. O. and S. Thore, "Retraining in an Interdependent System of Labor Markets: A Network Analysis," *European Journal of Operational Research*, 44 (1990) 349–356.
9. Goreux, L. M. and A. S. Manne, *Multi-Level Planning: Case Studies in Mexico*, North-Holland, Amsterdam 1973.
10. Heady, E. O., editor, *Economic Models and Quantitative Methods for Decisions and Planning in Agriculture*, Iowa State University Press, Ames 1971.

11. Kendrick, D. A. and A. J. Stoutjesdijk, *The Planning of Industrial Investment Programs*, Johns Hopkins University Press, Baltimore 1978.
12. Koopmans, T. C., editor, *Activity Analysis of Production and Allocation*, John Wiley, New York 1951.
13. Koopmans, T. C., *Three Essays on the State of Economic Science*, McGraw-Hill, New York 1957.
14. Leontief, W. W., *The Structure of American Economy 1919–1939*, 2nd edition, Oxford University Press, New York 1951.
15. Lindahl, E., *Studies in the Theory of Money and Capital*, Allen and Unwin, London 1939.
16. Manne, A. S., "ETA: A Model for Energy Technology Assessment," *Bell Journal of Economics*, 7 (1976) 379–406.
17. Morgenstern, O. and G. L. Thompson, "Un Modèle de Croissance en Économie Ouverte," *Économies et Societés*, 5 (1971) 1703–1728.
18. Morgenstern, O. and G. L. Thompson, "A Note on an Open Expanding Economy Model," *Naval Research Logistics Quarterly*, 19 (1972) 557–559.
19. Morgenstern, O. and G. L. Thompson, *Mathematical Theory of Expanding and Contracting Economies*, D. C. Heath and Co., Lexington, MA 1976.
20. Pigou, A. C., *The Economics of Welfare*, Macmillan, London, fourth ed. 1952.
21. Takayama, T. and G. G. Judge, "An Interregional Activity Analysis Model of the Agricultural Sector," *Journal of Farm Economics*, 49 (1965) 349–365.
22. Takayama, T. and G. G. Judge, *Spatial and Temporal Price and Allocation Models*, North-Holland, Amsterdam 1971.
23. Thompson, G. L. and S. Thore, "Economic Disequilibrium by Mathematical Programming," *Journal of Optimization Theory and Applications*, 71 (1991) 169–187.
24. Thore, S., *Economic Logistics: The Optimization of Spatial and Sectoral Resource, Production, and Distribution Systems*, Greenwood Press, Westport, Conn., in press 1991.
25. Thore, S. and S. Isser, "A Goaling Format for National Energy Security," *Mathematical Modelling*, 9 (1987) 51–62.
26. Weyant, J. P., "General Economic Equilibrium as a Unifying Concept in Energy-Economic Modeling," *Management Science*, 31 (1985) 548–563.

13

Industry Modeling: One Production Location

We have already in Chapter 5 encountered the concept of a "production activity." An individual activity is characterized by fixed input requirements and fixed outputs per unit level of operation. Consider, for instance, the building of residential homes. Many individual activities are required to build a residential home, from constructing the foundation to putting on the roof. To build twice as many homes of each category, twice as much mortar, twice as many electrician hours, etc., are needed.

By an industry we mean the collective facilities required for the production of a suitable aggregate of goods and services which are subject to economic demand, such as the housing industry, the health industry, the fertilizer industry or the airframe industry. Mathematically, the industry can be specified by listing the individual production activities that together make up the industry, and their unit inputs and unit outputs.

To illustrate the modeling procedures, we shall choose a numerical example from agriculture. Agricultural products are typically homogeneous and are commonly sold at the wholesale level by bulk rather than under brand names. Consumer demand is stable. The assumption of a fixed and given demand thus seems reasonable enough. On the production side, the individual production activities involve standard technologies which are well known, such as growing, storing, and distributing staple agricultural products.

Consider an agricultural region where the farmers plant two crops, corn and wheat. Three resources are needed for each crop: land, fertilizer, and machinery. The matrix A of unit input requirements is:

$$\begin{array}{l} \\ \text{Land} \\ \text{Fertilizer} \\ \text{Machinery} \end{array} \begin{array}{c} \textit{Growing corn} \quad \textit{Growing wheat} \\ \left[\begin{array}{cc} 1 \text{ acre} & 1 \text{ acre} \\ 2.5 \text{ tons/acre} & 1.75 \text{ tons/acre} \\ 0.5 \text{ days/acre} & 0.60 \text{ days/acre} \end{array}\right] \end{array} = A$$

There are two production activities, growing corn and growing wheat. The level of operation of each activity is defined as the cultivation of 1 acre of land. Each column of the matrix displays the input requirements necessary to operate an activity at unit level.

The matrix B of unit output coefficients is:

$$\begin{array}{l} \\ \text{Corn} \\ \text{Wheat} \end{array} \begin{array}{cc} \textit{Growing corn} & \textit{Growing wheat} \\ \left[\begin{array}{c} \text{120 bushels corn/acre} \\ 0 \end{array}\right. & \left.\begin{array}{c} 0 \\ \text{85 bushels wheat/acre} \end{array}\right] \end{array} = B$$

Each column in the B matrix shows the quantities of outputs obtained when operating an activity at unit level.

Let the two component column vector x denote the levels of operation of activities, with x_1 being the level of operation of the first activity (growing corn) and x_2 the level of operation of the second activity (growing wheat).

Form the matrix product Ax. It is the column vector

$$\begin{bmatrix} x_1 & + & x_2 \\ 2.5x_1 & + & 1.75x_2 \\ 0.5x_1 & + & 0.60x_2 \end{bmatrix}$$

which is the vector of all inputs. Similarly, form the product Bx. It is obtained as

$$\begin{bmatrix} 120x_1 \\ 85x_2 \end{bmatrix}$$

which is the vector of all outputs.

Next, assume that all inputs carry a fixed and known unit cost charge, as displayed by the row vector

$$q = [\$25/\text{acre}, \$95/\text{ton}, \$500/\text{day}].$$

Form the matrix product qAx which is the total cost of all inputs. First calculate the row vector

$$qA = [512.5 \quad 491.3]$$

and then find

$$qAx = (qA)x = 512.5x_1 + 491.3x_2.$$

The following additional data are provided. Total demand (to be denoted by d) is given by the column vector

$$d = \begin{bmatrix} \text{50,000 bushels of corn} \\ \text{120,000 bushels of wheat} \end{bmatrix}$$

Total available land (the column vector X) is

$$X = \begin{bmatrix} \text{600 corn acres} \\ \text{1500 wheat acres} \end{bmatrix}$$

The linear program in (13.1) is then the basic industry model:

Minimize $\quad qAx$

$$\text{Subject to} \quad Bx \geq d \qquad (13.1)$$
$$x \leq X$$
$$x \geq 0$$

Program (13.1) instructs us to find an optimal planting schedule to minimize the total cost of all industry operations subject to three sets of constraints: the output of each consumer product must suffice to cover demand d, the level of operation of each activity cannot exceed its capacity limit, and each activity must be nonnegative.

The data box for program (13.1) is shown below:.

	x_1	x_2	
p_1	120	0	$\geq$ 50,000
p_2	0	85	$\geq$ 120,000
s_1	1	0	$\leq$ 600
s_2	0	1	$\leq$ 1,500
	512.5	491.3	

To find the numerical solution to this program, solve the GAMS program CORN on page 323. The computer output shows that $x_1^* = 416.67$ acres should be planted in corn and $x_2^* = 1411.77$ acres should be planted in wheat. Both capacity constraints are slack.

For the general industry model, the following notation is used:

$i = 1, \ldots, m$	is the index of the inputs, m the largest index.
$j = 1, \ldots, n$	is the index of the activities, n the largest index.
$k = 1, \ldots, r$	is the index of the outputs.
$x = (x_1, \ldots, x_n)$	is the (column) vector of (unknown) activity levels.
$X = (X_1, \ldots, X_n)$	is the (column) vector of (known) capacity levels.
$d = (d_1, \ldots, d_r)$	is the (column) vector of (known) consumer demands.
$q = (q_1, \ldots, q_m)$	is the (row) vector of (known) input prices.
$p = (p_1, \ldots, p_r)$	is the (row) vector of (unknown) output prices.
$s = (s_1, \ldots, s_n)$	is the (row) vector of (unknown) upper bound costs.
$A = \|a_{ij}\|$	is the $m \times n$ matrix of input coefficients, where a_{ij} is the quantity of input i required when activity j is operated at unit level.
$B = \|b_{kj}\|$	is the $r \times n$ matrix of output coefficients, where b_{kj} is the quantity of output k produced when activity j is operated at unit level.

The formulation is based on the assumption that the industry buys all inputs at fixed and known prices and that it faces a fixed and known demand for its output. In other words, the supply curve for each of the inputs is horizontal and the demand curve for each of the outputs is vertical. The problem is to satisfy the demand at lowest possible cost.

The operation of most activities is associated with the use of real capital, such as machinery, floor space, etc. and the installed capacity then puts a limit on the level of operation of the activity. (If there is some activity which has no capacity limit, one may yet formally enter some suitable very large number as the upper bound; it will then always be redundant.)

Inspecting program (13.1) for the general case, clearly if the demands are too large or the capacity bounds are too small there will be no feasible solution to this linear program, and hence no optimal solution. It is therefore necessary to assume that the parameters are chosen so that optimal solutions do exist.

We next turn to the corresponding dual program and its interpretation. Denoting the dual variables in our numerical example as p_1, p_2, s_1, s_2 (see the left hand margin in the data box on page 165), the numerical solution gives $p_1^* = \$4.27$ per bushel of corn and $p_2^* = \$0.78$ per bushel of wheat. The optimal values of s_1 and s_2 are zero because the capacity constraints are slack.

Assuming that the stated programming model gives an exhaustive representation of the cultivation and marketing of corn and wheat in this region, we shall interpret p_1^* and p_2^* as the market prices of corn and wheat, respectively. That is, we identify the imputed costs with market prices. This is a crucial step of inference which will be discussed at some length in a moment.

There are dual constraints and relations of complementary slackness of the form

$$\begin{aligned} 120p_1^* + 0p_2^* &\le 512.5, \qquad x_1^*(512.5 - 120p_1^* - 0p_2^*) = 0 \\ 0p_1^* + 85p_2^* &\le 491.3, \qquad x_2^*(491.3 - 0p_1^* - 85p_2^*) = 0. \end{aligned} \tag{13.2}$$

Inserting the optimal values found, shows that the gross revenue obtained from selling the produce obtained from operating each activity at unit level is exactly exhausted by its corresponding costs.

Turning to the general formulation (13.1), we can state the dual program as

$$\begin{aligned} &\text{Maximize} \quad pd + sX \\ &\text{Subject to} \quad pB + s \le (qA) \\ &\qquad\qquad\quad p \ge 0,\ s \le 0 \end{aligned} \tag{13.3}$$

The dual variable vectors p and s in (13.3) have the following interpretations: p is the imputed cost vector and s is the capacity charge vector. As indicated above, we shall identify the imputed cost p with the market price. The charge s_j (which is nonpositive) measures the additional production cost or surcharge, caused by the fact that activity j is limited by its upper bound capacity X_j. The unit price (or imputed cost) p_k of output k is calculated so that the costs of inputs plus the capacity costs will just be covered by the total revenue collected when the goods produced are sold at these prices.

Also from the data box on page 165, we can derive the *complementary slackness* conditions in vector form:

$$p^*(Bx^* - d) = 0 \tag{13.4}$$

$$s^*(x^* - X) = 0 \tag{13.5}$$

$$[p^*B + s^* - (qA)]x^* = 0. \tag{13.6}$$

We also know that at the optimum

$$(qA)x^* = p^*d + s^*X \tag{13.7}$$

that is, the optimal objective functions of the primal and dual problem are equal.

We now give the economic interpretations of conditions (13.4–7) (which are guaranteed to hold at the optimal solution) by first stating them in component form. We discuss them in order.

(i) Condition (13.4) in component form is

$$p_k^*[(Bx^*)_k - d_k] = 0 \qquad \text{for } k = 1, \ldots, r$$

where the notation $(\ )_k$ means the kth element of the vector. This means two things: (a) If $p_k^* > 0$, that is, output good k has a positive price, then $(Bx^*)_k = d_k$ that is, there is equality between supply and demand meaning that the market *clears*. (b) If the market does not clear, i.e., $(Bx^*)_k > d_k$, then $p_k^* = 0$. Stated another way this result means that if output good k is overproduced then it is a free good.

(ii) Writing (13.5) in component form gives

$$s_j^*(x_j^* - X_j) = 0 \qquad \text{for } j = 1, \ldots, n$$

which can be stated in two ways: (a) If $s_j^* < 0$, that is, if there is a capacity charge for activity j, then $x_j^* = X_j$, that is, the activity is being operated at full capacity. (b) If $x_j^* < X_j$ then $s_j^* = 0$, that is, if the activity is not run at capacity, then its capacity charge is 0.

(iii) In component form (13.6) becomes

$$[(p^*B)_j + s_j^* - (qA)_j]x_j^* = 0 \qquad \text{for } j = 1, \ldots, n$$

which means that the net profit from operating any activity is nonpositive. In other words activities are *profitless*.More specifically, two statements can be made: (a) If $x_j^* > 0$, that is activity j is run with positive intensity then

$$(p^*B)_j = (qA)_j - s_j^* \qquad \text{for } j = 1, \ldots, n.$$

That is, the total revenue $(p^*B)_j$ received by activity j just equals the total cost of its inputs $(qA)_j$ plus the capacity charge $-s_j^*$ for that activity. (b) If $(p^*B)_j < (qA)_j - s_j^*$, i.e., if activity j loses money, then $x_j^* = 0$, meaning activity j is closed down. Briefly this means that *unprofitable activities* are not operated.

The words "profit" and "profitable" (and "profitless" and "unprofitable") as used right now refer to an imagined accounting situation where the capacity charge is included among current costs. Actual accounting practice in this matter may vary from case to case. Assume that the producer owns the productive capacity himself (the machinery, or the trucks, or the plant, or other real capital that defines the capacity limit in question). The productive capacity is part of his equity in the firm. The capacity charge, which is only an imputed cost, does not have to be paid in cash. Nevertheless, we may imagine that the producer is charging himself a separate cost for the ownership of his equity. There will be a positive cash profit *without* the capacity charge, but the imputed profit calculated *net* of the capacity charge is zero.

A positive cash profit signals the presence of one or several capacity limits. A positive cash profit is generated by capacity scarcity.

(iv) If we rewrite (13.7) as

$$p^*d = (qA)x^* - s^*X$$

the interpretation is clear. The left hand side, p^*d, is the total revenue to be received from all activities; the right hand side is the sum of all input costs, $(qA)x^*$, plus the sum of all capacity charges, $-s^*X$. Briefly this condition means that *total revenue equals total cost*.

Intermediate Goods

In the preceding account, all goods were divided into two categories: industry inputs and consumer goods. In addition, there may be intermediate goods which are both inputs and outputs: they are manufactured by industries and used up by the same or other industries as inputs for further production along the production chain. For instance, in the fertilizer industry, sulfuric acid is an intermediate good. The production of superphosphate (a final good) requires inputs of phosphate rock (a raw material) and sulfuric acid. Sulfuric acid, in its turn, is manufactured from elemental sulfur (a raw material). Other examples are: flour, which is an intermediate product between wheat and bread; sheet steel, which is an intermediate product between iron ore and automobiles, etc.

Returning to the agricultural example discussed above, suppose that the farmers face a demand for 10,000 hogs per year as well as the previous demand for corn and wheat. The farmers feed the hogs corn and wheat raised on the farms. Corn and wheat now become intermediate as well as final goods. Assume that each hog requires 18 bushels of corn and 7 bushels of wheat to grow to slaughtering age.

We shall now distinguish three inputs (land, fertilizer, machinery), two intermediate goods (corn for hog feed, wheat for hog feed), and two final goods (corn for sale, wheat for sale). There are five activities

$j = 1$ growing corn for sale

$j = 2$ growing wheat for sale

$j = 3$ growing corn for hog feed

$j = 4$ growing wheat for hog feed

$j = 5$ raising hogs

The vectors and matrices previously defined are now broken up into separate parts corresponding to intermediate goods, having superscript I, and final goods, having superscript F. We also use the superscript P for primary raw materials used as inputs. The matrices of input coefficients are:

$$\begin{array}{l} \\ \text{Land} \\ \text{Fertilizer} \\ \text{Machinery} \end{array} \begin{array}{c} \begin{array}{ccccc} j=1 & j=2 & j=3 & j=4 & j=5 \end{array} \\ \begin{bmatrix} 1 & 1 & 1 & 1 & 0 \\ 2.5 & 1.75 & 2.5 & 1.75 & 0 \\ 0.5 & 0.60 & 0.5 & 0.60 & 0 \end{bmatrix} \end{array} = A^P$$

$$\begin{array}{l} \text{Corn for hog feed} \\ \text{Wheat for hog feed} \end{array} \overset{\begin{array}{ccccc} j=1 & j=2 & j=3 & j=4 & j=5 \end{array}}{\begin{bmatrix} 0 & 0 & 0 & 0 & 18 \\ 0 & 0 & 0 & 0 & 7 \end{bmatrix}} = A^I$$

and the matrices of output coefficients are

$$\begin{array}{l} \text{Corn for hog feed} \\ \text{Wheat for hog feed} \end{array} \overset{\begin{array}{ccccc} j=1 & j=2 & j=3 & j=4 & j=5 \end{array}}{\begin{bmatrix} 0 & 0 & 120 & 0 & 0 \\ 0 & 0 & 0 & 85 & 0 \end{bmatrix}} = B^I$$

$$\begin{array}{l} \text{Corn for sale} \\ \text{Wheat for sale} \\ \text{Hogs} \end{array} \overset{\begin{array}{ccccc} j=1 & j=2 & j=3 & j=4 & j=5 \end{array}}{\begin{bmatrix} 120 & 0 & 0 & 0 & 0 \\ 0 & 85 & 0 & 0 & 0 \\ 0 & 0 & 0 & 0 & 1 \end{bmatrix}} = B^F$$

of intermediate goods and final consumer goods, respectively.

In order to accommodate the needs for corn and wheat to raise hogs, while meeting the previous final demands, the upper bounds on acres planted must now be raised. In fact we will drop them and obtain the new linear program whose data box is given below.

	x_1	x_2	x_3	x_4	x_5	
p_1^F	120	0	0	0	0	$\geq$ 50,000
p_2^F	0	85	0	0	0	$\geq$ 120,000
p_3^F	0	0	0	0	1	$\geq$ 10,000
p_1^I	0	0	120	0	−18	= 0
p_2^I	0	0	0	85	−7	= 0
	512.5	491.3	512.5	491.3	50	

It is assumed that each hog requires an out of pocket cost of $50 for shelter, vaccinations, etc. To find the new solution solve the GAMS program HOGS on page 324.

The new solution becomes

$$x_1^* + x_3^* = 1916 \text{ acres planted to corn}$$
$$x_2^* + x_4^* = 2235 \text{ acres planted to wheat}$$
$$x_5^* = 10{,}000 \text{ hogs produced.}$$

The optimal dual solution is:

$$p_1^F = 4.271 \text{ \$/bushel of corn}$$
$$p_2^F = 5.78 \text{ \$/bushel of wheat}$$
$$p_3^F = 167.3 \text{ \$/hog.}$$

The imputed prices for corn and wheat are unchanged. Note that the number of acres needed for corn has increased more than 4.5 times and the number of acres planted to wheat has gone up by more than 1.5 times. Clearly the production of meat is much more costly in terms of acres required than corn or wheat.

For the general case the primal minimizing problem is given in (13.8) below.

$$\begin{aligned} \text{Minimize} \quad & (qA^P)x \\ \text{Subject to} \quad & B^F x \geq d \\ & B^I x - A^I x = 0 \\ & x \leq X \\ & x \geq 0 \end{aligned} \tag{13.8}$$

Similarly we can write the dual maximizing problem as in (13.9).

$$\begin{aligned} \text{Maximize} \quad & p^F d + sX \\ \text{Subject to} \quad & p^F B^F + p^I(B^I - A^I) + s \leq (qA^P) \\ & p^F, p^I \geq 0, \quad s \leq 0. \end{aligned} \tag{13.9}$$

Interpretations of the dual variables are similar to those of the previous model. The optimal value of p^I will make the market for intermediate goods be in equilibrium. The previously derived results will hold after being modified to include terms for the implied costs or revenues from intermediate goods, and capacity costs associated with the upper bounds.

When Can a Dual Variable Be Interpreted as a Market Price?

Up to now, we have taken great care always to identify dual variables as "imputed unit costs" or "imputed unit values." They were not (except accidentally) the same as the market prices. For instance, we have several times used constraints for the local availability of labor. The dual of such a constraint was interpreted to be the imputed wage rate. This imputed rate was a micro concept referring to an optimal allocation and imputation scheme for a single firm or group of firms, but it is not, except accidentally, the actual market wage rate.

When the modeling effort, as presently, is being extended to cover an entire industry, i.e. all micro units producing the good or goods in question, the situation becomes different. We may then actually *define* the vector of equilibrium prices p^* in the markets by the relations of complementary slackness (13.4) through (13.6). In other words, when the equilibrium price is positive, the market must clear. (If supply exceeds demand, the price must drop to zero.) Further, through the mechanism of competition and free entry of new competitors, any positive profit must be wiped out. The profit (calculated net of all relevant costs, both direct cash costs and imputed costs) can only be zero or negative (in the latter case the activity will not be operated).

Note that the vector of prices p^* establishes equilibrium only with respect to the particular programming model that has been formulated and solved. The vector of equilibrium prices is therefore a theoretical concept referring to a particular model description of the market. If the model is changed, by introducing additional unknown variables or by adjoining additional constraints, the particular vector p^* will typically no longer be the equilibrium solution. Instead, there will be a new vector of dual variables and a new set of equilibrium prices.

For instance, a model builder may decide that some positive profit is necessary as a reward to the managers of the firms. The supply of managerial ability must then be incorporated as one of the quantity constraints of the model. The dual variable corresponding to this new upper bounded constraint will be the imputed unit cost to be paid in the model for managerial ability. The unit cost of operating any activity will now include the implied unit cost of managerial ability. All *net* profit from operating an activity will still vanish.

The challenge to the managers is to provide leadership whose value, as measured in the competitive marketplace, is at least as large as the dual variable of the managerial constraint. If they are unable to do so, competitive pressures will, in the long run, cause either a reduction in their compensation, or their replacement by other, better managers.

On the Optimizing Properties of Competitive Prices

A competitive economy for which the dual variables of all market balances can be interpreted as competitive prices, possesses some surprising mathematical properties which for a long time have intrigued economists and politicians alike. To some, these properties show that the competitive system is "the best of all worlds." To others, it is the root of suppression and exploitation of the working "proletariat."

To see what is involved, return to the simple corn and wheat model (13.1) and consider the totality of all direct constraints, all dual constraints, and all conditions of complementary slackness:

$$\begin{array}{rrr} Bx^* \geq d, & p^*(Bx^* - d) = 0, & x^* \leq X, \\ s^*(X - x^*) = 0, & x^* \geq 0, & p^*B + s^* \leq (qA), \\ [(qA) - p^*B - s^*]x^* = 0, & p^* \geq 0, & s^* \leq 0. \end{array} \qquad (13.10)$$

As we have seen, the economic interpretations of these conditions are: (i) all markets for final consumer goods must be in equilibrium; and (ii) no activity may be operated at a profit.

There is a fundamental mathematical result in linear programming that states that the solution to the system of relations that is formed by the totality of all direct constraints, all dual constraints, and all conditions of complementary slackness constitutes an optimal solution to the primal and to the dual program. That is, consider a collection of vectors x^*, p^*, s^* that solves (13.10). Then, in particular, x^* is an optimal solution to the primal program (13.1), and total costs are minimized.

(In the present instance that result is obvious enough, noting that the profit of operating any activity is nonpositive. It follows that the total profit in the industry is also nonpositive. But at the optimum, total costs equal total imputed revenue. Hence, those total costs must actually be minimal.)

We now realize that there are two distinct ways of presenting the industry model. One is to assume at the beginning that costs are minimized, just the way we did it in the text. One calculates the duals of the market balances and discusses whether they may be identified with market prices. The alternative approach is to start with the competitive assumptions (13.10). Then one *concludes* that costs are minimized.

The mathematical issues now discussed are noncontroversial. Adherents of free markets and capitalism, and the bureaucrats in the planning secretariat of a state socialistic country will have no difficulty agreeing on the mathematics. But when it comes to drawing policy conclusions, they will arrive at very different results. The market economist who starts out from the cost minimization formulation, will interpret it as a mathematical "potential function." The potential—total costs—is chosen because the formulated program (13.1) together with its corresponding dual produces the desired formulation (13.10).

To the central planner there is no need to interpret total costs as an "economic potential" function. To him, it is natural enough to minimize total costs. But he, too, will find the equivalent formulation (13.10) intriguing. He realizes that prices need to be set so that the system (13.10) is satisfied. But rather than letting markets set prices, the central economy of state socialism will rely on a planning secretariat (like the powerful GOSPLAN in the USSR) to solve program (13.1), to calculate the duals p^* and to establish those prices by decree.

Most real-life economies are neither totally competitive, nor totally centrally planned. The corn and wheat example might refer to some particular region in a developing third world country. The economy might be only partly monetized so that much of the produce is consumed locally on the farms. The distribution system might be deficient, with some produce rotting in substandard warehouses. Farming operations might be guided by tradition rather than economic considerations. Formulating program (13.1) (or some more sophisticated version) and solving it may then point to potential opportunities for moving the actual economy closer toward efficient use.

Price-Sensitive Demand

So far, we have only dealt with the supply side of the market for consumer goods. Demand was taken to be fixed and known (the vector d). We now briefly discuss the demand side as well. The consumers are assumed to have given and known *partial demand functions* for all goods $k = 1, \ldots, r$, exhibiting the demand for each good as a function of prices. (Consumer income and the prices of all other goods beyond the list $k = 1, \ldots, r$ are taken to be exogenous.) Assume that, after inverting the demand functions, the demand price of each good is obtained as

$$p_k = \alpha_k - \beta_k d_k \qquad \text{for } k = 1, \ldots, r \tag{13.11}$$

where a_k and b_k are given positive numbers. In vector form this equation reads simply

$$p(d) = \alpha - \beta d \tag{13.12}$$

Thus the demand price function is a line with negative slope, see Figure 2 in Chapter 3. The demand price for good k is the highest price a consumer would be willing to pay to acquire the amount d_k of the product. The demand for each product is no longer fixed and known, but must be determined together with the production amounts and market prices.

Following the procedure that we used in Chapter 3, we first integrate each demand price function (13.11) to obtain

$$\alpha_k d_k - 0.5\beta_k d_k^2 + \text{integration constant} \tag{13.13}$$

The nonlinear version of (13.1) is (after suppressing a constant of integration for each consumer good)

$$\text{Maximize} \quad \sum_{k=1}^{k} (\alpha_k d_k - 0.5\beta_k d_k^2) - (qA)x \tag{13.14}$$

$$\text{Subject to}\quad \begin{aligned} d - Bx &\leq 0 \\ x &\leq X \\ d,\ x &\geq 0 \end{aligned}$$

The maximand is an economic potential function. It is formed by summing all integrated demand price functions, and deducting total input resource cost. There is no economically meaningful interpretation for the potential function. It is formed for operational purposes only.

Making use of the rules given in Chapter 4 for deriving the Kuhn-Tucker conditions corresponding to (13.14), we first write the data box of the problem:

	d	x	
p	$I^{(k)}$	$-B$	≤ 0
s	0	$I^{(n)}$	$\leq X$
	$\alpha - \beta d$	$-(qA)$	

where $I^{(k)}$ is the $k \times k$ identity matrix and $I^{(n)}$ is the $n \times n$ identity matrix. The Lagrange multiplier vectors for the problem are denoted by p and s (they are both row vectors). The Kuhn-Tucker conditions are

$$\begin{aligned} d^* - Bx^* &\leq 0, \\ p^*(Bx^* - d^*) &= 0, \\ x^* &\leq X, \\ s^*(X - x^*) &= 0, \\ d^*,\ x^* &\geq 0 \end{aligned} \tag{13.15}$$

(which we recognize from the linear formulation) and also

$$\begin{aligned} p_k^* &\geq \alpha_k - \beta d_k^* \\ [p_k^*(\alpha_k - \beta d_k^*)]d_k^* &= 0, \qquad k = 1, \ldots, r, \end{aligned} \tag{13.16}$$

$$\begin{aligned} -p^*B + s^* &\geq -(qA) \\ [(qA) - p^*B + s^*]x^* &= 0, \qquad p^* \geq 0, \quad s^* \geq 0. \end{aligned} \tag{13.17}$$

Conditions (13.16) state that the market price p_k^* of each consumer good k must not fall short of its demand price. If a positive quantity of the good is bought, the market price must equal the demand price. But if the market price exceeds the demand price, nothing is bought. Conditions (13.17), relating to the cost side, are the same exhaustion conditions as before: The net profit of operating any activity is nonpositive (the capacity charge, if any, has to be included in the costs). If the activity is actually operated, the profit is zero. If the net profit is negative, the activity is not operated. (The capacity constraints $x \leq X$ appear now the "right way" in the direct program, so that their dual variable vector s is nonnegative.)

The potential function was designed so that the Kuhn-Tucker conditions express the desired equilibrium conditions.

Exercises

1. An industry produces three final goods $k = 1, 2, 3$. The demand is $d_1 = 4{,}000$ units, $d_2 = 3{,}600$ units and $d_3 = 5{,}000$ units, respectively. There are three different activities $j = 1, 2, 3$. Each activity requires three resources $i = 1, 2, 3$. The matrix $A = \|a_{ij}\|$ of unit resource requirements and the matrix $B = \|b_{kj}\|$ of unit outputs are, respectively

$$A = \begin{bmatrix} 2.4 & 4.0 & 2.4 \\ 1.0 & 3.6 & 1.6 \\ 3.6 & 3.0 & 1.8 \end{bmatrix} \qquad B = \begin{bmatrix} 18 & 10 & 12 \\ 16 & 10 & 15 \\ 15 & 20 & 10 \end{bmatrix}$$

Each element a_{ij} gives the amount of resource i required to operate activity j at unit level. Each element b_{kj} gives the amount of consumer good k obtained when activity j is operated at unit level.

The prices of the three resources are \$25, \$16, and \$20, respectively.

The level of operation x_j of each activity j is bounded both from below and from above, as follows

activity	*lower limit*	*upper limit*
$j = 1$	40	200
$j = 2$	80	180
$j = 3$	60	120

The upper limits reflect existing installed productive capacities. The lower limits are imposed by management in order to protect local employment.

(a) Construct a linear programming model whose solution will give the optimal operation level of each activity. Define dual variables and write down the dual problem. Interpret the dual variables and the dual constraints.

(b) Solve the problem numerically. Analyze the net return and the cost of operating each activity. Are activities operated at a profit, at the breakeven point, or at a loss? Determine the market prices of the three goods.

2. The main products of the U.S. apple industry are fresh picked apples and applesauce. On-tree apples are harvested from September through November, stored (in regular or controlled atmosphere) or processed into applesauce. The following two activities are distinguished:

$j = 1$ harvesting 1 lb. of on-tree apples, storage and packing,

$j = 2$ harvesting 1 lb. of on-tree apples, and processing it into applesauce.

The input unit requirements and the unit outputs are displayed in the table below:

		Activities	
		$j = 1$	$j = 2$
Inputs	on-tree apples, lbs.	1	1
	labor hours	0.02	0.02
	capital hours	0.01	0.02
Outputs	packed retail apples, lbs.	1	0
	applesauce cans	0	3

The prices of inputs are: price of 1 lbs. of on-tree apples \$0.15, price of 1 labor hour \$4.00, price of 1 capital hour \$20.00. The final demand is 3,000 million lbs. packed retail apples and 500 million cans of applesauce.

Determine the optimal production pattern in the industry, and the market prices of packed retail apples, and of applesauce.

(For realistic data on the U.S. apple industry, see H. W. Fuchs, R. O. Farrish, R. W. Sohall, "A Model of the U.S. Apply Industry: A Quadratic Interregional Intertemporal Activity Analysis Formulation," *American Journal of Agricultural Economics*, Nov. 1974.)

3. Using the same data as in Exercise 2, replace now the assumption of vertical demand curves by the price dependent demand relations

$$x_1 = 4000 - 200p_1$$
$$x_2 = 900 - 50p_2$$

where p_1 is the unknown price of a pound of packed retail apples and p_2 is the unknown price of a can of applesauce. Solving for the demand price functions we get

$$p_1 = 20 - 0.005x_1$$
$$p_2 = 16 - 0.020x_2$$

(a) Write down the economic potential function and state the nonlinear programming problem.

(b) Derive and interpret the Kuhn-Tucker conditions.

14

Industrial Modeling: Spatial Networks

It is rather curious to note that the spatial dimension seldom appears in textbook presentations of economic theory. Economic relationships are conveniently formulated with no reference to the geographical location of the participating economic subjects. (The obvious exceptions are in expositions of the theory of international trade.)

And yet, how can one understand the spectacular development of modern economies without pointing to the development of new markets in developing countries and the search for raw materials and energy sources in remote locations? As transportation and distribution costs come down, the logistics networks that connect resources with final consumer demand become ever longer and more complex.

The constitutent elements of the network now envisaged are industrial activities together with transportation activities. Raw materials and intermediate goods are bought at one location and used as inputs for activities at another. Finished products are shipped from the factory or the farm to distribution centers, eventually to reach the consumer through wholesalers and retailers. The modelling task at hand is to determine the level of operations of the various industrial activities at each production location and to determine the optimal routing of outputs from production locations to demand points which will satisfy the given demands.

We have already studied the simple transportation model in Chapter 1. For the purpose of our present analysis, it is helpful to note that the transportation of a single commodity along a link in a transportation network can formally be represented as the operation of a "transportation activity." The unit level of operation of a transportation activity may be the number of railway cars running from an originating node to a destination node, or else the quantity transported on each such railway car. Alternative modes of transportation such as trucks, barges, airplanes, etc., can be represented as separate alternative activities. The inputs to the transportation activities are labor, fuel and the various transportation vehicles involved. If the unit costs of these inputs were all given and known, the unit costs of transportation would also be given and known. We mention this not because we propose to deal with transportation in such a detailed fashion but because we want you to understand the underlying mathematical assumptions concerning transportation and other inputs, and why we shall be able to develop an industry model which combines production and transportation activities.

The spatial equilibrium model we are going to state is an extension of the industry model of the previous chapter to include production and demand each being located at several different places. We state the notation needed for the new model:

$i = 1, \ldots, m$ is the index of inputs.

$j = 1, \ldots, n$ is the index of the activities.

$k = 1, \ldots, r$ is the index of the outputs.

h and $l = 1, \ldots, f$ are the indices of the locations; the letter h will preferably be used when a location serves as an origin (a plant) and the letter l will be used when a location is considered as a destination (a demand point).

$x_h = (x_{h1}, \ldots, x_{hn})$ is the (column) vector of activities in region h.

$X_h = (X_{h1}, \ldots, X_{hn})$ is the (column) vector of activity upper bounds in region h.

$d_h = (d_{h1}, \ldots, d_{hr})$ is the (column) vector of demands in region h.

$q_h = (q_{h1}, \ldots, q_{hm})$ is the (row) vector of input prices in region h.

$p_h = (p_{h1}, \ldots, p_{hr})$ is the (row) vector of output costs in region h.

$v_h = (v_{h1}, \ldots, v_{hr})$ is the (row) vector of factory costs in region h.

$s_h = (s_{h1}, \ldots, s_{hr})$ is the (row) vector of upper bound costs.

$c_{hl} = (c_{hl1}, \ldots, c_{hlr})$ is the (row) vector of unit shipping charges between regions h and l.

$t_{hl} = (t_{hl1}, \ldots, t_{hlr})$ is the (column) vector of quantities shipped from region h to region l.

$A_h = \|a_{hij}\|$ is the $m \times n$ matrix of input coefficients in region h.

$B_h = \|b_{hkj}\|$ is the $r \times n$ matrix of output coefficients in region h.

The notation now introduced enables us to specify the production decisions in an industry taken at a number of different locations, and the flow of each output from plants to demand points. In order to determine the operation of the various production activities, and the routing of transportation, we state the general industry spatial model as in (14.1).

$$\text{Minimize} \quad \sum_{h=1}^{f} (q_h A_h) x_h + \sum_{h=1}^{f} \sum_{l=1}^{f} c_{hl} t_{hl} \tag{14.1}$$

$$\text{Subject to} \quad B_h x_h - \sum_{l=1}^{f} t_{hl} \geq 0, \qquad h = 1, \ldots, f$$

$$\sum_{h=1}^{f} t_{hl} \geq d_l, \qquad l = 1, \ldots, f$$

$$x_h \le X_h, \qquad h = 1, \ldots, f$$
$$x_h, t_{hl} \ge 0, \qquad h, l = 1, \ldots, f$$

The objective is to minimize total production and transportation costs. The first set of constraints in (14.1) is

$$B_h x_h - \sum_{l=1}^{f} t_{hl} \ge 0 \tag{14.2}$$

stating that the total amount shipped from location h is at most equal to the production there. The second set of constraints in (14.1) is

$$\sum_{h=1}^{f} t_{hl} \ge d_l \tag{14.3}$$

which requires that the total amount shipped to region h is at least as much as the demand there. The third constraint in (14.1) is

$$x_h \le X_h \tag{14.4}$$

requiring that the activities in region h must be no larger than their upper bounds.

We now associate the vector of dual variables v_h with (14.2), the vector of dual variables p_l with (14.3) and the vector of dual variables s_h with (14.4).

Using them, the dual problem is:

$$\text{Maximize} \quad \sum_{l=1}^{f} p_l d_l + \sum_{h=1}^{f} s_h X_h \tag{14.5}$$

$$\begin{aligned} \text{Subject to} \quad v_h B_h + s_h &\le (q_h A_h), & h &= 1, \ldots, f \\ p_l - v_h &\le c_{hl}, & h, l &= 1, \ldots, f \\ v_h, p_h &\ge 0, & h &= 1, \ldots, f \\ s_h &\le 0, & h &= 1, \ldots, f \end{aligned}$$

The interpretations for the dual variables are similar to those for the model in the preceding chapter, except that there now are two output imputed cost (or price) vectors: v_h represents the prices of the outputs at the factory door, and p_l represents the prices at region l. The second set of constraints shows the connection between them. To see the connection we note that t_{hl} is the primal variable associated with the second constraint in (14.5) so that the corresponding complementary slackness condition is

$$(p_l^* - v_h^* - c_{hl}) t_{hl}^* = 0.$$

Hence if $t_{hlk}^* > 0$ for some output k, it follows that

$$p_{lk}^* = v_h^* + c_{hlk} \tag{14.6}$$

Recalling that p_{lk} and v_{hk} are nonnegative, this means: if there is a positive shipment of good k from region h to region l, then the cost p_{lk} of good k at region l is the factory cost v_{hk}^* at region h plus the shipment cost c_{hlk} from region h to region l.

Decentralization

The linear programming problem constructed just now seems reasonable provided the entire industry is owned by one large corporation or government, which operates both the transportation and the production facilities at all locations specified. But suppose that the industry is made up of several corporations, each one operating at just a few locations. Who then, would be the master planner who would formulate and solve program (14.1)?

The answer is that the optimal solution derived still is a prescription for the optimal behavior of each participant in the industry, in the sense that if everybody else adheres to that solution then it will also be optimal for each single participant also to do so. This holds for each local production manager. It even holds for a hypothetical manager of routing of transportation. In order to see this, assume that the optimal solution to program (14.1) has already been established at all production facilities except at location h; the optimal transportation along all routes has also been established so that the local required output at location h (which equals local demand plus net out-shipments from h to other regions) is known. It only remains to determine the production plan at location h. Inspecting program (14.1), we see that it boils down to a single production problem for location h, identical to the program (13.1) in Chapter 13.

Arguing along a different track, assume next that the optimal solution to program (14.1) has been established at *all* production facilities but let the transportation routing between regions remain to be determined. Inspecting program (14.1) this time, we see that it boils down to a conventional network problem with given influxes (the local outputs) and given effluxes (local demands).

To conclude, the master program (14.1) defines a totality of individual plans, both for individual production managers and for a manager of transportation, which have the property that each single such plan defines optimal behavior, given that all the other individual plans are implemented.

Distribution Networks

The format of program (14.1) is general enough to cover also cases of wholesale and retail distribution. Put the vector $x^{(h)} = 0$ at one or several locations h and there will then be no production in these places; but there may still be a positive final demand at the location, or the location could even be used as a transshipment location for the routing of output from plants to demand locations. We illustrate by working an example of the distribution of farm products to cities.

Example 1. Let us continue with the farm example of the preceding chapter but expand it to a problem having two farms F_1 and F_2 producing corn and wheat which are sent to fulfill demands at three cities C_1, C_2, and C_3 as shown in Figure 14.1. The matrices of input coefficients are the same for both farms, namely:

$$\begin{array}{cc} \textit{Corn} & \textit{Wheat} \\ \textit{acre} & \textit{acre} \end{array}$$

$$A_1 = A_2 = \begin{bmatrix} 1 & 1 \\ 2.5 & 1.75 \\ 0.5 & 0.60 \end{bmatrix} \begin{array}{l} \text{Land (acres)} \\ \text{Fertilizer (tons/acre)} \\ \text{Machinery (days/acre)} \end{array}$$

Figure 14.1

Network for distribution of grain from farms to cities.

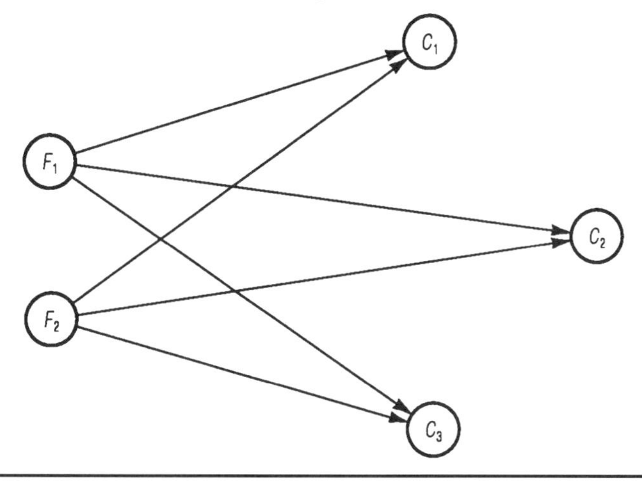

The matrices of output coefficients are

$$B_1 = \begin{array}{c} \begin{array}{cc} \textit{Corn} & \textit{Wheat} \\ \textit{acre} & \textit{acre} \end{array} \\ \left[\begin{array}{cc} 120 & 0 \\ 0 & 85 \end{array} \right] \end{array} \begin{array}{l} \text{bushels corn/acre} \\ \text{bushels wheat/acre} \end{array}$$

$$B_2 = \left[\begin{array}{cc} 135 & 0 \\ 0 & 75 \end{array} \right] \begin{array}{l} \text{bushels corn/acre} \\ \text{bushels wheat/acre} \end{array}$$

The out of pocket costs for each resource at each farm are

$$q_1 = (\$25/\text{acre} \quad \$95/\text{ton} \quad \$500/\text{day})$$
$$q_2 = (\$30/\text{acre} \quad \$100/\text{ton} \quad \$470/\text{day})$$

Farm 1 has up to 4000 acres that can be planted while Farm 2 has up to 3000 acres to plant. The per bushel transportation costs and yearly demands for corn and wheat at each city are:

	C_1	C_2	C_3
F_1	0.1	0.3	0.2
F_2	0.2	0.3	0.1
Corn demand (tons)	50,000	70,000	60,000
Wheat demand (tons)	120,000	140,000	135,000

In order to find the optimal planting amounts and distribution pattern we begin by calculating the unit production costs at each farm.

$$q_1 A_1 = (512.5,\ 491.3)$$
$$q_2 A_2 = (515,\ 487)$$

The two components of these vectors represent the per acre costs of planting an acre at each farm to corn and wheat, respectively.

We can now construct the data box for the linear program as follows:

	Corn	*Wheat*	*Corn*	*Wheat*	F_1 *Corn*			F_1 *Wheat*			F_2 *Corn*			F_2 *Wheat*			
	x_{11}	x_{12}	x_{21}	x_{22}	t_{111}	t_{121}	t_{131}	t_{112}	t_{122}	t_{132}	t_{211}	t_{221}	t_{231}	t_{212}	t_{222}	t_{232}	
v_{11}	120				−1	−1	−1										≥ 0
v_{12}		85						−1	−1	−1							≥ 0
v_{21}			135								−1	−1	−1				≥ 0
v_{22}				75										−1	−1	−1	≥ 0
p_{11}					1						1						$\geq$ 50,000
p_{21}						1						1					$\geq$ 70,000
p_{31}							1						1				$\geq$ 60,000
p_{12}								1						1			$\geq$ 120,000
p_{22}									1						1		$\geq$ 140,000
p_{32}										1						1	$\geq$ 135,000
s_1	1	1															$\leq$ 4,000
s_2			1	1													$\leq$ 3,000
	512.3	491.3	515	487	0.1	0.3	0.2	0.1	0.3	0.2	0.2	0.3	0.1	0.2	0.3	0.1	

The primal variables in the data box above have the following interpretations: x_{hj} is the number of acres planted to crop j at farm h; t_{hlj} number of bushels of crop j sent from farm h to city l. The dual variables in the data box have the following interpretations: v_{hj} is the imputed cost (or price) of crop j at farm h; p_{lj} is the imputed cost of crop j at city l; s_h is the imputed cost or value of additional acres at farm h.

The optimal solution given by solving the GAMS program FARMTOCITY on page 325 was: $x_{11}^* = 0$ and $x_{12}^* = 4000$ indicating that all acres of farm F_1 should be planted to wheat; also $x_{21}^* = 1333.3$, and $x_{22}^* = 733.3$ indicating that all the corn requirements of all the cities were produced by farm F_2; farm F_2 also produced some of the wheat requirements, but also had 1433.3 acres that were left unplanted. The dual variable associated with the upper bounds on acreage were, $s_1^* = -52.183$ indicating that it would be beneficial to expand farm F_1, and $s_2^* = 0$ which we know to be correct since farm F_2 has acreage that is not planted into crops. The rest of the solution involving shipments of grain from the farms to the cities and the imputed costs (or prices) of the grain at each of the locations is shown in Figures 14.2(a) for corn and Figure 14.2(b) for wheat. Note that the difference between the prices of a grain at the end and the beginning of an arrow on which positive shipment is made exactly equals the unit transportation cost. On arcs not used for shipping this difference is greater than or equal to the unit shipping cost.

The Distribution of Agricultural Harvest to Processing Plants

We can interchange the operations of transportation and production and consider a case in which agricultural inputs are produced on farms and shipped to plants for processing into finished food products.

Figure 14.2

Shipments of corn from farms to cities, and corn prices at each of these locations.

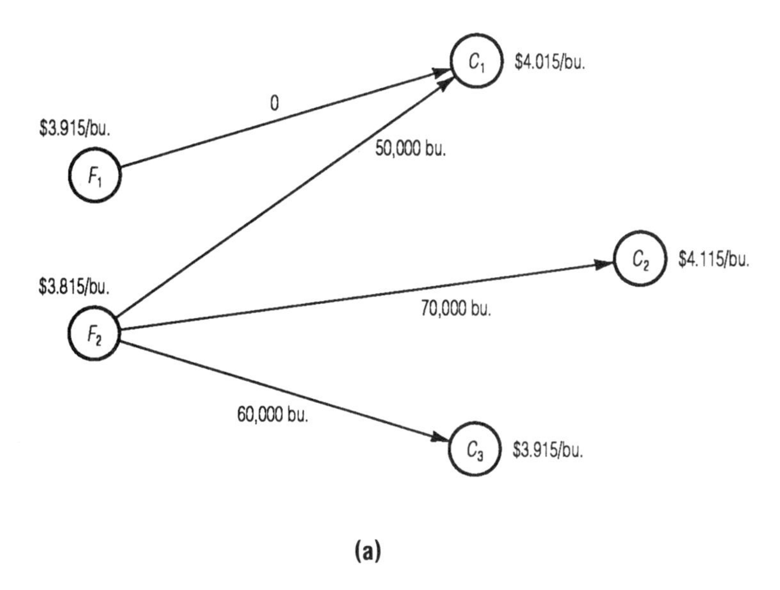

(a)

Shipments of wheat from farms to cities, and wheat prices at each of these locations.

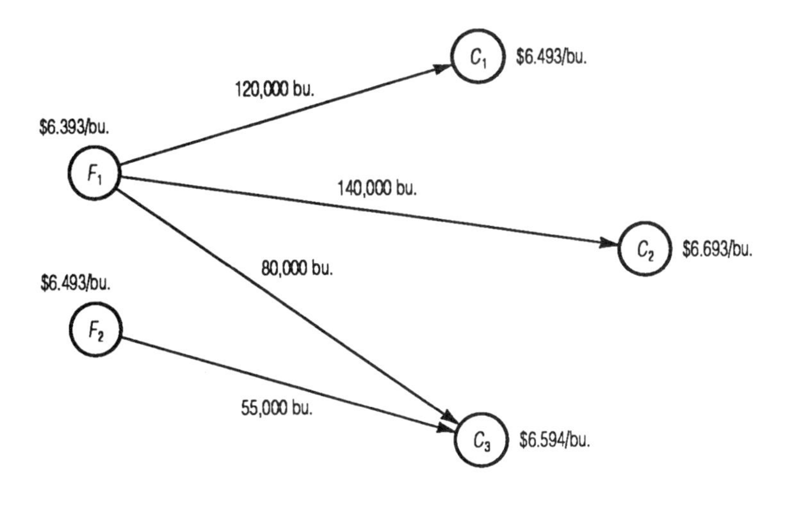

(b)

Example 2. To illustrate we consider an example of the harvesting and canning of pineapples.

There are three main pineapple growing regions in Honduras which produce 4,000, 5,000, and 6,000 lbs/day, respectively, during the harvesting season. There are two pineapple canning plants, each located on the Gulf of Mexico coastline, and each has its own harbor and export dock. Three resources are required to operate each plant: labor, capital goods (machinery, buildings, etc.), and harvested pineapples. Labor is paid $1.25/hour and capital resources are paid $0.40/capital hour. One of the plants is newer and is less labor intensive and more capital intensive than the other. The quantities of the three resources needed to make one case of canned pineapple are

	Plant 1	*Plant 2*
Labor (hours)	0.04	0.08
Capital ($)	2.0	1.45
Pineapples (lbs)	16.0	16.0

The unit transportation costs for shipping the freshly harvested pineapples from the growing regions to the canning plants are:

	Plant 1 (*$/lb*)	*Plant 2* (*$/lb*)
Region 1	0.02	0.04
Region 2	0.01	0.03
Region 3	0.04	0.01

If the world price for a case of canned pineapple at the shipping dock is $12.50, what is the best way to process the pineapple production each day?

To solve the problem let x_1 and x_2 be the amounts processed in each plant, and let t_{hl} be the quantity in pounds/day shipped from growing region h to plant l. The input matrix is then

$$A = \begin{bmatrix} 0.04 & 0.08 \\ 2.00 & 1.45 \end{bmatrix}$$

(The input requirement of 16 lbs. pineapples/case will be incorporated in the constraints.) Let $q = (1.25 \quad 0.4)$ be the input price vector so that

$$qA = (0.85 \quad 0.68)$$

is the input cost vector. The data box for the problem appears below.

	t_{11}	t_{12}	t_{21}	t_{22}	t_{31}	t_{32}	x_1	x_2	z	
u_1	1	1								≤ 4000
u_2			1	1						≤ 5000
u_3					1	1				≤ 6000
u_4	−1		−1		−1		16			$= 0$
u_5		−1		−1		−1		16		$= 0$
v							−1	−1	1	$= 0$
	−0.02	−0.04	−0.01	−0.03	−0.04	−0.01	−0.85	−0.68	12.5	

Figure 14.3

Numerical solution for pineapple example.

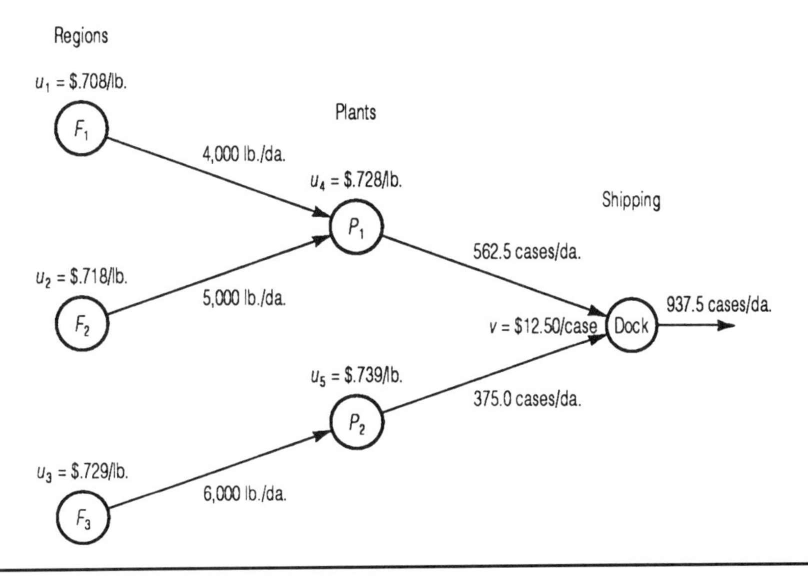

The variable z is the sum of the production in both plants and hence is the country's total daily production of canned pineapples. The dual variables u_1, u_2, and u_3 are the imputed values of harvested pineapples at each growing region. The dual variables u_4 and u_5 are the imputed values of pineapples arriving at each of the canning plants raw materials gates. The dual variable v, which has to be \$12.50, the world price of a case of canned pineapples, is the value of the finished goods at the export docks. Solution of the GAMS program PINEAPPLE on page 327 produced the solution shown graphically in Figure 14.3.

You should check that the appreciation in value on a shipping arc that is used exactly equals the unit shipping cost. On arcs not used, the appreciation in value is less than the shipping cost that would be required to use such arcs.

Exercises

1. Answer the following questions about Example 1 by making several computer runs, (or else by using ranging analysis if your computer program provides it).
   (a) Increase the demand for wheat at city C_3 and show that, at least for a certain range of demands, the wheat supply curve is horizontal.
   (b) Repeat (a) for the supply curve for corn by changing the demand for corn at C_1.
2. In Example 2 assume that instead of selling the canned pineapple at the dock all of the output is shipped either to New York or Los Angeles in order to get higher prices. Los Angeles has a maximum daily demand of 400 cases/day while New York has a maximum demand of 600 cases/day. The shipping costs are \$0.001/case mile. New

York is 1500 sea miles from Honduras. Los Angeles is 800 sea miles from the north coast of Honduras and there is an additional charge of $1 per case when the cargo ship carrying the pineapples goes through the Panama Canal. The price of a case of pineapples is $18 in New York and $15 in Los Angeles. Enlarge the linear program shown in the data box on page 184 and solve to find the optimal distribution of the canned pineapple. Could you have predicted this result without actually solving the problem? Explain the significance of each of the primal and dual variables.

15

Goals, Environmental Economics, & Pigou Taxes

Sometimes an economic policy maker might feel concerned that the proposed market solutions, such as those which we discussed in Chapters 13 and 14, involve excessive exploitation of depletable resources (for instance, scarce minerals, crude oil or ground water). In other cases, the aim may be to stimulate the demand for some particular kinds of resources, such as laborers having physical or mental handicaps. A common feature of these diverse circumstances is that so-called negative external economies are felt to arise from the competitive market solution and that there is a wish by policy makers to intervene in the working of these free markets. It will be assumed that the intervention can be characterized by the setting of goals and that such goals have been ranked in order of their relative importance.

The technique of *goal programming* to be discussed in this chapter permits an economic modeler to deal with soft constraints, such as those which the market does not explicitly take into account. Such soft constraints can be violated, but at a cost. A goal or target level is laid down for each of a number of unknown variables, and a mathematical program is formulated, designed to search for some optimal realization of these unknowns that comes as close as possible to the goals. Penalties are levied on deviations between goals and actual performance. The penalties are cash charges assessed by some controlling agency, or may just reflect an ordinal system of priorities entertained by a policy maker. The more urgent the goal, the greater the penalty assessed for violation of the corresponding constraint. In any event, the objective of the goal program is to minimize the sum of all penalties.

The companion technique of *goal focusing* applies when the formulation of the goals is attached to a prior mathematical program existing in its own right but where it is now desired to temper the objective of that program, requiring the solution values to come as close as possible to the goals. The objective function of the goal focusing

Figure 15.1

Weekly production limits and penalties.

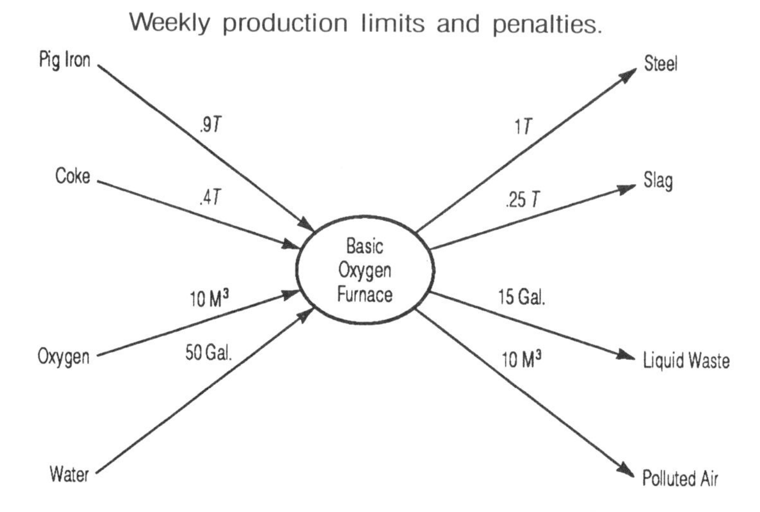

program is defined as the objective of the prior (non-goaled) program adjusted by the sum of all penalties. That is, while the prior objective ("market efficiency," say) is still sought as long as the goals so permit, one introduces the possibility of a trade-off if all goals cannot be realized exactly. The final answer may have less efficiency in order to avoid paying penalties.

In the political discussion of the need to preserve the environment, two types of methods of enforcement are proposed: (i) direct regulation of industry; and (ii) taxes levied directly on the use of scarce resources by industry. As we shall see, the direct and the dual programs in goal focusing correspond in a fashion to these two approaches. The direct program includes constraints laying down the various goals. The dual program determines the corresponding taxes which, if assessed, would induce the users of resources to modify these uses as required.

In order to illustrate the basic technique of goal programming, we first turn to a simple numerical example involving a steel mill that wishes to produce 100 tons of finished steel in a given week. The production process is illustrated in Figure 15.1. The company has ample supplies of pig iron, coke, oxygen, and water. However, its output of pollutants is monitored by the county office of pollution and charges are made for excess production of waste products according to the schedule below.

Pollutant	*Weekly Upper Limit*	*Charges for Excess*
Slag	20 T/wk	4 \$/T
Liquid Waste	1200 Gal/wk	15 \$/Gal
Polluted Air	900 M^3	18 \$/M^3

The following notation, which will be used throughout the chapter, is helpful.

g = goal or target value of a variable.

g^+ = excess performance ("over-performance") relative to goal.

g^- = deficit performance ("under-performance") relative to goal.

The actual performance of a variable is then related to the goal through the relation

$$\text{actual performance} - g^+ + g^- = g.$$

It must be assumed that g^+ and g^- are both nonnegative, and that $g^+g^- = 0$, i.e. these two unknown deviations cannot both be positive at the same time. As we shall see in what follows, this latter condition will always be automatically fulfilled by the programming formulations to be written down.

The steel maker pays two kinds of penalties: lost revenue if the quantity of steel sold falls short of the production target; and charges for excess outputs of wastes. The purpose of the linear program shown below is to determine a production policy that minimizes the sum of all such penalties.

x_1	g_1^-	g_2^+	g_3^+	g_4^+	
1	1	0	0	0	≥ 100
0.25	0	−1	0	0	≤ 20
15	0	0	−1	0	≤ 1200
10	0	0	0	−1	≤ 900
0	p	4	15	18	

In the databox, p is the price for a ton of steel. Clearly the best production mix will depend on that price. In the databox, x_1 is the production of steel, g_1^- is the deficit in steel production, g_2^+ is the excess production of slag, g_3^+ is the excess production of liquid waste, and g_4^+ is the excess production of polluted air.

The solution to the problem was found by solving the GAMS program STEEL on page 328 for several values of p. The results are shown in the table below.

Steel p	*Steel Produced* x_1	*Steel not Produced* g_1^-	*Excess Slag Produced* g_2^+	*Excess Liquid Waste Produced* g_3^+	*Pollutant Air Produced* g_4^+
200	80	20	0	0	0
350	90	10	2.5	150	0
500	100	0	5.0	300	100

Note that when steel has a low price, $p = 200$, no excess production of any waste product is made, and the steel manufacturer foregoes $4,000 of revenue due to lost sales. When the price of steel is higher, $p = 350$, the steel maker raises his steel production by 10 tons. In so doing he violates his limits on slag and liquid waste production, and so has to pay penalties of $2260. Finally, at a high steel price, $p = 500$, the steel maker makes his goal production, but also violates all of his pollution limits and pays penalties of $6,320.

Clearly the ability of taxes to control the production of pollutants will depend on the profitability of the firm. The monitoring agency must take that into account when setting penalties for pollutant production.

Resource Usage

The ideas of goal programming having been explained, we next turn to the case of goal focusing in industry modeling. In Chapter 13 we studied the production problem of an industry facing a given and known demand for each good produced. Resources and other inputs could be procured as required, at given and known prices. In other words, the supply curves for inputs were all horizontal. In the notation of Chapter 13, the demand for input i was $\sum_j a_{ij}x_j$.

Suppose, however, that a policymaker is concerned with the resulting use of resources. He or she may feel that the exploitation of some resources is excessive and detrimental in the long run, such as the deforestation of wildlife tracts and tropical rain forest, eventually leading to erosion of soil and the change of climate. The employment of other resources may be felt to be lacking, such as the use of unskilled labor, workers with handicaps etc. Suppose that it is possible to encapsulate the various considerations regarding the use of input i into a single numerical goal g_i. The goal is a desirable target, but its exact achievement is not required. Deviations from the goal are permitted, both in the positive direction (an overfulfillment or excess is denoted by g_i^+) and in the negative direction (an underfulfillment or deficit is denoted by g_i^-). Mathematically, any use of resource i can then be written

$$\sum_j a_{ij}\, x_j = g_i + g_i^+ - g_i^- \tag{15.1}$$

with g_i^+ and g_i^- both being nonnegative and $g_i^+ g_i^- = 0$, i.e., at least one of the two deviations must equal zero.

In vector notation, the same relation reads

$$Ax = g + g^+ - g^- \tag{15.2}$$

where each of the three column vectors, g, g^+, and g^- has the dimension m.

Deviations from a goal are associated with penalties. Let the dollars/unit penalty for overshooting goal g_i be M_i, and let the dollars/unit penalty for undershooting be N_i. For instance, in the case of supply of ground water there will be some large penalty to be paid for overwithdrawal from the aquifer. No penalty will be levied for withdrawals of ground water that are less than the goal.

Define penalty row vectors $M = [M_i]$ and $N = [N_i]$, each having dimension m. The total penalties then are $Mg^+ + Ng^-$ dollars. The larger the penalty that is associated with deviation from a goal, the more likely it is that the goal will be satisfied.

Whether penalties are charged in cash, or just have to be suffered as a pyschological inconvenience by management, in the programming formulation to follow they will under all circumstances be counted as costs of doing business, just like the cost of buying raw materials, power, water, etc.

The problem faced by an industry who has goals constraints on its use of raw materials can be stated by modifying the linear program of (13.1) by adding the goal constraints in (15.2) and penalty costs to the objective function. We obtain the following goal program:

$$\begin{aligned} \text{Minimize} \quad & (qA)x + Mg^+ + Ng^- \\ \text{Subject to} \quad & Bx \geq d \\ & x \leq X \\ & Ax - g^+ + g^- = g \\ & x, g^+, g^- \geq 0 \end{aligned} \tag{15.3}$$

The program minimizes the sum of all input costs plus all penalties, subject to a market condition for each output, capacity constraints and the goal constraints.

As long as there is some deviation from the goals, the presence of the penalty term will cause the optimal value of the minimand to decrease. In any case, the program will search for a combination of deviations that makes the net value of the program as small as possible.

Note that it is not necessary to introduce the requirement $g_i^+ g_i^- = 0$ explicitly; it will automatically be satisfied at the point of solution. (For assume, *per contra*, that both g_i^+ and g_i^- were positive. It would then be possible to lower the value of the maximand by shaving off some small positive constant from them both. One would be able to continue this procedure until one of the two deviations was reduced to zero.)

The dual program to (15.3) is given by

$$\begin{aligned} &\text{Maximize} \quad pd + sX + tg \\ &\text{Subject to} \quad pB + s + tA \leq (qA) \\ &\qquad -t \leq M \\ &\qquad t \leq N \\ &\qquad p \geq 0, \quad s \leq 0 \quad \text{and } t \text{ unrestricted in sign} \end{aligned} \tag{15.4}$$

where p, s, and t are row vectors of dual variables associated with the three sets of constraints in (15.3). As we shall see immediately, the unrestricted variable t_i is a shadow price that is assessed whenever the goal is not met exactly. If the actual resource use falls short of the goal, its shadow price is positive and it becomes a bonus or subsidy that stimulates increased use of the resource. If the actual resource use exceeds the goal, its shadow price is negative and it is then a cost charge that decreases the use of the resource.

It is clear that the following results will hold at the point of optimum:

(i) There is equilibrium in all output markets.

(ii) Capacity charges arise for activities which are operated at their maximal level.

(iii) For the purpose of calculating the profit of operating any activity, both the capacity charge, if any, and the possible adjustment of resource prices due to the goal relations, should be taken into account. The vector of adjusted resource prices is $(q - t)$.

(iv) Unit profits being calculated in the fashion now explained, the net profit from operating any activity is nonpositive. If an activity is actually operated on a positive level, the profit vanishes. For the first set of constraints in (15.4), together with complementary slackness, give

$$\begin{aligned} p^*B + s^* + t^*A &\leq (qA) \\ [p^*B + s^* - (q - t^*)A]x^* &= 0 \end{aligned} \tag{15.5}$$

If the optimal use of input i exceeds the goal, so that the deviation g_i^{+*} is positive, the dual t_i^* equals the negative of the unit penalty for overshooting, $-M_i$. If the optimal use of input i falls short of its goal, so that the deviation g_i^{-*} is positive, the dual t_i^* equals the unit penalty for underfulfillment N_i. If the optimal use coincides with the goal, the dual t_i^* will take on some numerical value (positive or negative) that falls between these two extremes, i.e.,

$-M_i \leq t_i^* \leq N_i$. For the two last sets of constraints of program (15.4) give, together with complementary slackness

$$-t_i^* \leq M_i \quad \text{and} \quad g_i^{+*}(-t_i^* - M_i) = 0 \tag{15.6}$$

for $i = 1, \ldots, m$. Also

$$t_i^* \leq N_i \quad \text{and} \quad g_i^{-*}(t_i^* - N_i) = 0 \tag{15.7}$$

for $i = 1, \ldots, m$.

(v) Total sales revenues equal total costs (including capacity charges and penalties but deducting possible resource bonuses). For the duality theorem and some elementary manipulation using the relations of complementary slackness gives:

$$p^*d = (q - t^*)Ax^* - s^*X. \tag{15.8}$$

A key question in all goal programming is this: Who is going to *enforce* the optimal solution? Clearly, some mechanism of enforcement is needed, otherwise the solution will revert to the free market solution. Few producers will voluntarily adjust their use of inputs unless they are induced to do so, by being forced to pay goal penalties, or be able to accept goal subsidies, directly or indirectly.

There are several answers to this question. One possibility is social and attitudinal change: some producers may become aware of the urgency of environmental factors; they will then act as if bonuses and penalties are assessed for goal deviations. But no bonuses would actually be paid and no penalties collected in dollars and cents. Another possibility is that the local or the central government actually pays the bonuses and collects penalties in cash. Examples of the latter are provided by the U.S. steel industry which since the mid 1960s has had to comply with environmental guidelines, and to pay cash fines for excessive pollution of air and/or water.

A third possibility is that local or central government computes the goal constraint dual variable $t = (t_i)$ and introduces a system of unit *subsidies* and *excise taxes* connected with the use of resources. The effective cash price that each producer would have to pay for resource i would then be $q_i - t_i$. The possibility of such subsidies and excise taxes was discussed by A. C. Pigou back in 1915 in his book *The Economics of Welfare*. (Such an excise tax is often called a *Pigou tax*). The use of Pigou taxes have become widespread in Western countries, *cf.* excises on cigarettes, liquor and gasoline.

Speaking in terms of modern welfare analysis, the purpose of the Pigou tax is to *internalize* the negative external economies associated with the use of the good in question. But a Pigou tax is not the only way this can be done. Sometimes it is possible to define *property rights* to the environmental factors which are being damaged, and to let the owner of these property rights charge a market price for the use of his property. For instance, the owner of a large wilderness tract may charge cash for hunting permits, or the owner of a river may charge a fee for permitting an upstream factory to release toxic waste into his waters.

Example 1. To illustrate what has now been said, consider the case of the growing of rice in a developing country. There are two methods of cultivation: a traditional labor intensive method using a conventional variety of rice (activity #1), and a more recently developed method of cultivation based on intensive fertilization and the use of pesticides (activity #2). Specifically, the unit input requirements are, per ton of harvested rice

	low yield $j = 1$	*high yield* $j = 2$
water $i = 1$ (in hundreds of gallon months)	10	6
labor $i = 2$ (in person years)	0.77	0.43
land $i = 3$ (hectares)	0.67	0.33
fertilizer $i = 4$ (tons)	0.01	0.04
pesticides $i = 5$ (tons)	0	0.01

The unit cost of each of the five factors of production are 1.50, 2.00, 6.00, 12.00 and 20.00, respectively, expressed in the local currency.

Total demand for rice is 1.2 million tons. This figure is a bit higher than the maximal harvest of 1.0 million tons that can be brought in using the conventional method alone. Due to a shortage of seeds and farm consultants, the new high yielding method can at most produce a total of 0.4 million tons.

New land can be brought under cultivation through irrigation (a horizontal supply curve of land).

Water for irrigation purposes is drawn from a large river. An environmental study has recommended that an acceptable figure for the total diversion of water for irrigation purposes is 11 hundreds of millions of gallon months. Water use above this figure would lower the water level in several upstream lakes, with detrimental effects on the living conditions in these areas.

There is also a concern about the use of pesticides and a target figure of 2500 tons has been established.

Formulate a goal focusing model that would solve for the optimal use of the two methods of cultivation, given that the goal for the use of pesticides has top priority, and that the target figure for irrigation water is ranked second!

In order to solve the problem, we first compute the vector qA which comes out as (20.68, 12.52). One then arrives at the goal focusing problem spelled out by the data box below.

	x_1	x_2	g_1^+	g_5^+	g_1^-	g_5^-	
p	1	1					≥ 1.20
s_1	1						≤ 1.00
s_2		1					≤ 0.40
t_1	10	6	-1		$+1$		$= 11$
t_2		0.01		-1		$+1$	$= 0.0025$
	20.68	12.52	111	999	0	0	

The unit penalties of 111 and 999 have been used to indicate the relative priorities of the two goals formulated (there is no penalty for use of water or pesticides that falls short of the stated targets). The GAMS program for this model is RESGOAL on page 329.

To see how goals affect the optimal solution, it is instructive first to solve this problem without goals. One simple way to achieve this in the problem formulation is to replace the penalties for goal violation by zeros throughout. Thus, replacing "111" and "999" by zeros in RESGOAL, one finds the optimal solution

$$x_1^* = 0.800, \qquad x_2^* = 0.400.$$

The use of water would then be $10 \times 0.800 + 6 \times 0.400 = 10.4$ and the use of pesticides would be $0.01 \times 0.400 = 0.004$. The use of pesticides is above its goal level.

Next, let us solve the goal-focusing problem as originally formulated in RESGOAL. This time the optimal solution is

$$x_1^* = 0.950, \qquad x_2^* = 0.250, \qquad g_1^{+*} = g_1^{-*} = g_5^{+*} = g_5^{-*} = 0.$$

In order to meet the goals, it turns out that the use of the new high yield cultivation technology must be rolled back from 0.400 to 0.250. The use of water is then $10 \times 0.950 + 6 \times 0.250 = 11.0$ which is the permitted target figure. The use of pesticides is $0.01 \times 0.250 = 0.0025$, i.e., also equal to the desired target.

The duals of the constraints are $p_1^* = 25.25$, $s_1^* = s_2^* = 0$, $t_1^* = -0.457$, $t_2^* = -999$, respectively.

One way to implement the goal focusing optimal solution would be for government to introduce a system of Pigou taxes placed on the use of sensitive inputs. The rice growers would pay a tax = 0.457 for each hundred gallon month of irrigation water, and a tax = 999 for each ton of pesticides used. These taxes are in addition to the regular market prices (1.50 and 20, respectively) quoted for these goods. With these taxes, the rice growers would break exactly even, while operating each activity. The unit profit from low yield farming is apparent from the tabulation below

Market price of rice	25.25
Unit costs:	
cash costs of inputs	20.68
Pigou tax to be paid on use of water $0.457 \times 10 =$	4.57
Total unit costs	25.25

and the unit profit from high yield farming can be inferred from the calculation

Market price of rice	25.25
Unit costs:	
cash costs of inputs	12.52
Pigou tax to be paid on use of water $0.457 \times 6 =$	2.74
Pigou tax to be paid on use of pesticides $999 \times 0.01 =$	9.99
Total unit costs	25.25

In this numerical example it was possible to satisfy both targets exactly. In retrospect we realize that it would have been possible to replace the "soft" constraints of goal focusing by hard constraints, simply requiring the use of water and pesticides to fall below the stipulated target figures.

But if the target figures are lowered, it may no longer be possible to satisfy the given demand without incurring penalties. To see this, the reader is invited to recompute the solution for the case when the target use of water is just 9 hundreds of millions of gallon months and the target figure of pesticides is just 1600 tons.

Reining in Price-Responsive Resource Supply: Nonlinear Goal Programming

In the present chapter we have discussed how the free market system sometimes leads to an excessive use of scarce or non-renewable resources. To the casual observer, this might perhaps sound surprising because one might think that as a resource becomes more scarce, its price would rise. Potential users would then look for cheaper substitutes. For instance, when the price of silver rose threefold during the bull market in silver at the end of the 1970's, the photographic industry, which is a large user of silver, started to look for novel electronic processes which would not require silver compounds in the manufacture of film.

The examples of air pollution and water pollution that we have mentioned show that this mechanism does not always work. The reason is that the ownership of air and water is usually not defined. When no ownership exists, the resource is a "free" commodity with the nominal price equal to (or close to) zero.

We now turn to another category of resources which do have a market and a market-determined price. Responding to a conventional "law of supply," the supply of the resource may even become more plentiful at a higher price. And yet, society may have serious concerns about the depletion of the resource. Consider the case of the rapid destruction of the tropical rain forests of the southern hemisphere. Land usually does have ownership, and tracts of land located in a rain forest can be bought and sold by private parties. High land prices accelerate the deforestation of such tracts and their conversion to agricultural land (for the cultivation of crops or for cattle ranching), for road construction, or for the development of urban residential areas.

The negative externalities that eventually appear include the lowering of the water table, erosion, climatic changes and the expansion of the deserts. But the costs of such negative externalities are not assigned to those who caused them.

We now show how the technique of goal programming can be employed to formulate an optimal plan for the husbanding of scarce resources the supply of which responds positively to price.

To make our ideas specific, consider an industry using two different activities to convert three resources into two consumer goods. The supply of each resource is price-sensitive; let the supply price of resource i be

$$p_i(w_i) = \gamma_i + \delta_i w_i, \qquad \text{for } i = 1, 2, 3 \tag{15.9}$$

where w_i is the quantity of resource i supplied.

Use the letter x_j to denote the level of operation of activity j, to be determined. The matrix of unit input requirements is

$$A = \begin{bmatrix} a_{11} & a_{12} \\ a_{21} & a_{22} \\ a_{31} & a_{32} \end{bmatrix}$$

and the matrix of output coefficients is

$$B = \begin{bmatrix} b_{11} & b_{12} \\ b_{21} & b_{22} \end{bmatrix}$$

The industry faces a given and known demand d_k for each output $k = 1,2$.

Proceeding as before, let us now set a quantitative target or goal g_i for the use of resource i, and let g_i^- and g_i^+ be the deficiency and excess usages. Then we will have

$$w_i - g_i^+ + g_i^- = g_i \qquad \text{for } i = 1, 2, 3 \tag{15.10}$$

Penalties can be attached to either or both under-utilization and over-utilization of the resources. In the present application, a penalty will be levied only in the case of over-utilization (exploitation) of a resource. The relative magnitude of such penalties will mirror the relative importance of the various goals, as conceived by the planner. For instance, we may regard the goal attached to the *first* resource to have the highest priority, and the two goals attached to the *second* and *third* resource as being less urgent but at about equal importance. We may then use the numerical figures $M_1 = 9999$, $M_2 = M_3 = 999$ as the unit penalties.

In order to state the nonlinear goal programming problem we first integrate the price functions (15.9) to obtain the nonlinear function f

$$f_i(w_i) = \int p_i(w_i)dw_i = \gamma_i w_i + 0.5\delta_i w_i^2 \tag{15.11}$$

(A constant of integration has been suppressed.) The goal program is now

$$\text{Minimize} \quad f_1(w_1) + f_2(w_2) + f_3(w_3) + 9999g_1^+ + 999g_2^+ + 999g_3^+ \tag{15.12}$$

$$\begin{aligned} \text{Subject to} \qquad b_{11}x_1 + b_{12}x_2 &\geq d_1 \\ b_{21}x_1 + b_{22}x_2 &\geq d_2 \\ a_{11}x_1 + a_{12}x_2 - w_1 &\leq 0 \\ a_{21}x_1 + a_{22}x_2 - w_2 &\leq 0 \\ a_{31}x_1 + a_{32}x_2 - w_3 &\leq 0 \\ w_1 - g_1^+ &= g_1 \\ w_2 - g_2^+ &= g_2 \\ w_3 - g_3^+ &= g_3 \\ x_1, x_2, w_1, w_2, w_3, g_1^+, g_2^+, g_3^+ &\geq 0 \end{aligned}$$

Example 2. In a certain county strip mining is permitted in two regions. The coal is transported by rail to two large electric utilities 1 and 2 where it is used to generate electricity. The demand for coal by the utilities is 3,200 tons and 2,400 tons, respectively. Marginal costs are $100 + 20w_1$ when strip-mining w_1 tons in region 1 and $60 + 26w_2$ when mining w_2 tons in region 2. The distances from regions 1 and 2 to the utilities 1 and 2, and the demands there are:

	Utility 1	*Utility 2*
Region 1	400 miles	300 miles
Region 2	200 miles	250 miles
Demand	3,200 tons	2,400 tons

The unit railway charges are \$0.1 per ton-mile.

There is environmental concern about the effects of strip mining in each region. Region 1 is considered to be the most sensitive, and a goal has been set of 2,000 tons to be mined and the penalty for violating the goal is 9999. In region 2 the goal is 4,500 tons, and the violation penalty is set at 999. Let w_i be the quantity of coal produced in region i and let x_{ij} be the quantity of coal shipped from region i to utility j. Also define the nonlinear functions

$$\begin{aligned} f_1(w_1) &= 100w_1 + 10w_1^2 \\ f_2(w_2) &= 60w_2 + 13w_2^2 \end{aligned} \qquad (15.13)$$

obtained by integrating the marginal cost functions for mining in each region.

The data box for the nonlinear goal programming model of the problem appears below. The objective is minimization.

x_{11}	x_{12}	x_{21}	x_{22}	w_1	w_2	g_1^+	g_2^+	
1	1			−1				≤ 0
		1	1		−1			≤ 0
1		1						$\geq 3{,}200$
	1		1					$\geq 2{,}400$
				1		−1		$= 2{,}000$
					1		−1	$= 4{,}500$
40	30	20	25	$f_1'(w_1^*)$	$f_2'(w_2^*)$	9999	999	

The GAMS program to solve the data box is STRIPMINE on page 330.

Exercises

1. A city runs several facilities for the disposal of household waste. Two methods are used: incineration and landfill. The cost of operations are as follows:

	man hours required per unit of waste	*capital hours required per unit of waste*
incineration	0.4	1.0
landfill	0.2	2.0

The cost of a man hour is \$3.00; the cost of a capital hour is \$0.40.

The total amount of waste that needs to be processed each week is 1,400 truckloads.

Both incineration and landfill create environmental problems. The city has formulated the following targets:

(a) *Incineration*. Each unit of waste incinerated releases 20 grams of pollutants into the air. The city would like the total release not to exceed 15,000 grams per week.

(b) *Landfill*. The total acreage that can be used for landfill is limited, and it is desired that the total volume of household waste dumped in the landfills should not exceed 600 units per week.

Formulate a goal programming model that can be used to determine the optimal level of operation of the incineration plants and the landfills. Discuss two alternatives: (i) The goal of air pollution is considered more important than the goal on the utilization of land; the model-builder will therefore use unit penalties for exceeding the two target figures equal to 999 and 777, respectively. (ii) The goal on the utilization of land is the more important one; the unit penalties to be used are 777 and 999, respectively.

2. Nuclear waste is transported from two nuclear power plants A and B to two waste dumps, E and F. The transportation is by truck. The road system is mainly through sparsely populated regions, but passes through two towns C and D. The distances are as follows:

(A,C)	200 miles	(A,D)	250 miles
(B,C)	300 miles	(B,D)	280 miles
(C,E)	200 miles	(C,F)	300 miles
(D,E)	220 miles	(D,F)	320 miles

The transportation cost is \$0.02 per ton of nuclear waste transported one mile.

The volume of waste that needs to be disposed of is 600 tons per week at A and 400 tons at B. The maximum receiving capacity at the dump E is 300 tons per week, and 1200 tons per week at F.

The inhabitants in the two towns C and D are concerned about the hazards involved, and a planning commission has formulated the following recommended targets:

total nuclear waste passing town C each week: 350 tons
total nuclear waste passing town D each week: 550 tons

There is a large hospital in town C and several schools and the planning commission considers the target for town C must take precedence over the target for town D. Formulate a goal focusing model what would solve for the optimal routing of nuclear waste. Define dual variables. Write down the dual program and interpret it. Is it possible to design a system of road tolls that could be used to implement the optimal solution?

3. Scottish trawlers fish for cod in three regions in the North Sea, $i = 1, 2, 3$. The catch is brought to four ports, $u = 1, 2, 3, 4$. The quantities demanded at the ports are 4, 3, 5, and 4 thousand pounds, respectively.

The catch in each region is denoted by s_j, $i = 1, 2, 3$. By the use of modern gear, it is expected that it would be technically feasible to catch quantities up to 5, 8, and 14 thousand pounds in the three regions, respectively. However, there is much concern about the possible overfishing and the depletion of the stock of fish. An environmental study has been conducted, recommending that the catch in the regions be limited to 4, 8, and 12 thousand pounds, respectively. The first region, $i = 1$, is supposed to be the most sensitive and the first priority must be to meet the goal in this region. The second region, $i = 2$, is somewhat less sensitive, and the goal in the third region $i = 3$ has the lowest priority.

The unit costs (in pound sterling per thousand pounds) of catching fish and bringing it to port are displayed in the table below:

	Port			
Region	$j = 1$	$j = 2$	$j = 3$	$j = 4$
$i = 1$	0.30	0.30	0.15	0.70
$i = 2$	0.10	0.15	0.05	0.40
$i = 3$	0.40	0.40	0.20	0.70

Formulate a goal programming model that will solve for the optimal catch in each region and the optimal routes of transportation from regions to ports. Write the data box. Define dual variables and interpret them. Write the corresponding dual program.

Solution on a computer shows that the optimal catches are $s_1^* = 4$, $s_2^* = 8$, $s_3^* = 4$, respectively. (The goals at regions $i = 1, 2$ are filled, but two thousand pounds above the goal will be caught in region $i = 3$.) The optimal quantities transported from fishing regions to ports (denoted by x_{ij}, $i = 1, 2, 3$ and $j = 1, 2, 3, 4$) are $x_{11}^* = 3$, $x_{13}^* = 1$, $x_{21}^* = 21$, $x_{22}^* = 3$, $x_{24}^* = 4$, $x_{33}^* = 4$. Determine the optimal values of all dual variables. Write down all relations of complementary slackness and check that they are satisfied.

4. Solve the problem whose data box appears on page 197 using the GAMS program `STRIPMINE` on page 330. Interpret the solutions.

16

The Planning of Industrial Investment Programs

Chapter 11 covered capital budgeting, which deals with the situation of a single manager who must choose an optimal bundle of investment "projects" which satisfy constraints on the resulting cash flows now and in future periods. Each project was characterized by a flow of payments (costs) and receipts (revenues) over time.

How can a manager gauge the expected flow of revenue that would result from a particular investment project if carried out? This flow is not really exogeneous at all. Those future revenues depend upon future production decisions. There is no guarantee that productive capacity, once installed, will be fully utilized at all times. Firms typically operate many production activities and produce many outputs. They may make investments which could increase the productive capacity of one or several activities. A farmer may buy a combine for harvesting his wheat, or an automated cotton picker for harvesting his cotton. There is no certain flow of returns from either of these two investment decisions. The actual returns will depend upon the acreages that are allocated to growing wheat and cotton, now and in the future.

Nevertheless, many managers no doubt have a pretty good idea of how a particular project is going to fit into the greater scheme of things. Simple capital budgeting analysis, based on the assumption of a given time flows of receipts, is perfectly valid if the employment of the new productive capacity and future production plans is assumed to be known. But turning, as we shall now, to the investment decisions in an entire industry, it is clear that the employment of newly installed capacity will typically be part and parcel of the evaluation of these decisions.

For one thing, investment decisions and production decisions are often made by different individuals. A developer may decide to build a new shopping mall. Retailers then make decisions whether they want to locate in the mall. A hospital may install some expensive electronic imaging technology. Doctors then decide which patients, if any, should be sent there.

For another thing, investment in infrastructure such as electric power generation, agricultural irrigation, and commuter passenger trains, are typically made by public or publicly controlled authorities. The administrators of such bodies may have very vague ideas of how the investment will eventually be put into productive use.

The World Bank regularly sends groups of economists to developing countries to judge the credit worthiness of proposed development projects. To assist such evaluation, the Bank has promoted the mathematical modeling of industrial investment programs. For instance, the Bank has conducted studies of the fertilizer industry in Kenya, Uganda and Tanzania. Economists directly or indirectly associated with the Bank have modeled the mechanical engineering industry in Korea, the timber industry in Turkey and in West African countries, and the electric power industry in India. The present chapter surveys the mathematical methods employed for such industrial investment planning.

A key concept in investment planning is "productive capacity." Investment is undertaken in order to expand productive capacity. At any given point in time, productive capacity is limited by the existing productive facilities—machinery, equipment, and plants. For instance, an automobile manufacturer is able to turn out at most 1,000 cars a week from a particular assembly line, or an aluminum smelter can pour at most 1,000 tons of aluminum ingots a day.

We have already in Chapter 13 defined the capacity limit X_j of productive activity $j = 1, \ldots, n$ as the upper limit on the possible level of operation of the activity:

$$x_j \leq X_j, \qquad j = 1, \ldots, n. \tag{16.1}$$

The purpose of investment is to construct additional productive capacity, say ΔX_j, so that the constraints (16.1) are replaced by

$$x_j \leq X_j + \Delta X_j, \qquad j = 1, \ldots, n. \tag{16.2}$$

As already stated, the installation of new capacity entails flows over time of costs and revenues. The time flow of revenues depends upon intertemporal production decisions, however the costs of construction are certain to be incurred. We first discuss costs.

The Cost of Capacity Expansion

To build new productive capacity, a firm may incur many kinds of costs, such as costs for research and development, and retraining of labor. But the large cost items are those of buying or constructing new equipment, machinery, and plant, that is, new real capital.

The word "capital" is a tricky word. Karl Marx wrote a large treatise on the subject, and so have many other economists, both before and after him. Capital can mean at least three different things: (i) a collection of durable means of production, like machinery and plants; (ii) the monetary value of such items; (iii) the ownership to these means of production.

The value of capital can be calculated from the cost side, as the cost actually sunk into its construction and acquisition. That is the way we are going to do it now. Sometimes

Figure 16.1

Schedule depicting the cost of capacity expansion.

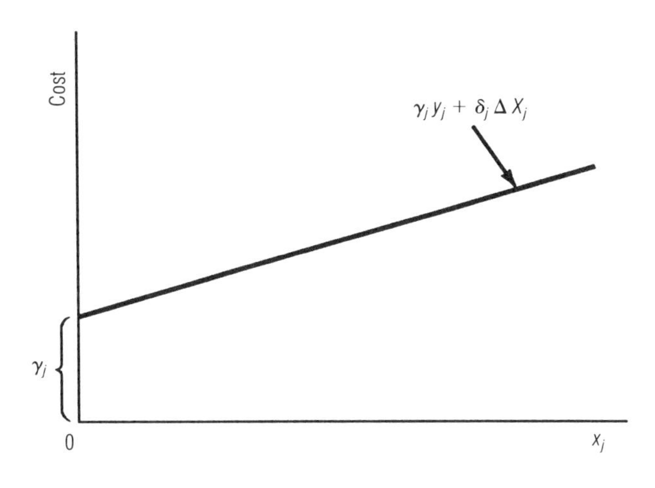

it has also been proposed to calculate the value of capital from the revenue side, as the present value of a future stream of revenues. But, as explained previously, that begs the question of how the capital is actually going to be employed in future production decisions.

Figure 16.1 shows a schedule relating installation costs to installed additional productive capacity ΔX_j (capacity to operate activity j). The schedule illustrates the presence of both fixed costs, the intercept γ_j, and variable costs, the quantity $\delta_j \Delta X_j$. Mathematically, total installation costs are given by the equation

$$\gamma_j y_j + \delta_j \Delta X_j \tag{16.3}$$

where, as stated,

γ_j = fixed-charge portion of capacity costs

δ_j = slope of linear portion of capacity expansion cost function

and

y_j = a binary variable, equal to 0 if $\Delta X_j = 0$ but equal to 1 if $\Delta X_j > 0$.

The schedule has a discontinuity at the origin. If no new capacity is added, the cost is zero. If any positive amount of new capacity is added, the entire fixed charge γ_j must be paid (as well as variable costs).

In order to express mathematically the role of a binary variable y_j, we adjoin to the schedule (16.3) the condition

$$\Delta X_j < N_j y_j \tag{16.4}$$

where N_j is the maximum amount of incremental capacity increase that is possible. (Just as there are upper limits to current production, there are also upper limits to investment in new capacity. For instance, while the current operations of an airline are limited by the number of aircraft already on hand, the number of new planes that the airline may add to its fleet in any one time period is limited by the capacity of the aircraft manufacturer.) Inspecting (16.4), we see that if y_j equals unity, then ΔX_j is free to assume its maximum value. But if y_j equals zero, (16.4) forces ΔX_j to equal zero as well.

The fixed cost γ_j reflects costs that will be incurred regardless of the size of the capacity expansion. Examples are R&D costs, expenditures incurred in buying patents, the acquisition of land for the construction of new plant—in fact, all cost elements that cannot be directly associated with the scale of operation of the activity. The presence of such fixed costs leads to *economies of scale* which exist whenever the average costs

$$(\gamma_j y_j + \delta_j \Delta X_j)/\Delta X_j \tag{16.5}$$

fall when productive capacity is expanded. (Consider a point on the schedule Figure 16.1. Draw a ray from the origin to the point. The slope of that ray measures the average costs (16.5). As the point travels to the right in the diagram, the slope of the ray decreases.)

The presence of strong economies of scale in an industry tends to lead to a concentration of large firms. Small firms have difficulties surviving. Modern biotechnology firms provide an example. Very large research and development costs have caused a shake-out in the biotechnology industry, and only the largest companies have the resources that it takes to pursue the race to develop and test new genetically engineered drugs.

We now need to introduce time explicitly by dividing the planning time span into successive time periods $t = 1, \ldots, T$. Using subscripts indicating the current time period, the installation costs (16.3) should then be written

$$\gamma_j y_{tj} + \delta_j \Delta X_{tj}, \qquad t = 1, \ldots, T \tag{16.6}$$

where y_{tj} is a binary variable, and ΔX_{tj} satisfies

$$\Delta X_{tj} \leq N_j y_{tj}, \qquad t = 1, \ldots, T \tag{16.7}$$

where N_j is the maximum amount of capacity increase that is possible in any one period. The expressions (16.6) give the time flows of actual cash disbursements.

Next, it is necessary to *periodize* these disbursements, that is, to spread the costs of expanded capacity over its useful economic life.

Obviously, what is needed is some kind of discounting formula that achieves what is desired. We have already earlier (in Chapter 11) learned how to calculate the net present value (NPV). Here we need a discounting technique, involving the use of the *capital recovery factor* (CRF). It is defined to be the rental value on the capital sunk in an investment project. More specifically, the capital recovery factor is defined to be the factor that converts the capital costs associated with a given investment project into an even stream of payments which are sufficient to repay the original capital costs plus interest charges during the expected life time of the project. We shall denote the capital recovery factor by the Greek letter σ, where $0 \leq \sigma \leq 1$.

If there were no interest charges, the capital recovery factor would simply equal the reciprocal of the expected useful life time of the project. Consider an example: A manager installs some machinery at the beginning of year 1, at the cost of \$50,000. The expected life time of the equipment is four years. The capital recovery factor is then 0.25.

The presence of interest charges makes the calculation slightly more complicated. Let the discount rate be 10% annually. The total sum of all cost charges calculated over four years and discounted to the end of the expected life span of the equipment is then $\sigma \times 50{,}000(1.1^3 + 1.1^2 + 1.1 + 1)$ which should equal the value of the initial outlay discounted to the same point in time, viz. $1.1^4 \times 50{,}000$. Solving for σ gives

$$\sigma = 1.1^4/(1.1^3 + 1.1^2 + 1.1 + 1) = 0.315.$$

More generally, assume that the initial investment outlay is K dollars and let the investment project have an expected life of L years. The interest rate is $100r$ per cent. The total sum of all cost charges accumulating during the course of the project, and calculated at the end of year L is then

$$\sigma K[(1 + r)^{L-1} + (1 + r)^{L-2} + \ldots + (1 + r) + 1]$$

which should exhaust the value of the outlay at this time, $(1 + r)^L K$. One then has

$$\sigma = (1 + r)^L/[(1 + r)^{L-1} + (1 + r)^{L-2} + \ldots + (1 + r) + 1]$$

or, summing the geometric series in the denominator and simplifying

$$\sigma = r/[1 - (1 + r)^{-L}]. \tag{16.8}$$

The periodized capital charges in period t are obtained by *cumulating* the charges arising from capacity expansion in all earlier periods τ including the current one, $\tau = 1, \ldots, t$:

$$\sum_{\tau=1}^{t} \sigma(\gamma_j y_{\tau j} + \delta_j \Delta X_{\tau j}). \tag{16.9}$$

This formula holds for each activity j.

Total capital charges arising over the entire planning span, for all activities, and discounted to the present, are then obtained as

$$\sum_{t=1}^{T} \left[\sum_{\tau=1}^{\tau} \sum_{j=1}^{n} \sigma(\gamma_j y_{\tau j} + \delta_j \Delta X_{\tau j}) \right] \Big/ (1 + r)^t. \tag{16.10}$$

An Intertemporal Programming Model of Capacity Expansion

We outline a programming model that solves simultaneously for the optimal capacity expansion and optimal production in each time period of the planning span. As we shall see, the result is a mixed integer programming model with binary variables.

The notation is

$i = 1, \ldots, m$	is the index of the inputs, m the largest index.
$j = 1, \ldots, r$	is the index of the activities, n the largest index.
$k = 1, \ldots, r$	is the index of the outputs, r the largest index.
$t, \tau = 1, \ldots, T$	are indices of time periods, T the horizon.
$x_t = (x_{t1}, \ldots, x_{tn})$	is the (column) vector of (unknown) activity levels planned for period t.

$X_t = (X_{t1}, \ldots, X_{tn})$	is the (column) vector of (known) capacity levels holding in period t.
$d_t = (d_{t1}, \ldots, d_{tn})$	is the (column) vector of (known) consumer demands in period t.
$q_t = (q_{t1}, \ldots, q_{tm})$	is the (row) vector of (known) input prices in period t.
$A = \|a_{ij}\|$	is the $m \times n$ matrix of input coefficients, where a_{ij} is the quantity of input i required when activity j is operated at unit level.
$B = \|b_{kj}\|$	is the $r \times n$ matrix of output coefficients, where b_{kj} is the quantity of output k produced when activity j is operated at unit level.

The starting point is the following intertemporal industry model *without* capacity expansion:

$$\begin{aligned} \text{Minimize} \quad & \sum_{t=1}^{T} q_t A x_t/(1+r)^t \\ \text{Subject to} \quad & B x_t \geq d_t \\ & x_t \leq X_t \\ & x_t \geq 0, \qquad t = 1, \ldots, T \end{aligned} \tag{16.11}$$

Program (16.11) is a straight-forward intertemporal generalization of the basic industry model discussed in Chapter 13. The program minimizes total discounted input costs accumulating over the entire planning span, subject to the conditions that final demand in each period be met, and that no activity can ever be operated beyond its current capacity limit.

The input coefficients a_{ij} and output coefficients b_{kj} are assumed to remain constant over time. This can always formally be accomplished by adopting the convention that any change of technology over time can be treated as the introduction of a new and separate technology.

Notice that program (16.11) can be broken up into T separate programs, one for each time period. (In terms of the decentralization theory discussed in Chapter 7, the "master" program (16.11) is "completely decomposable." There are no constraints tying individual divisions together.) Each such separate program is a simple industry model for a single time period. So, the solution of (16.11) actually becomes the solution of a succession of single time period problems.

Now we are set to deal with the possibility of added productive capacity. The capacity constraints in (16.11) are amended to permit capacity expansion in each time period, and the minimand will then consist of the present value of both current input costs and capital expansion costs. The resulting program is (using vector notation throughout):

$$\begin{aligned} \text{Minimize} \quad & \sum_{t=1}^{T} q_t A x_t/(1+r)^t \\ & + \sum_{t=1}^{T} \left[\sum_{\tau=1}^{t} \sigma(\gamma y_\tau + \delta \Delta X_\tau) \right] \Big/ (1+r)^t \end{aligned} \tag{16.12}$$

$$
\begin{aligned}
\text{Subject to} \quad & Bx_t \geq d_t, && t = 1, \ldots, T \\
& x_t - \sum_{\tau=1}^{t} \Delta X_\tau \leq X_0, && t = 1, \ldots, T \\
& \Delta X_t - N y_t \leq 0, && t = 1, \ldots, T \\
& x_t, \Delta X_t \geq 0, && t = 1, \ldots, T \\
& y_{tj} = 0 \text{ or } 1, && j = 1, \ldots, n, \quad t = 1, \ldots, T
\end{aligned}
$$

where the initial capacity on hand at the beginning of the first period has been denoted X_0 and N is a vector of upper limits.

Before turning to the numerical examples, consider the same mathematical program (16.12) for the particular case when it happens that all optimal activity levels x_t^*, $t = 1, \ldots, T$ are already known. Then (16.12) becomes

$$
\text{Minimize} \quad \sum_{t=1}^{T} \left[\sum_{\tau=1}^{t} \sigma(\gamma y_\tau + \delta \Delta X_\tau) \right] \Big/ (1 + r)^t \tag{16.13}
$$

$$
\begin{aligned}
\text{Subject to} \quad & \sum_{\tau=1}^{t} \Delta X_\tau \geq x_t^* - X_0, && t = 1, \ldots, T \\
& \Delta X_t - N y_t \leq 0, && t = 1, \ldots, T \\
& \Delta X_t \geq 0, && t = 1, \ldots, T \\
& y_{tj} = 0 \text{ or } 1, && j = 1, \ldots, n, \quad t = 1, \ldots, T
\end{aligned}
$$

which is a capital budgeting problem of the same type that was treated in Chapter 11.

Example 1. Returning to the farming economy discussed in the text in Chapter 13, involving the cultivation of corn and wheat, and where the productive processes were constrained by the availability of arable land as

$$
X_0 = \begin{bmatrix} 600 \text{ corn acres} \\ 1500 \text{ wheat acres} \end{bmatrix}
$$

we shall now allow for the possibility that the farmers may put more land under the plough by razing tropical rain forest. As we shall see, there may exist powerful market incentives for farmers to act in this manner.

The costs of capacity expansion include the purchase of forest land, the burning of trees and underbrush, and cultivation by using heavy machinery. Let these costs in each year t, $t = 1, 2, 3$ be given by the cost function

$$
40{,}000 y_{tj} + 100 \Delta X_{tj}.
$$

The parameters of the cost function do not depend upon the intended use of the land, whether it be for growing corn $j = 1$ or for growing wheat $j = 2$. The fixed cost is \$40,000, which may reflect the costs of the purchase of land and machinery and erecting temporary living quarters for work crews, building access roads etc. The fixed cost in year t is incurred only if land is cleared in that period ($y_{tj} = 1$, $j = 1,2$). There is no fixed charge if no additional land is cleared ($y_{tj} = 0$, $j = 1,2$). The variable cost is \$100 per acre of land cleared, whether destined for the cultivation of corn or of wheat. Available resources permit no more than 1,000 acres of new land to be cleared in any one time period.

In order to provide the desired optimizaton formulation, we first note that the purpose of the binary variables y_{tj} is to see to it that the constraints

$$\Delta X_{tj} \leq 1000 y_{tj}$$

are satisfied.

Next we evaluate the capital recovery factor. Assume that the discount rate is 10% and that the expected life of the land clearing project is 10 years (hopefully, the current senseless destruction of tropical rain forest will eventually be brought to a halt, and many tracts of tropical rain forest eventually be restored). Inserting into the formula (16.8), one finds

$$\sigma = 0.1/(1 - 1.1^{-10}) = 0.1627.$$

In words, the rental cost of capital invested in land clearing is 16.27% per year.

The market prices of resources (land, fertilizer, machinery) are assumed to remain constant over time, viz.

$$q_t = (\$25/\text{acre}, \$95/\text{ton}, \$500/\text{day}), \qquad t = 1, 2, 3.$$

The matrices of input requirements (A) and of unit outputs (B) also remain unchanged over time; here, too, we shall use the same data as in Chapter 13.

On the consumer demand side, however, we need to make some slight adjustments of the assumptions. Land clearing and the expansion of capacity is ultimately driven by a growing consumer demand. Assume that the expected demand in the three planning periods is

	year 1	*year 2*	*year 3*
corn	50,000	80,000	100,000
wheat	120,000	200,000	275,000

Demand in the first year is the same as before. It is expected to grow quickly from there on.

The weights of the minimand appearing in program (16.12) are calculated below:

unknown	*coefficient*
x_{11}	$512.5/1.1 = 465.9$
x_{12}	$491.3/1.1 = 446.6$
x_{21}	$512.5/1.1^2 = 423.5$
x_{22}	$491.3/1.1^2 = 406.0$
x_{31}	$512.5/1.1^3 = 385.0$
x_{32}	$491.3/1.1^3 = 369.1$
y_{11}, y_{12}	$0.1627 \times 40000(1/1.1 + 1/1.1^2 + 1/1.1^3) = 16190$
y_{21}, y_{22}	$0.1627 \times 40000(1/1.1^2 + 1/1.1^3) = 10270$
y_{31}, y_{32}	$0.1627 \times 40000/1.1^3 = 4891$
$\Delta X_{11}, \Delta X_{12}$	$0.1627 \times 100\ (1/1.1 + 1/1.1^2 + 1/1.1^3) = 40.47$
$\Delta X_{21}, \Delta X_{22}$	$0.1627 \times 100\ (1/1.1^2 + 1/1.1^3) = 25.68$
$\Delta X_{31}, \Delta X_{32}$	$0.1627 \times 100/1.1^3 = 12.23$

(Here and elsewhere, the results of computations are rounded off to four figures.)

The data box is displayed below with the weights calculated above entered in the bottom row.

x_{11}	x_{12}	x_{21}	x_{22}	x_{31}	x_{32}	y_{11}	y_{12}	y_{21}	y_{22}	y_{31}	y_{32}	ΔX_{11}	ΔX_{12}	ΔX_{21}	ΔX_{22}	ΔX_{31}	ΔX_{32}	
120	0																	$\geq$ 50,000
0	85																	$\geq$ 120,000
1	0											−1						$\leq$ 600
0	1												−1					$\leq$ 1,500
		120	0															$\geq$ 80,000
		0	85															$\geq$ 200,000
		1	0									−1		−1				$\leq$ 600
		0	1										−1		−1			$\leq$ 1,500
				120	0													$\geq$ 100,000
				0	85													$\geq$ 275,000
				1	0							−1		−1		−1		$\leq$ 600
				0	1								−1		−1		−1	$\leq$ 1,500
						−1000						1						$\leq$ 0
							−1000						1					$\leq$ 0
								−1000						1				$\leq$ 0
									−1000						1			$\leq$ 0
										−1000						1		$\leq$ 0
											−1000						1	$\leq$ 0
465.9	446.6	423.5	406.0	385.0	369.1	16190	16190	10270	10270	4891	4891	40.47	40.47	25.68	25.68	12.23	12.23	

To solve this problem we solve the GAMS program NEWLAND on page 331. The unknown y variables all have to be specified as binary (0–1 variables).

The optimal solution is exhibited below.

		year $t = 1$	*year* $t = 2$	*year* $t = 3$
corn	actual level of operation x_{t1}	416.7	666.7	833.3
	capacity X_{t1}	600	666.7	833.3
wheat	actual level of operation x_{t1}	1412	2353	3235
	capacity X_{t2}	1500	2353	3253

Entries show acres actually cultivated, and potentially available after land development.

In order to meet the expanded demand for corn, 66.7 acres of new corn land have to be cleared in year 2, and an additional 166.7 acres in year 3. As to wheat, there is a need to clear 853 acres of new wheat land in year 2, and 882 more acres in year 3. This annual razing of tropical rain forest is always within the capacity bound (1,000 new acres per year for any crop).

Example 2. The numerical problem we have looked at should introduce you to the mechanics of writing an investment model. But to see how the investment calculus actually comes into play, we need to change the assumptions slightly. You will notice that there are no independent investment decisions in Example 1. The demand constraint in each time period forces output to cover demand.

Output and capacity therefore are uniquely governed by demand, and the required investment in new capacity must be undertaken regardless of cost.

While retaining the assumption of a fixed and given demand in year 1 (a vertical demand curve), assume now that any quantity of produce can be sold in the market in the two subsequent years as long as it is priced competitively (horizontal demand curves). Specifically, let the market prices of produce be (in dollars per bushel)

	year 2	*year 3*
corn	4.30	4.50
wheat	5.90	7.00

The problem at hand then becomes converted into a profit maximization problem, maximizing the difference between the discounted stream of revenues and the discounted stream of costs. The weights of the maximand are calculated below:

unknown	*coefficient*
x_{11}	$-512.5/1.1 = -465.9$
x_{12}	$-491.3/1.1 = -446.6$
x_{21}	$4.30 \times 120/1.1^2 - 512.5/1.1^2 = 2.893$
x_{22}	$5.90 \times 85/1.1^2 - 491.3/1.1^2 = 8.471$
x_{31}	$4.50 \times 120/1.1^3 - 512.5/1.1^3 = 20.66$
x_{32}	$7.00 \times 85/1.1^3 - 491.3/1.1^3 = 77.95$
y_{11}, y_{12}	$-0.1627 \times 40000(1/1.1 + 1/1.1^2 + 1/1.1^3) = -16190$
y_{21}, y_{22}	$-0.1627 \times 40000(1/1.1^2 + 1/1.1^3) = -10270$
y_{31}, y_{32}	$-0.1627 \times 40000/1.1^3 = -4891$
$\Delta X_{11}, \Delta X_{12}$	$-0.1627 \times 100\ (1/1.1 + 1/1.1^2 + 1/1.1^3) = -40.47$
$\Delta X_{21}, \Delta X_{22}$	$-0.1627 \times 100\ (1/1.1^2 + 1/1.1^3) = -25.68$
$\Delta X_{31}, \Delta X_{32}$	$-0.1627 \times 100\ /1.1^3 = -12.23$

The data box is displayed below.

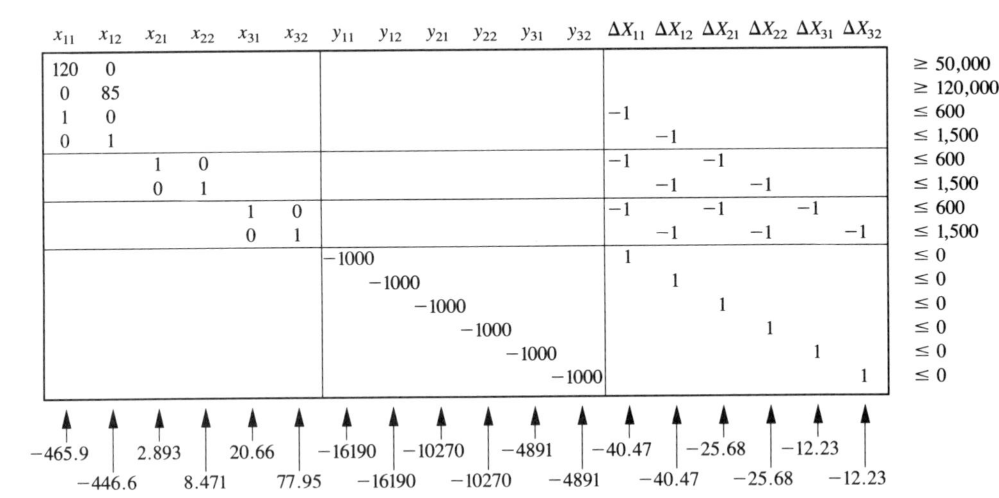

x_{11}	x_{12}	x_{21}	x_{22}	x_{31}	x_{32}	y_{11}	y_{12}	y_{21}	y_{22}	y_{31}	y_{32}	ΔX_{11}	ΔX_{12}	ΔX_{21}	ΔX_{22}	ΔX_{31}	ΔX_{32}	
120	0																	≥ 50,000
0	85																	≥ 120,000
1	0											−1						≤ 600
0	1												−1					≤ 1,500
		1	0									−1		−1				≤ 600
		0	1										−1		−1			≤ 1,500
				1	0							−1		−1		−1		≤ 600
				0	1								−1		−1		−1	≤ 1,500
						−1000						1						≤ 0
							−1000						1					≤ 0
								−1000						1				≤ 0
									−1000						1			≤ 0
										−1000						1		≤ 0
											−1000						1	≤ 0
−465.9	−446.6	2.893	8.471	20.66	77.95	−16190	−16190	−10270	−10270	−4891	−4891	−40.47	−40.47	−25.68	−25.68	−12.23	−12.23	

Now look at the optimal solution, displayed below.

		year $t = 1$	*year* $t = 2$	*year* $t = 3$
corn	actual level of operation x_{t1}	416.7	600.0	1600.0
	capacity X_{t1}	600	600.0	1600.00
wheat	actual level of operation x_{t1}	1412	3500	4500
	capacity X_{t2}	2500	3500	4500

The current production in year 1 is the same as before, of course, because of the requirement to cover current demand. But in addition, in that very first period, the farmers start a feverish razing of tropical rain forest, clearing the maximum amount of 1,000 acres of wheatland. Why? Not in order to build capacity that is going to be used right away. There is sufficient initial capacity on hand already (1500 acres) to permit the optimal level of cultivaton of wheat in year 1 (1412 acres). The added capacity is earmarked for expanded cultivation *in the future*, that is, in years 2 and 3. It is the farmer's expectation of high future prices that drives their current investment decisions.

Exercises

1. Show that if the life of an investment project is infinite, i.e., $L = +\infty$, then the capital recovery factor equals the rate of interest, that is $\sigma = r$.

2. Perform numerical experiments to investigate how the optimal solution to Example 1 in the main text depends upon the discount rate. What happens if the rate is changed from 10% to 12%? If it is lowered to 7%?

3. Discuss how one could develop a goal programming model for restricting the razing of tropical rain forest. Write the programming model and use the Kuhn-Tucker conditions to characterize the nature of the optimal solution obtained.

17

Activity Analysis

Activity analysis was developed by T. Koopmans in 1951. Production is modeled through elementary processes called activities, which we have already met repeatedly in this book. Each activity requires certain inputs and produces certain outputs. The activities are chained together to cover an entire vertical production process ranging from the employment of scarce primary inputs (labor and raw materials) to the manufacture of final outputs. There are vertical supply curves of all primary inputs and horizontal demand curves for all final outputs.

Activity analysis is often assumed to refer to the entire productive sector of a nation's economy. It exhibits the alternative uses of the endowments of natural resources and the alternative baskets of final outputs that can be obtained. Often textbooks allude to these basic decisions by way of an example of "butter versus guns": how and for what purpose should a nation's resources be employed? The dilemma is illustrated by a "production possibility curve" for the entire economy, depicting the alternative combinations of butter and guns that the available resources will sustain. The quantity of butter manufactured is measured along the horizontal axis; the quantity of guns manufactured along the vertical axis. With vertical supply curves of all primary inputs, and linear activities transforming primary goods to intermediate goods and final goods, the production possibility curve (or frontier) can be obtained as a convex polyhedron (explanations and illustrations will be provided later). With fixed and given demand prices for both butter and guns, a price slope is defined in the diagram. The optimal solutions will lie on a corner or along a facet to the polyhedron.

Activity analysis covers a larger part of an economy than does an industry model, because it traces the vertical production chain back to the use of scarce primary inputs. Consider for instance all production chains that lead to the manufacture of an automobile. Following the production chain backwards, the automobile industry is dependent upon deliveries from the steel industry; the steel industry is dependent upon deliveries from the mining industry. Also, the automobile industry is dependent upon deliveries from the tire industry; the tire industry depends upon rubber production (synthetic and natural).

Figure 17.1

Feasible output set is shaded. The efficiency frontier is the solid line $A - B - C - D$. Points E and F are inefficient. Point G is infeasible.

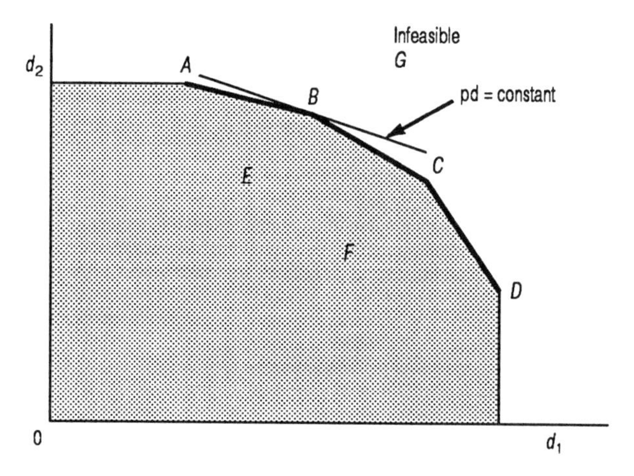

Nowdays, automobiles also contain quite advanced digital computer equipment; the computer industry depends upon the computer chip industry, etc. Each industry along these chains may consider the supply prices of the preceding industries as given and known (as in Chapters 1 and 2). When we reach the initial link of the chain (mining, natural rubber, computer chip knowhow) the supplies are limited by the natural resources of the country.

We model the activities of an economy using the following notation:

$i = 1, \ldots, m$	is the index of the inputs, m is the largest index.
$j = 1, \ldots, n$	is the index of the activities, n the largest.
$k = 1, \ldots, r$	is the index of the outputs, r the largest.
$x = (x_1, \ldots, x_n)$	is the (column) vector of (unknown) activity levels.
$X = (x_1, \ldots, X_n)$	is the (column) vector of (known) activity upper bounds.
$d = (d_1, \ldots, d_r)$	is the (column) vector of (unknown) final demand.
$W = (W_1, \ldots, W_m)$	is the (column) vector of (known) supplies of primary resources.
$p = (p_1, \ldots, p_r)$	is the (row) vector of (adjustable) output prices.
$A = \|a_{ij}\|$	is the $m \times n$ matrix of input coefficients, where a_{ij} is the quantity of input i required when activity j is operated at unit level.
$B = \|b_{kj}\|$	is the $m \times r$ matrix of output coefficients, where b_{kj} is quantity of output k produced when activity j is operated at unit level.

The basic idea of activity analysis is the following: Given the endowment vector W of primary resources and the upper bound vector X on activities, how shall the economy

Figure 17.2

Dominating set for d.

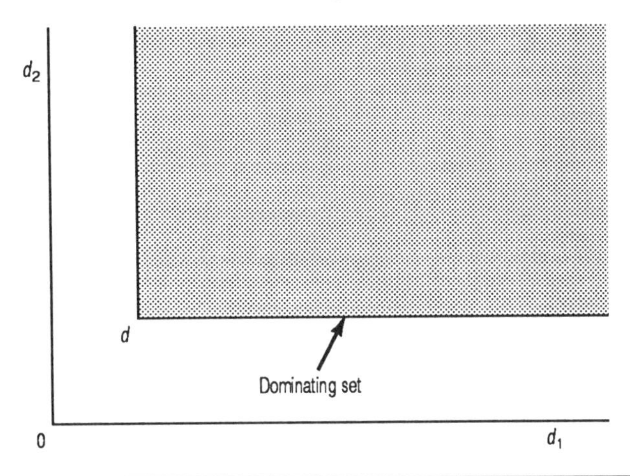

choose to operate its productive activities to maximize the resulting vector of outputs? To answer this question we observe first that the set of feasible combinations of final demand, d, is defined by the following set of constraints:

$$\begin{aligned} d - Bx &\leq 0 \\ Ax &\leq W \\ x &\leq X \\ d, x &\geq 0 \end{aligned} \tag{17.1}$$

The first constraint in (17.1) says that d is constrained by the output vector Bx; the second constraint says that the resources used, Ax, should be at most equal to the available amounts of primary resources; the third constraint restricts vector x to be less than its upper bound vector X; and the fourth constraint requires d and x to be nonnegative.

The solution set of the final outputs d of (17.1) is a polyhedral convex set such as that shown in Figure 17.1. (A convex polyhedral set, i.e., a convex polyhedron, is a convex set spanned by a finite number of points.) This is a two dimensional representation of an m-dimensional space; the horizontal axis could represent "butter" and the vertical axis "guns"—two final goods that both lay their claims on the endowments of primary resources.

A point $d^{(1)}$ is said to *dominate* d if $d_k^{(1)} \geq d_k$ for $k = 1, \ldots, r$, with at least one inequality being strict. The set of all points $d^{(1)}$ that dominate point d is shown geometrically in Figure 17.2. Observe that any point $d^{(1)}$ located to the "north-east" of d is in the dominating set. Since points in the dominating set of d are preferred to d, the only solutions to conditions (17.1) of interest are the undominated points.

Returning to Figure 17.1, we observe that point E is dominated by B and F is dominated by both B and C. Point G is not dominated, but is infeasible, because it does not satisfy (17.1), hence is not of interest. The set of undominated feasible points is called the *efficiency frontier* and is indicated by the points A, B, C, D and the solid lines connecting them. Clearly the economy will want to choose one of the points on the efficiency frontier because such points are undominated.

How does an economy make a choice of one of the points on the efficiency frontier at which to operate? It can make its choice by selecting the final demand price vector p, and solving the primal linear program in (17.2).

$$\begin{aligned} &\text{Maximize} \quad pd \\ &\text{Subject to} \quad d - Bx \leq 0 \\ &\qquad\qquad Ax \leq W \\ &\qquad\qquad x \leq X \\ &\qquad\qquad d, x \geq 0 \end{aligned} \tag{17.2}$$

Observe that the constraints of (17.2) are just those in (17.1).

Since the components of p are positive, $p > 0$, it follows that the locus of a constant value of the objective function, i.e., the locus of the equation px = constant, is a hyperplane in the output space. In two dimensions, the hyperplane is a line, such as the one shown tangent to point B in Figure 17.1. As the price vector p is varied, but still keeping $p > 0$, the locus of efficient points is traced out by the set of solutions to (17.2). As in Figure 17.1, the locus of efficient points in the two-dimensional case is downward sloping to the right.

The dual problem to (17.2) is given by (17.3).

$$\begin{aligned} &\text{Minimize} \quad qW + sX \\ &\text{Subject to} \quad u \geq p \\ &\qquad\qquad -uB + qA + s \geq 0 \\ &\qquad\qquad u, q, s \geq 0 \end{aligned} \tag{17.3}$$

The dual variables u, q, and s have the following dimensions and interpretations:

$u = (u_1, \ldots, u_r)$ is a (row) vector whose ith component u_k gives the imputed value of being able to increase d_k by a small amount; note that $u_k \geq p_k$.

$q = (q_1, \ldots, q_m)$ is a (row) vector whose ith component q_i gives the imputed value of increasing primary resource W_i by a small amount.

$s = (s_1, \ldots, s_n)$ is a (row) vector whose jth component s_j gives the imputed value of increasing X_j by a small amount.

Thus u, q, and s can be interpreted as the prices the economy should be willing to pay for more of the commodities they measure.

The following results hold at the optimal solution:

(i) There is equilibrium in all output and input markets. For the market constraints appearing in the direct program, together with complementary slackness show that

$$\begin{aligned} d^* - Bx^* \leq 0 \quad &\text{and} \quad u^*(d^* - Bx^*) = 0 \\ Ax^* \leq W \quad &\text{and} \quad q^*(Ax^* - W) = 0 \end{aligned} \tag{17.4}$$

The standard case is that the price in a market is positive, so that the market clears (there is equality between demand and supply). But if a market is in disequilibrium, then the price in that market must have dropped to zero.

(ii) The fixed output price of a final good cannot exceed its market price. If a positive quantity of the good is purchased, there is equality between the two. For the first set of inequalities in the dual program (17.3) give, together with complementary slackness

$$u^* \geq p \qquad \text{and} \qquad (u^* - p)d^* = 0 \tag{17.5}$$

The remaining results are similar to those that we have already met before:

(iii) Capacity charges arise for activities which are operated at a positive level.

(iv) The net profit of operating any activity is nonpositive (the unit costs should include the capacity charge, if any). If the activity is operated, the profit must vanish.

For details, see the corresponding list of results in Chapter 13. Finally, the duality theorem gives

$$pd^* = q^*W + s^*X \tag{17.6}$$

Intermediate Goods

Intermediate goods are both inputs and outputs, being produced at an earlier stage of the production chain and eventually fully used up at a later stage of the chain. Using the amended notation explained in the corresponding section in Chapter 13, let A^P and A^I denote the matrices of primary input coefficients and intermediate input coefficients, respectively; let B^F and B^I denote the matrices of final output coefficients and intermediate output coefficients respectively. Program (17.2) should then be amended to read

$$\begin{aligned} &\text{Maximize} \quad pd \\ &\text{Subject to} \quad d - B^F x \leq 0 \\ &\qquad (A^I - B^I)x = 0 \\ &\qquad A^P x \leq W \\ &\qquad x \leq X \\ &\qquad d, x \geq 0 \end{aligned} \tag{17.7}$$

There is now one market condition for each type of goods: final goods, intermediate goods and primary goods. Denote the corresponding dual variables by u^F, U^I, and q, respectively. The dual program reads

$$\begin{aligned} &\text{Minimize} \quad qW + sX \\ &\text{Subject to} \quad u^F \geq p \\ &\qquad -u^F B^F + u^I(A^I - B^I) + qA^P + s \geq 0 \\ &\qquad u^F, u^I, q, s \geq 0 \end{aligned} \tag{17.8}$$

The market for intermediate goods will be in equilibrium, as will the other goods markets. Unit costs will exhaust unit profits as before, assuming that each good, including an intermediate good, is charged its market price. (The cost calculation also includes a capacity charge, when appropriate.)

Decentralization Properties

Who is the master planner who would formulate and solve program (17.2)? As will now be explained, a competitive free economy will behave as if there existed a master planner who solves program (17.2). Using the famous term of Adam Smith, we may term the master planner the "invisible hand."

The invisible hand operates by communicating prices throughout the economy. In particular, the invisible hand solves for the duals of the input constraints in program (17.2), which are the shadow prices of the primary inputs. All buyers of primary inputs thereupon take these prices as given and known and formulate production plans accordingly.

In other words, the market formation can be conceived of as finding the solution to a *two-level programming problem*. The problem on the first level is the master problem (17.2) solved by the invisible hand. The problem on the second level is obtained by feeding the calculated shadow prices of all inputs into an individual production problem for each single industry. This second problem is one of maximizing profits in the face of fixed and given prices both on the output side (remember that the demand curves are all supposed to be horizontal) and on the input side (using the shadow prices just now computed). Each producer chooses a mix of activities designed to maximize his profits, subject only to the capacity conditions on the activities. Together, the producers must satisfy all the collective market demand constraint (total output must suffice to cover demand).

It is easy to demonstrate that the solution to the master problem also solves the delegated industry problem. For example, return to program (17.3) and suppose that the vector of shadow prices of all primary inputs q has been determined by the master planner and found to be equal to q^*. Inserting them into the dual program (17.3) gives

$$\begin{aligned} &\text{Minimize} \quad q^* W + sX \\ &\text{Subject to} \quad u \geq p \\ &\qquad -uB + s \geq -q^*A \\ &\qquad u, s \geq 0 \end{aligned} \tag{17.9}$$

Dropping the first (constant) term of the objective function in (17.9), the corresponding primal problem is:

$$\begin{aligned} &\text{Maximize} \quad pd - (q^*A)x \\ &\text{Subject to} \quad d - Bx \leq 0 \\ &\qquad x \leq X \\ &\qquad d, x \geq 0 \end{aligned} \tag{17.10}$$

which is an industry problem at the end of the production chain. Note that the objective function of (17.10) consists of revenues, pd, minus costs $(q^*A)x$; i.e., it is net profit which is to be maximized.

Example 1. Consider an economy involving the following activities: agriculture $(j = 1)$; transportation by truck $(j = 2)$; transportation by rail $(j = 3)$; manufacturing $(j = 4)$.

The unit requirements for each activity are listed in the table below.

		Transportation		
	Agriculture	*by Truck*	*by Rail*	*Manufacturing*
Land	2	0	0	0
Energy resources	4.5	12	10	0.5
Capital goods	3	4	6	1.5
Transportation services	0	0	0	0.4

There are three primary goods used as inputs: land $(i = 1)$, energy resources $(i = 2)$ and capital goods $(i = 3)$. The dimension of each input coefficient is a quantity per unit level of operation of the activity. Land may be measured in millions of acres, energy in million BTUs and inputs of capital goods in millions of dollars. There is one intermediate good: transportation services. Transportation services are produced by activities $j = 2$ and $j = 3$; these services are themselves an input used in the manufacturing industry $j = 4$. Transportation services may be measured in millions of pounds transported, or in pound miles (quantity multiplied by distance).

The first three rows in the table above are the matrix A^P. The last row is A^I (it is just a vector).

In this simple example, each activity has just one single output. The unit level of operation of an activity is defined as the level which generates 1 unit of output. The unit outputs of each activity are listed below.

		Transportation		
Output	*Agriculture*	*by Truck*	*by Rail*	*Manufacturing*
Final: Food	1	0	0	0
Manufactured Goods	0	0	0	1
Intermediate: Transportation	0	1	1	0

There are two categories of final goods: food $(k = 1)$ and manufactured goods $(k = 2)$. Food is measured in total calorie content. The quantity of manufactured goods is measured in millions of dollars.

The top two rows above are the matrix B^F. The last row is B^I.

Let the given endowments of primary goods (the vector W) be: land 100; energy 357.5; capital goods 227.5. The prices of the final goods (the vector p) are: food 36; manufactured goods 29.2. In this simple numerical example, we disregard the possible presence of capacity limits on the activities. Program (17.7) then reads

Figure 17.3

Optimal solution to numerical example.

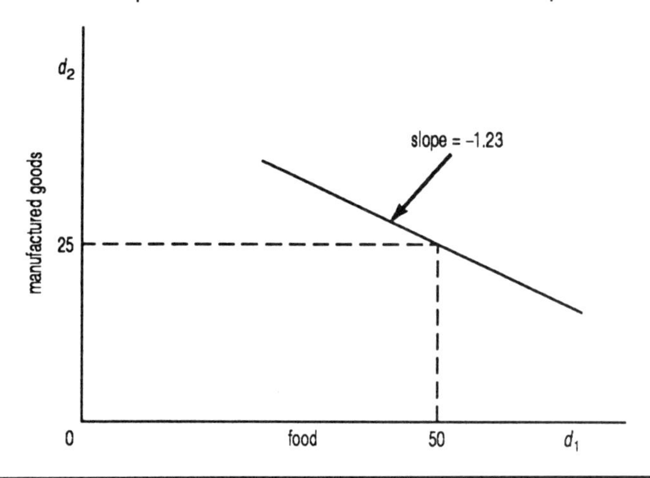

$$\text{Maximize} \quad 36d_1 + 29.2d_2$$

$$\begin{aligned} \text{Subject to} \qquad d_1 - x_1 &\leq 0 \\ d_2 - x_4 &\leq 0 \\ -x_2 - x_3 + 0.4x_4 &= 0 \\ 2x_1 &\leq 100 \\ 4.5x_1 + 12x_2 + 10x_3 + 0.5x_4 &\leq 357.5 \\ 3x_1 + 4x_2 + 6x_3 + 1.5x_4 &\leq 227.5 \\ d_1, d_2, x_1, x_2, x_3, x_4 &\geq 0 \end{aligned} \tag{17.11}$$

The optimal solution found by solving the GAMS program KOOPMANS on page 333 is

$$x_1^* = x_1^* = 50, \qquad x_2^* = 10, \qquad x_3^* = 0, \qquad d_2^* = x_4^* = 25.$$

Thus the activity transportation by rail will not be operated, because it is not competitive with transportation by truck.

The dual optimal solution is not unique. One optimal solution is

$$u_1^F{}^* = 36, \qquad u_2^F{}^* = 29.2$$
$$u_1^I{}^* = 48$$
$$q_1^* = 4.5, \qquad q_2^* = 2, \qquad q_3^* = 6.$$

There exist infinitely many other optimal dual solutions. As a matter of fact, it is possible to choose the price of the intermediate good arbitrarily (as long as it is chosen from some given interval), and the prices of the primary goods will then be uniquely determined.

The Frontier of Efficient Combinations of Outputs of Final Goods

The optimal solution of the numerical example dealt with is illustrated in the diagram in Figure 17.3, showing the space of the final goods (food and manufactured goods). The point $d_1^* = 50$, $d_2^* = 25$ has been plotted, together with the price direction (slope) $-p_1/p_2 = -36/29.2 = -1.23$ which was employed in generating this optimal solution. By construction, assuming that the prices of the final goods p_1 and p_2 stand in this proportion to each other, this point represents the highest possible total value of final demand that can be attained.

We can now undertake a series of numerical experiments, varying the prices p_1 and p_2 parametrically, each time solving the linear program anew and recording the optimal point (d_1^*, d_2^*) as in the table below.

numerical experiment	p_1	p_2	*slope* $-p_1/p_2$	d_1^*	d_2^*
1	36	29.2	−1.23	50	25
2	36	9	−4	50	25
3	36	4	−9	50	25
4	36	36	−1	50	25
5	9	36	−0.25	0	69.64
6	4	36	−0.11	0	69.64
7	44	50	−0.88	0	69.64
8	45	50	−0.9	50	25

We also plot the result of each experiment in Figure 17.4, exhibiting each time both the optimal solution found and the price direction that generated it. As long as the price direction (slope) remains fairly steep, $-p_1/p_2 \leq -0.9$, the optimal solution always is the point $(50, 25)$. But for a flatter slope such as $-p_1/p_2 \geq -0.88$, the optimal solution is $(0, 69.64)$.

Apparently there exists some critical value of $-p_1/p_2$ when the optimal solution flips from the point $B = (50, 25)$ to $A = (0, 69.64)$. It is easy to see that this critical value is

$$-p_1/p_2 = -(69.64 - 25)/50 = -0.89$$

i.e., the slope of the line AB itself.

The line segment AB including its end points is called the *frontier* (or locus) *of efficient combinations of outputs* of final goods. The optimal solutions in the parametric experiments that we have conducted trace the frontier, varying each price p_k, $k = 1, 2$, over the range of positive values $0 < p_k < \infty$. An efficient combination of outputs is one which can be obtained as the optimal solution to such a linear program, with suitable positive values for p_1 and p_2.

The entire area $ABCO$ (shaded in Figure 17.4) is the area of all feasible solutions to the given activity analysis program, i.e. the locus of all combinations of final goods that satisfy the given constraints and thus are possible to realize. It is the *production possibility region*. The curve ABC may be called the production possibility frontier.

Of all the points along BC, only point B can be obtained as the optimal solution to the activity analysis program. Points along BC other than B are necessarily *suboptimal*

Figure 17.4

Results of the numerical experiment.

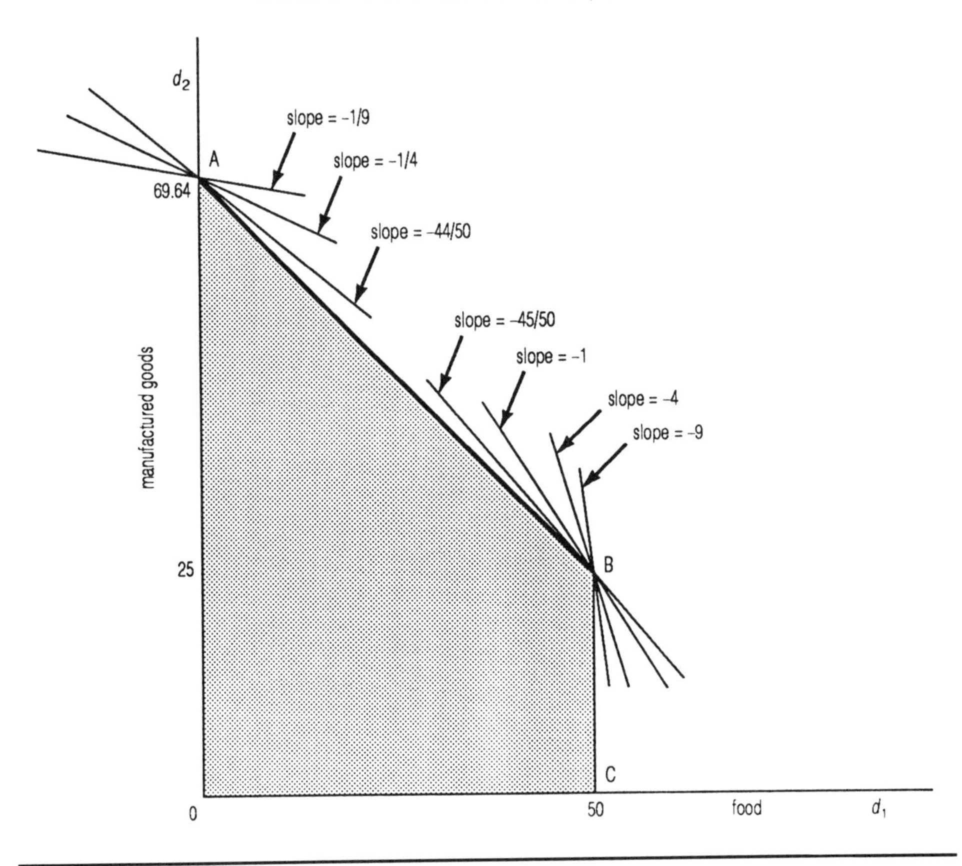

points, i.e., it is possible to increase the deliveries of one final good (manufactured goods) without decreasing the deliveries of the other (food). At an efficient point, however, it is not possible to increase the output of one final good without having to decrease the output of the other.

Which Efficient Output Point Will the Consumers Choose?

In the small prototype economy that we have constructed, the efficiency frontier spells out all the optimal output combinations that can be attained and which are thus available to the consumers. To each such combination corresponds a price ratio of the consumer goods. But which of these alternatives will the consumers actually choose?

Economists investigating consumer behavior have pursued two different approaches. One approach is to postulate the existence of a set of demand functions for all goods and services. A demand function for a single good depends upon the price of the good (the "own" price elasticity), the prices of other goods ("cross" elasticities), and consumer income.

In earlier chapters in this book we have repeatedly encountered *partial* demand functions for one single commodity of a few related commodities, assuming that income and the price of all other goods were kept constant (the *ceteris paribus* assumption of partial economic theory). By inverting such a partial demand function, we have made use of the corresponding partial demand price function.

The activity analysis model is a model of an entire economy, and deals with the optimal resource allocation and production in an economy, so that partial demand functions can't be used. The two commodities d_1 = food and d_2 = manufactured goods are taken as an example of an exhaustive list of all consumer goods and services, and what is needed is the demand for various sets of these goods.

The alternative approach to consumer behavior is the theory of preference fields (utility). Based upon work done by W. Pareto around the turn of the century, this approach is usually formulated by means of a set of axioms spelling out the meaning of the statement that a given "bundle" of goods A would be preferred to another bundle B, or that B would be preferred to A, or that a consumer would be "indifferent" facing a choice between A and B (see Figure 17.5 below).

The locus of indifferent bundles is called an indifference curve (in the case of more than two goods: an indifference surface). A series of indifference curves (each such curve corresponding to a given level of indifference) form an *indifference map*. Pareto showed that such a map may be viewed as the level curves of an ordinal utility function, that is, a concave and monotonically increasing function where the value of the function is an ordinal number (subject to comparisons such as, "greater than," "less than," "equal to") rather than a conventional cardinal number.

Under suitable mathematical regularity conditions, the existence of an ordinal utility function implies the existence of well-behaved demand functions.

It is possible to begin instead with the assumption that demand functions exist. Following P. A. Samuelson, we may then carry out the following thought experiment.

Figure 17.5

Indifference curves for bundles of goods.

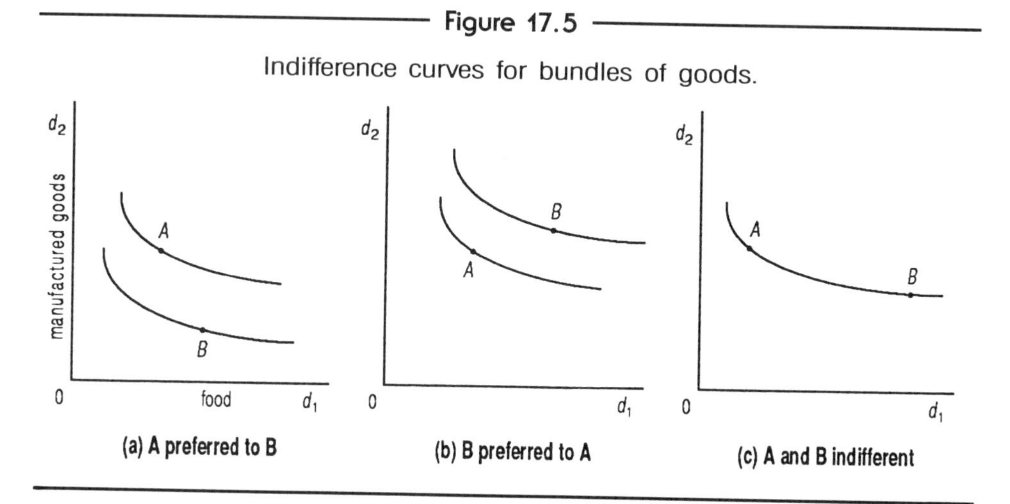

Figure 17.6

Construction of ordinal preference functions.

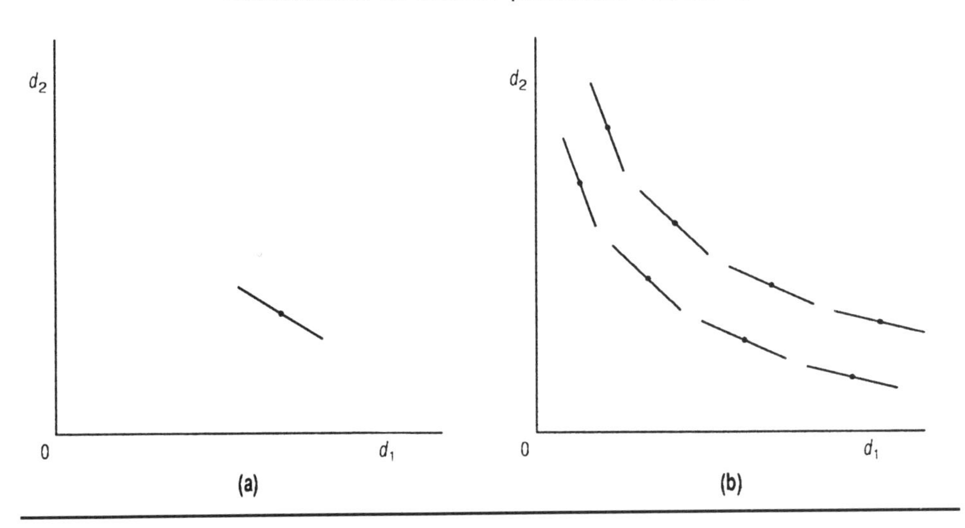

The demand functions depend upon prices and consumer incomes as parameters. Consider one particular set of numerical values of these parameters, and calculate the demand of each good. Plot the obtained point in the preference field together with the price ratios that generated it. [See Figure 17.6(a)].

Next, consider a new set of numerical values of the parameters. Calculate the demands for each good again, and plot the obtained point together with its directional elements. Imagine continuing these experiments so that we fill the entire preference field with observed points together with their corresponding directional elements.

Under suitable mathematical regularity conditions, the price directions may be integrated to obtain a corresponding ordinal preference function. Geometrically, the price directional elements are the tangent lines of the indifference curves. Thus, the succession of experiments has revealed the mathematical nature of the underlying preference field. (This is sometimes called the doctrine of revealed preference.)

To conclude, the two approaches of demand theory and utility theory to the analysis of consumer behavior may be viewed as logically equivalent.

Rather than using the partial demand price functions of earlier chapters, we may now define the *indirect demand functions* for our numerical example to be:

food	$f_1(d_1) = 12 - 0.4d_1$
manufactured goods	$f_2(d_2) = 15 - 0.25d_2$

Given the point (d_1, d_2) in the preference field, the indirect demand functions spell out the price directional elements that would have induced the consumer to choose the point (d_1, d_2) in the first place. In other words, they provide the price directional elements at each point in the quantity space. They do not depend upon income. (See L. Hurwicz and H. Uzawa, "On the Integrability of Demand Functions" in J. S. Chipman, L. Hurwicz, M. Richter, H. S. Sonnenschein, editors, *Preferences, Utility and Demand*, Jovanovich, New York 1971.)

After integrating the demand price functions we can state the nonlinear programming problem

$$
\begin{aligned}
\text{Maximum} \quad & 12d_1 - 0.2d_1^2 + 15d_2 - 0.125d_2^2 \\
\text{Subject to} \quad & d_1 - x_1 \leq 0 \\
& d_2 - x_4 \leq 0 \\
& -x_2 - x_3 + 0.4x_4 = 0 \\
& 2x_1 \leq 100 \\
& 4.5x_1 + 12x_2 + 10x_3 + 0.5x_4 \leq 357.5 \\
& 3x_1 + 4x_2 + 6x_3 + 1.5x_4 \leq 227.5 \\
& d, x \geq 0
\end{aligned}
\tag{17.12}
$$

The solution to this problem will select a unique consumption point on the production frontier *AB* in Figure 17.4. You are asked to complete the solution to this problem in Exercise 1.

Exercises

1. (a) Solve the nonlinear programming problem in (17.12). Denote the Lagrange multipliers of the constraints by p_1, p_2, u^I, q_1, q_2, q_3 respectively. Write down the Kuhn-Tucker conditions and check that they are satisfied at the solution point that you have found. What is the economic significance of these conditions?

   (b) Draw a graph of the feasible production points like the one in Figure 5.7 and locate the optimal solution you found in (a). Show that the line *AB* is tangent to an indifference curve at the solution point.

   (c) Rearrange the Kuhn-Tucker conditions and show that at the point of optimum (denoted by an asterisk)

   $$p_1^* d_1^* + p_2^* d_2^* = 100q_1^* + 357.5q_2^* + 227.5q_3^*$$

   Interpret this relation!

2. In an activity analysis model there are

   3 primary goods
   2 intermediate goods
   2 final goods
   5 activities.

The matrices of unit input requirements are shown below

	Activities				
Primary goods	3.5	0	0	0.3	0.3
	0	5	4.5	0	0
	2	8	9	0	0
Intermediate goods	0	0	0	1	0
	0	0	0	0	1

The top matrix is A^P, the bottom matrix is A^I. The matrices of outputs are

	Activities				
Final outputs	1	0	0	0	0
	0	0	0	1	1
Intermediate goods	0	1	0	0	0
	0	0	1	0	0

The top matrix is B^F; the bottom matrix is B^I. There are given and fixed "endowments" of all resources, viz. 100, 350 and 225 respectively.

Construct the locus of efficient points.

3. An activity analysis model features

   $k = 1, 2$ final goods,
   one intermediate good,
   $i = 1, 2$ primary goods (resources).

There are four activities, $j = 1, 2, 3, 4$.

Beginning with the unit requirements needed to operate the various activities, the matrix of unit resource requirements is

$$A^P = [a_{ij}^P] = \begin{bmatrix} 4 & 2 & 3 & 4 \\ 6 & 10 & 5 & 8 \end{bmatrix}$$

and the row vector of unit requirements of the intermediate good is

$$a^I = [a_j^I] = [0 \quad 0 \quad 4 \quad 2]$$

Next, turning to the unit outputs of the various activities, the matrix of unit outputs of final goods is

$$B^F = [b_{kj}^F] = \begin{bmatrix} 0 & 4 & 0 & 0 \\ 0 & 0 & 4 & 2 \end{bmatrix}$$

and the row vector of outputs of the intermediate good is

$$b^I = [b_j^I] = [1 \quad 0 \quad 0 \quad 0]$$

The prices of the two final goods are taken to be 0.8 and 2.5, respectively (horizontal demand schedules). The supplies of resources are price-responsive; the supply price functions of the two resources are

$$12 + 4w_1$$
$$8 + 6w_2$$

respectively, with w_i, $i = 1, 2$ denoting the quantity of resource i supplied.

Write down the nonlinear program that can be used to solve this activity analysis economy. Define Lagrange multipliers and write down all Kuhn-Tucker conditions and provide an economic interpretation of each such condition.

18

Energy Modeling

The production and distribution of energy is of strategic importance to the Western economies. The oil crises of the 1970s involving dramatic increases in the price of oil demonstrated how vulnerable the modern economy is to disturbances in the flow of oil.

Coal, oil and natural gas are important sources of energy in the U.S. In some countries, hydroelectric power provides for much of the energy needs. Nuclear power is a much debated source of energy.

In this chapter we shall draw upon techniques already explained in previous chapters to analyze the production and distribution of energy. First we demonstrate the use of a network with gain factors along the various links.

Consider the prototype network illustrated in Figure 18.1. The network shows the flow of oil products through a production system including distillation, catalytic cracking and blending. There are two inputs, two different grades of crude oil, entering nodes 1 and 2 as influxes. The first step in the production process is distillation through a so-called distillation column. There are two grades of distillates, represented as nodes 3 and 4 respectively. Crude oil at node 1 only yields the distillates at node 3; crude oil at node 2 can be used to obtain the distillates either at node 3 or node 4. The next step in the refinery process is cracking and blending. The result is gasoline at node 5.

In this simple example there are two primary goods (crude oil at nodes 1 and 2), two intermediate products (distillates at nodes 3 and 4) and one final demand (gasoline at node 5). There are five production activities, viz.

activities $(1,3)$, $(2,3)$ and $(2,4)$:	distillation
activities $(3,5)$ and $(4,5)$:	cracking and blending

We shall associate a flow variable x_{ij} with each arc (i,j). The flow x_{ij} is the quantity of energy that enters arc (i,j) at node i as an input. Defining e_{ij} as the *thermal efficiency* of the activity, the energy output that arrives at node j, is $e_{ij}x_{ij}$. The factor e_{ij} is a "gain factor" or a factor of amplification or attenuation along link (i,j).

Figure 18.1

Energy network with gain factors.

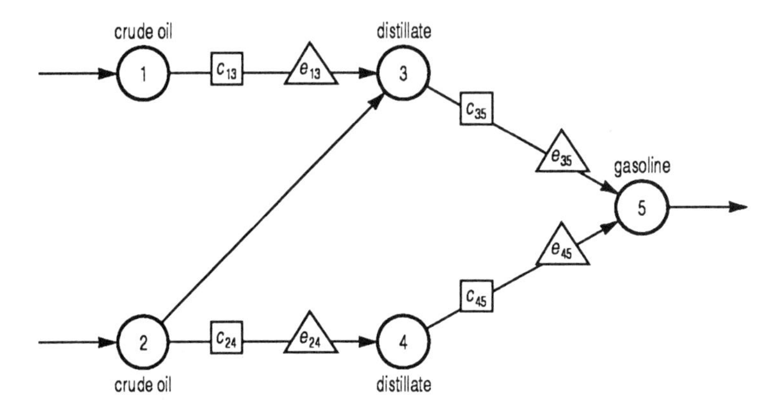

The complete notation to be used in this small network prototype is exhibited below:

$i, j = 1, \ldots, n$ various stages of production and refinement of energy sources, represented as nodes in network.

(i,j) productive activity converting energy at node i into energy at node j.

c_{ij}, c nonenergy input costs incurred in operating activity (i,j), calculated per unit of energy at node i; the corresponding (row) vector is written c (it has as many entries as there are activities).

e_{ij} thermal efficiency of activity (i,j), calculated as energy content of one unit of output per energy content of one unit of input.

x_{ij}, x amount of energy from node i sent to productive activity (i,j); the corresponding (column) vector is written x.

$b = (b_1, \ldots, b_n)$ (column) vector of energy supplies (negative entries) and energy demands (positive entries), given and known.

In order to set up the network problem, we define the *node arc incidence matrix* as

$$M = \begin{array}{c} \\ 1 \\ 2 \\ 3 \\ 4 \\ 5 \end{array} \begin{array}{c} \begin{array}{ccccc} (1,3) & (2,3) & (2,4) & (3,5) & (4,5) \end{array} \\ \begin{bmatrix} -1 & 0 & 0 & 0 & 0 \\ 0 & -1 & -1 & 0 & 0 \\ e_{13} & e_{23} & 0 & -1 & 0 \\ 0 & 0 & e_{24} & 0 & -1 \\ 0 & 0 & 0 & e_{35} & e_{45} \end{bmatrix} \end{array}$$

There is one column for each arc in the network, and one row for each node. There are exactly two nonzero entries in each column; -1 in the row of the 'from node' of the arc and e_{ij} in the row of the 'to node' of the arc. For example, in the first column labeled arc $(1, 3)$ there is a -1 in row 1 and e_{13} in row 3; all other entries in the column are 0. If we look at row 3 of M corresponding to node 3 we see that there are -1's in row 3 corresponding to arcs pointing out from node 3, and gain factors with a plus sign corresponding to the arc pointing into node 3.

We can now write the *conservation of flow conditions*

$$Mx = b. \tag{18.1}$$

The rule for entering elements on the right hand side is: enter a supply at a node with a minus sign, and enter a demand at a node with a plus sign; if there is neither a supply or a demand at the node, enter zero.

The network programming problem is

$$\begin{aligned} \text{Minimize} \quad & cx \\ \text{Subject to} \quad & Mx \geq b \\ & x \geq 0. \end{aligned} \tag{18.2}$$

The program minimizes total nonenergy input costs over the entire network subject to a conservation of flow condition at each node.

Note that the conservation of flow condition is now written as an inequality, stating that the net flow into a node via the arcs of the network must suffice to cover the net flow out of that node.

Why do we have to write the flow conditions in this manner? Remember that in the ordinary network problem without gain factors, dealt with in Chapter 7, the total flow into the network was equal to total flow out. Once that property was assured, it was indeed possible to satisfy all conservation flow conditions as equalities. But in the present case there may be amplification or attenuation of flow along the arcs, so that the total flow out of a node will in general no longer equal the total flow into the node. With given inflows into the network, it may then simply no longer be possible to obtain the desired outflows. It may no longer be possible to establish all conservation of flow conditions as equalities.

Next, consider the data box below where we have entered specific numeric values of the parameters.

	x_{13}	x_{23}	x_{24}	x_{35}	x_{45}	
u_1	-1	0	0	0	0	≥ -200
u_2	0	-1	-1	0	0	≥ -80
u_3	0.9	0.8	0	-1	0	$= 0$
u_4	0	0	0.9	0	-1	$= 0$
u_5	0	0	0	0.6	0.6	≥ 120
	4.5	6	6	19	12	

The vectors of inflows and outflows is $(-200, -80, 0, 0, 120)$, the vector of nonenergy unit costs along arcs is $(4.5, 6, 6, 19, 12)$ and the vector of gain factors is $(0.9, 0.8, 0.9, 0.6, 0.6)$. The dual variables are marked on the left.

The dual problem to program (18.2) is

$$\text{Maximize} \quad ub \tag{18.3}$$

$$\text{Subject to} \quad uM \le c, \qquad u \ge 0$$

Writing down the dual constraints, one by one, at the point of optimum and also remembering complementary slackness, one has

$$\begin{aligned}
-u_1^* + 0.9u_3^* &\le 4.5, & x_{13}^*(4.5 + u_1^* - 0.9u_3^*) &= 0 \\
-u_2^* + 0.8u_3^* &\le 6, & x_{23}^*(6 + u_2^* - 0.8u_3^*) &= 0 \\
-u_2^* + 0.9u_4^* &\le 6, & x_{24}^*(6 + u_2^* - 0.9u_4^*) &= 0 \\
-u_3^* + 0.6u_5^* &\le 19, & x_{35}^*(19 + u_3^* - 0.6u_5^*) &= 0 \\
-u_4^* + 0.6u_5^* &\le 12, & x_{45}^*(12 + u_4^* - 0.6u_5^*) &= 0
\end{aligned}$$

In the usual manner, we can identify the dual u_i^* with an imputed value of energy at node i. The relations listed above can then be interpreted in plain English as follows. Consider some arc, pointing out from a given node. The imputed appreciation along the arc of one unit of flow leaving the node cannot exceed the unit non-energy cost. (The imputed appreciation is calculated as the value of the *surviving* thermal energy at the destination node minus the value of a unit of energy at the node of origin.) If a positive flow is transmitted along the arc, the imputed appreciation equals the unit cost. But if the appreciation falls short of the unit cost, no flow is transmitted along this arc.

The optimal solutions, found by solving the GAMS program ENERGY on page 335, to the direct and dual problems are listed below

arc (i,j)	x_{ij}^*	*node i*	u_i^*
$(1,3)$	142.22	1	0
$(2,3)$	0	2	4.8
$(2,4)$	80	3	5
$(3,5)$	128	4	12
$(4,5)$	72	5	40

As it turns out, there is an excess supply at node 1 amounting to $200 - 142.22 = 57.18$. Accordingly, the imputed value of energy at that node has dropped to zero.

Arc $(2,3)$ is not utilized, so that there are only two optimal paths in the network: the path $1 \to 3 \to 5$ and the path $2 \to 4 \to 5$.

A Spatial Activity-Analysis Type Model of Electricity Generation

Many energy analysts monitoring fuel prices feel that local electric utilities play a key role in effecting the relative scarcity of alternative sources of energy. As a result of the oil price shocks of the 1970s, many utilities switched to coal as an alternative source of energy. As the demand for oil thus slackened, the price of oil gradually came down, and, in the late 1980s, a reverse process got under way: because of declining oil prices many utilities switched back to oil as a source of energy. One may predict that such substitution will eventually cause oil to become scarce again and the price of oil to rise.

We shall here present a spatial model of the flow of fuels to the electric utilities, and of the generation of electricity. The crucial feature of the model is a presentation of the choice that the individual electrical utility makes regarding its use of fuels. Unit fuel costs consist of the market price of the fuel at the point of delivery plus transportation costs. Depending upon its proximity to coal fields, gas pipelines, and oil distribution centers, each utility will choose a combination of activities for generating electricity that minimizes costs.

The production chain of the generation and delivery of electrical energy to final consumers includes the following three steps: the transportation of coal, oil, and gas from the various supply points to the electrical generation plants (a "transportation problem"); the generation of electricity at the plants owned by the utilities (an activity decision problem); and the distribution of electricity from these plants to consumers via a grid of high voltage transmission lines (a "transportation problem"). Focusing on the role of alternative sources of energy, we shall here develop a spatial activity analysis model that combines all three steps of supply. For simplicity, the local demand for electricity in each region is supposed to be fixed and known. We also allow for the possibility that electricity may be sent from a region which has excess capacity to one that is deficient. Our objective will be to minimize the total costs of supplying the demands for electricity in all regions.

We use the following notation:

$h, k = 1, \ldots, m$ regions.
$s = 1, \ldots, r$ fossil fuel types.
x_{hs} = amount (KWH) of electricity for region h produced by burning fuel s.
X_{hs} = maximum value of x_{hs}.
d_h = demand for electricity in region h.
f_{hs} = supply of fuel s in region h.
w_{hk} = KWH of electricity sent from region h to region k (for $h \neq k$).
t_{hks} = number of BTU's of fuel s sent from region h to region k.
c_{hks} = per unit shipping costs of sending fuel s from region h to region k.
a_{hs} = amount of fuel s needed to produce one unit of electricity in region h.
b_{hs} = unit operating cost for producing electricity at region h from fuel s.
g_{hk} = unit cost of power loss when sending a KWH from region h to region k.

The linear program for minimizing the total costs is now stated as follows:

$$\text{Minimize} \quad \sum_{h=1}^{m} \sum_{s=1}^{r} b_{hs} x_{hs} + \sum_{h=1}^{m} \sum_{k=1}^{m} g_{hk} w_{hk} + \sum_{h=1}^{m} \sum_{k=1}^{m} \sum_{s=1}^{r} c_{hks} t_{hks} \tag{18.4}$$

$$\text{Subject to} \quad \sum_{s=1}^{r} x_{hs} + \sum_{k=1}^{m} (w_{kh} - w_{hk}) \geq d_h \tag{18.5}$$

$$a_{hs} x_{hs} - \sum_{k=1}^{m} (t_{khs} - t_{hks}) \leq f_{hs} \tag{18.6}$$

$$x_{hs} \leq X_{hs} \tag{18.7}$$

$$x_{hs},\ w_{hk},\ t_{hks} \geq 0 \tag{18.8}$$

The objective function (18.4) has three summation terms. The first summation is the cost of generating electricity from all fuels at all locations; the second summation is the total cost of transshipping electricity between regions; and the third summation is the total cost of transshipping fuels between regions. Constraints (18.5) require that the total amount of electricity generated in region h, plus that transmitted into h from other regions, less that transmitted from h out to other regions, is enough to satisfy the demand in region h. Constraints (18.6) require that the amount of fuel s in region h required to generate x_{hs} units of electricity, plus the amount of fuel s shipped in region h, less the amount of fuel s shipped out of region h, is at most the amount f_{hs} of fuel s that region h has. Constraints (18.7) are just upper bounds on x_{hs} while constraints (18.8) are nonnegativity conditions.

A simple example will make the problem clear. In Figure 18.2 the graph of a example with two regions and two fuels is shown. The variables for the problem are marked on the arcs. At each node there are constraints. The data box of the problem shown below can easily be derived from the graph shown in Figure 18.2.

x_{11}	x_{12}	x_{21}	x_{22}	t_{121}	t_{211}	t_{222}	t_{212}	w_{12}	w_{21}	
1	1	0	0	0	0	0	0	-1	1	$\geq d_1$
0	0	1	1	0	0	0	0	1	-1	$\geq d_2$
a_{11}	0	0	0	1	-1	0	0	0	0	$\leq f_{11}$
0	a_{12}	0	0	0	0	1	-1	0	0	$\leq f_{12}$
0	0	a_{21}	0	-1	1	0	0	0	0	$\leq f_{21}$
0	0	0	a_{22}	0	0	-1	1	0	0	$\leq f_{22}$
1	0	0	0	0	0	0	0	0	0	$\leq X_{11}$
0	1	0	0	0	0	0	0	0	0	$\leq X_{12}$
0	0	1	0	0	0	0	0	0	0	$\leq X_{21}$
0	0	0	1	0	0	0	0	0	0	$\leq X_{22}$
b_{11}	b_{12}	b_{21}	b_{22}	c_{121}	c_{211}	c_{122}	c_{212}	g_{12}	g_{21}	

In order to better interpret this example we work with the following specific numbers. The units are written once on each line but apply to all the quantities on that line. (A BTU is a British Thermal Unit.)

$d_1 = 170,\quad d_2 = 135$ (Millions of KWH)

$f_{11} = 1.75,\quad f_{21} = 0.65$ (Trillions of BTUs of coal)

$f_{12} = 0.9,\quad f_{22} = 1.2$ (Trillions of BTUs of oil)

$X_{11} = 120,\quad X_{21} = 95$ (Millions of KWH)

$X_{12} = 80,\quad X_{22} = 55$ (Millions of KWH)

$a_{11} = 0.01144,\quad a_{21} = 0.0107$ (Trillions of BTUs of coal/Millions of KWH)

$a_{12} = 0.011,\quad a_{22} = 0.012$ (Trillions of BTUs of oil/Millions of KWH)

$b_{11} = 350,\quad b_{21} = 420$ (Millions \$/Millions of KWH)

$b_{12} = 280,\quad b_{22} = 310$ (Millions \$/Millions of KWH)

$c_{121} = 0.2,\quad c_{211} = 0.2$ (Millions \$/Trillions of BTUs of coal)

$c_{122} = 0.1,\quad c_{212} = 0.1$ (Millions \$/Trillions of BTUs of oil)

$g_{12} = 22.5,\quad g_{21} = 22.5$ (Millions \$/Millions of KWH)

Figure 18.2

Two region electricity generation example.

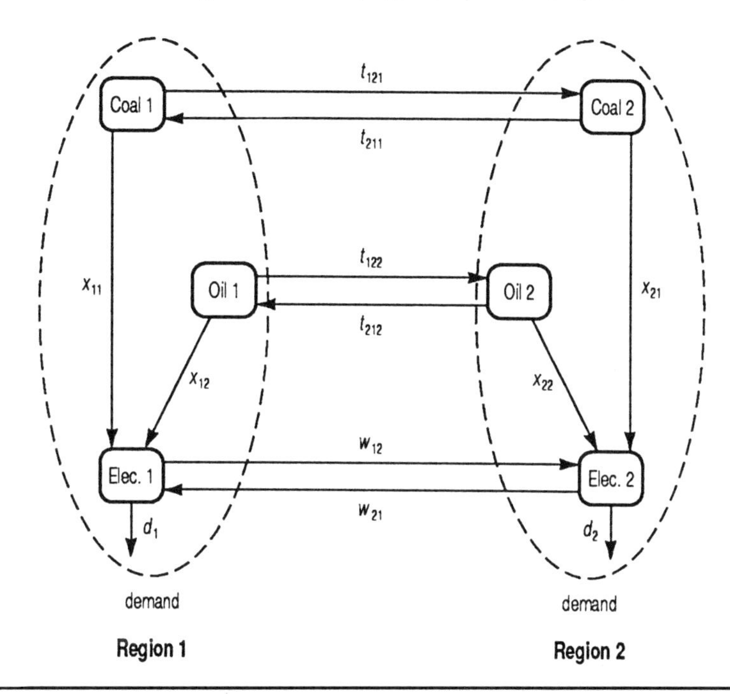

The optimal primal solution, found by solving the program ELECTRIC on page 335, is shown graphically in Figure 18.3.

Note that in the optimal solution, Region 1 ships generated electricity to Region 2. Also the maximum generating capacities of 120 for coal and 80 for oil are reached in Region 1. The maximum generating capacity for oil of 55 is reached in Region 2, but only 50 of the 95 units of capacity for coal generation are used in that region.

The dual solution of the problem is given below. The interpretations of each variable are given beside its value. Note that the imputed cost of generating electricity in Region 2 is 397.5 + 22.5 = 420.0, i.e., it is the cost of generating electricity in Region 1 and shipping it to Region 2.

1	−397.5	imputed cost of a million KWH in Region 1
2	-420.0	imputed cost of a million KWH in Region 2
3	0	imputed value of more coal in Region 1
4	0	imputed value of more oil in Region 1
5	0	imputed value of more coal in Region 2
6	0	imputed value of more oil in Region 2
7	47.5	imputed value of more coal generating capacity, Region 1
8	117.5	imputed value of more oil generating capacity, Region 1
9	0	imputed value of more coal generating capacity, Region 2
10	110.0	imputed value of more oil generating capacity, Region 2

Figure 18.3

Solution network for two region example.

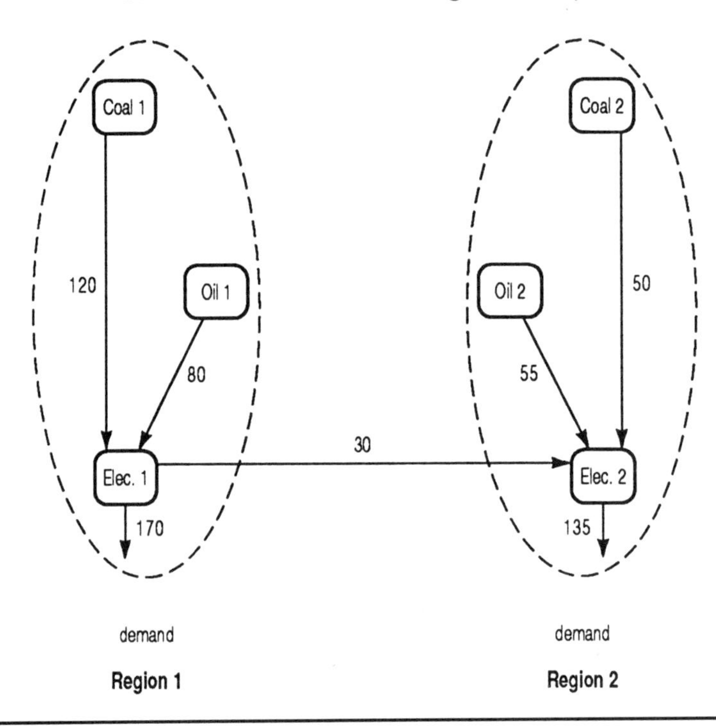

It is also clear that the best generating plant to expand is the oil burning plant in Region 1, since its imputed value is $117 per unit capacity expansion. The next best plant to expand is the oil burning plant in Region 2, followed by the coal burning plant in Region 1. Note that expanding the coal burning plant in Region 2 is of no value whatsoever, even though it is a small, relatively efficient plant.

Exercises

1. Resolve the problem in the data box on page 231 with the following right hand sides, explaining your answers in each case.
   (a) $(-100, -150, 0, 50, 150)$
   (b) $(-100, -150, 0, 150, 150)$.
2. This problem refers to the generation of electricity by electric utilities located in four regions A, B, C, D. The fuel used is either coal or oil. Each region has some local fuel supplies; in addition fuels can be hauled by truck or rail from one region to another.

The transportation network is exhibited below

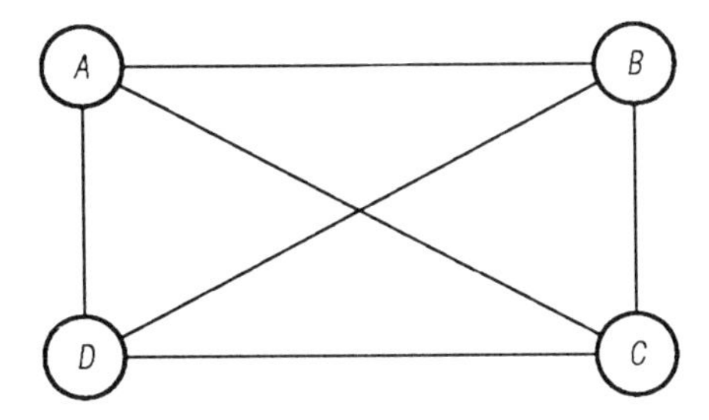

The distances are (in miles)

		To			
		A	*B*	*C*	*D*
From	*A*	0	100	130	80
	B	100	0	80	130
	C	130	80	0	100
	D	80	130	100	0

Quantities of fuels will be measured in million BTUs. The transportation costs are \$0.05 per million BTUs per mile when hauling coal, and \$0.01 per million BTUs per mile when hauling oil.

The local supplies of fuels are as follows (in trillions of BTUs; 1 trillion is the same as one million millions)

Region	*Coal*	*Oil*
A	1.85	0
B	1.00	0.435
C	1.60	0.30
D	0	0.30

The amount of electricity generated is measured in million KWH. The local demand is listed below (in million KWH):

	Demand
A	95
B	125
C	75
D	100

Each utility has available facilities for burning both coal and oil. There exist four different technologies:

activity 1	burning coal	older turbines
activity 2	burning coal	modern turbines
activity 3	burning oil	older turbines
activity 4	burning oil	modern turbines

The unit fuel requirements (in million BTUs per KWH electricity generated) are

Activity	*Coal*	*Oil*
1	0.01144	0
2	0.01000	0
3	0	0.0107
4	0	0.01000

All technologies are not available in all regions. For the available choices, consult the list below which also gives the maximal generating capacity of each activity (the capacity being measured in million KWH):

	1	2	3	4
A	80	90	30	—
B	80	100	—	60
C	15	20	20	20
D	40	—	30	30

The operating and maintenance costs (in $ per KWH electricity generated) are

Activity	*Cost*
1	0.025
2	0.020
3	0.004
4	0.003

Determine the optimal pattern of generation of electricity in each region, the use of fuels and the optimal shipments of fuels between regions.

19

Disequilibrium: Unemployment & Foreign Trade

To the economist, equilibrium in a market means that all participating subjects, both sellers and purchasers, can carry out their plans. A conventional demand curve plots planned demand as a function of various hypothetical price levels. A conventional supply curve plots planned supply as a function of price. At the point of intersection, planned demand = planned supply. The market clears. All participants can realize their plans (planned supply = actual deliveries and planned demand = actual demand). To use terms introduced into the economic vocabulary in the 1920s by Swedish economists Myrdal and Lindahl, the *ex ante* concepts become identical to *ex post* concepts.

Disequilibrium occurs when all agents cannot realize their *ex ante* intentions. If the market price is rigid or "sticky," the market may fail to clear. As illustrations, one may cite the lack of rental units in a city having rent control, unemployment of labor when there is a minimum wage, and government stockpiling programs of excess agricultural produce when there is a minimum price.

Consider the last case. Suppose that the Department of Agriculture imposes a minimum price on wheat. If there is a bumper crop, the government buys the excess supply rather than allowing wheat prices to fall. Now, is there really disequilibrium in this market? Would it perhaps not be more correct to say that the private demand plus government demand exactly matches supply, and that the result of the price support program is that equilibrium is established at the minimum price? In order to answer this question, remember the definition of disequilibrium just provided. At the enforced minimum price, the total wheat that farmers want to sell in the market exceeds the consumers' desired purchases. There is an excess supply in the market that the consumers do not want to buy. This *ex ante* dilemma is resolved by the government stepping in *ex post*, absorbing the surplus in the market. The total quantity purchased in the market

Figure 19.1

Supply curve for workers.

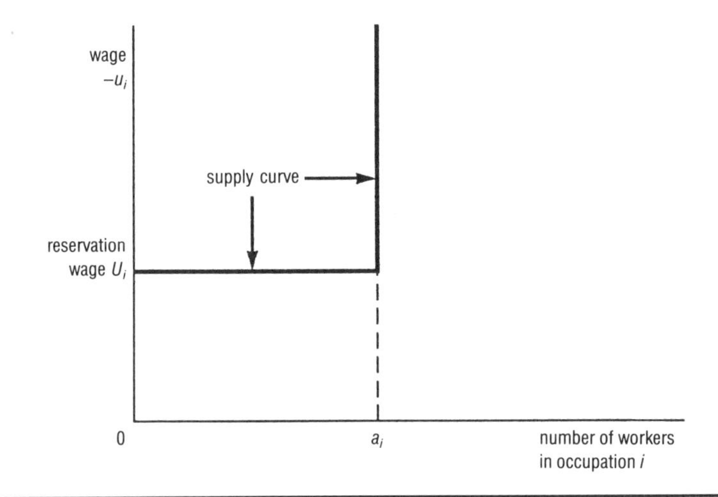

equals the quantity sold *ex post*; the *ex ante* market gap has been wiped out by the government stepping into the market *ex post*.

Rigidities may be introduced into a market from the outside in the form of government controls (price controls), or they may arise internally as consumers and producers fail to respond or respond only slowly to changing market conditions.

In particular, rigidities in the labor markets have been much discussed by economists. As is well known, there is no consensus among economists about the nature of unemployment. According to some economists (the "new classical macro-economists"), there exists no involuntary unemployment. The authors of this text do not share this view. To us, involuntary unemployment is an empirical fact that needs to be explained. Nominal wages sometimes fail to fall to the level where markets would be cleared. Nominal wages are "sticky downwards."

Several economic theories are able to produce such rigidities in labor markets. A common denominator for much of this thinking is the emphasis on the existence of so-called "implicit contracts" between employers and employees. During an act of employment, an association of some duration is set up between the employer and the employee and both parties have some interest in the continuity of this relation. Workers acquire nontransferable, firm-specific skills and knowledge about the nonwage attributes of a job through experience and on-the-job training. Transition, search and moving costs are incurred by both workers and employers when the association is broken.

Within the framework of a conventional model of comparative statics with full certainty, such wage rigidity takes the form of a wage floor, beneath which the wage cannot fall (a "reservation" wage rate). Rather than accepting a wage rate lower than the reservation wage, a worker may withdraw from active participation in the labor market and become unemployed.

To illustrate these ideas, we now present a transportation-type model of a labor market with retraining. The origin nodes of the transportation model represent the various occupations, and the directed links represent possible avenues of schooling and retraining. The retraining cost is formally dealt with as a "transportation cost" enabling a worker to transit from one occupation origin node to another occupation destination node.

The workers are divided among $i = 1, \ldots, n$ different occupations. Each occupation is represented both as an origin node and as a destination node. At the outset, the workers are located at the origin nodes. During the period of analysis, workers are offered the opportunity to "transit" from one occupation to another through schooling and training. A worker will then move from one origin node i to a destination node j, $i \neq j$. But if the worker chooses not to enroll in any such retraining program, he or she will retain the occupation classification $i = j$.

The supply curve for workers of each occupation i is illustrated in Figure 19.1. The total available number of workers in occupation i is a_i. But the wage rate is bounded from below, say $-u_i \geq U_i$, where u_i is the wage cost of workers of occupation i ($u_i < 0$) and U_i is the reservation wage.

The complete notation to be used is listed below.

$i, j = 1, \ldots, n$ indices of occupations (the index i is used for an origin node and the index j for a destination node).

a_i available number of workers of occupation i before possible retraining takes place.

g_i^- unemployment in occupation i.

b_j demand for workers of occupation i.

c_{ij} unit retraining cost ($c_{ij} = 0$ for $i = j$).

x_{ij} number of workers retrained and moving from occupation i to occupation j (x_{ij} with $i = j$ denotes the number of workers who manage to find employment without joining a retraining program).

U_i reservation wage.

u_i market cost of labor at origin node i, which satisfies $-u_i \geq U_i$.

v_j market wage of labor at destination node j.

We are now ready to write down the transportation program

$$\text{Minimize} \quad \sum_{i=1}^{n} \sum_{j=1}^{n} c_{ij} x_{ij} - \sum_{i=1}^{n} U_i g_i^- \tag{19.1}$$

$$\text{Subject to} \quad \sum_{j=1}^{n} x_{ij} + g_i^- = a_i, \qquad i = 1, \ldots, n$$

$$\sum_{i=1}^{n} x_{ij} \geq b_j, \qquad j = 1, \ldots, n$$

$$x_{ij} \geq 0, \; g_i^- \geq 0, \qquad i, j = 1, \ldots, n$$

The minimand is an economic potential function defined as the total retraining costs minus the total of wages foregone by all unemployed workers. There is no obvious economic reason for the inclusion of the second term, and the potential function is formed for operational purposes only. It has been chosen so that it peaks at the desired solution, which indeed it does as we shall see in a moment.

The first set of constraints spell out a market relation for each origin node i: the available supply a_i is either transmitted as a flow via the distribution net of the transportation model, or it stays at its supply node and $g_i^- > 0$. The second set of constraints is standard: total arrivals at a destination node must cover the local demand.

In order to understand the motivation for program (19.1), we write the corresponding dual program

$$\text{Maximize} \quad \sum_{i=1}^{n} a_i u_i + \sum_{j=1}^{n} b_j v_j \tag{19.2}$$

$$\begin{aligned} \text{Subject to} \quad & u_i + v_j \leq c_{ij}, && i,j = 1, \ldots, n \\ & u_i \leq -U_i, && i = 1, \ldots, n \\ & v_j \geq 0, && j = 1, \ldots, n \\ & u_i \text{ unrestricted in sign}, && i = 1, \ldots, n. \end{aligned}$$

The first set of dual constraints states that the increase in wage from an origin $(-u_i)$ to a destination (v_j) cannot exceed the retraining cost. And, by complementary slackness

$$x_{ij}^*(c_{ij} - u_i^* - v_j^*) = 0 \tag{19.3}$$

If a positive number of workers are retrained by flowing on the arc from node i to node j, the appreciation in wage precisely equals the retraining cost. But if the wage appreciation falls short of the retraining cost, no worker will select for that retraining program.

The second set of dual constraints, which can be rewritten as $-u_i \geq U_i$, $i = 1, \ldots, n$ retrieves the desired condition that the wage cannot fall below the reservation level. And, further

$$(g_i^-)^*(-u_i^* - U_i) = 0. \tag{19.4}$$

If there is unemployment in occupation i, the wage rate must have fallen to its reservation level. But if the wage stays above the reservation level, all workers in that occupation must be employed.

Because program (19.1) and its dual (19.2) generate all optimal conditions that one would want to associate with this model, we see why indeed the second term in the objective function (19.1) was chosen.

Example 1. Consider the following three occupations: health personnel, computer programmers, and mechanics; and let the data exhibited in tables below be given.

Occupation	*Available Labor (1000 of workers)*	*Labor Demand (1000 of workers)*	*Reservation Wage (1000 of \$)*
1 (health personnel)	400	300	35
2 (computer programmers)	200	240	36
3 (mechanics)	350	300	34

Retraining costs in 1000 of dollars

		To occupation		
		1	*2*	*3*
From occupation	*1*	0	2.5	0.8
	2	0.3	0	1
	3	1.2	3	0

Note that the total available labor (950 thousand workers) exceeds total demand (840 thousand) so that the difference (110 thousand) necessarily must wind up being unemployed.

Formulating program (19.1), we are then led to the data box shown below.

	x_{11}	x_{12}	x_{13}	x_{21}	x_{22}	x_{23}	x_{31}	x_{32}	x_{33}	g_1^-	g_2^-	g_3^-	
u_1	1	1	1							1			$= 400$
u_2				1	1	1					1		$= 200$
u_3							1	1	1			1	$= 350$
v_1	1			1			1						≥ 300
v_2		1			1			1					≥ 240
v_3			1			1			1				≥ 300
	0	2.5	0.8	0.3	0	1	1.2	3	0	−35	−36	−34	

The optimal direct solution found by solving the GAMS program `RETRAIN` on page 337 is

$$x_{11}^* = 300, \quad x_{22}^* = 200, \quad x_{32}^* = 40, \quad x_{33}^* = 300 \quad \text{and all other } x_{ij}^* = 0$$

$$g_1^{-*} = 100, \quad g_2^{-*} = 0, \quad g_3^{-*} = 10$$

and the optimal dual solution is

$$-u_1^* = v_1^* = 35, \qquad -u_2^* = v_2^* = 37, \qquad -u_3^* = v_3^* = 34.$$

This optimal solution is also illustrated in the graph Figure 19.2. It turns out that 40 thousand mechanics will enroll in a retraining program to become computer programmers, leaving 10 thousand unemployed mechanics. No health personnel will be retrained, and there will be 100 thousand unemployed health personnel.

The optimal wage of computer programmers is $37,000 annually, which is $1,000 above their reservation wage. So, there is equilibrium in the market for computer programmers. But for the other two occupations, there is disequilibrium and their wage rates have fallen to their reservation levels.

Activity Analysis with Rigid Prices of Primary Factors: The Possibility of Unemployment

Returning to the notation of Chapter 17, assume that the supply curve for one or several primary goods $i = 1, \ldots, m$ is kinked as in Figure 19.1. That is, the availability of each primary good is fixed and known, but there exists a threshold price level, called the

Figure 19.2

Graph of optimal solution. Numbers of transits between each pair of nodes shown below arrows.

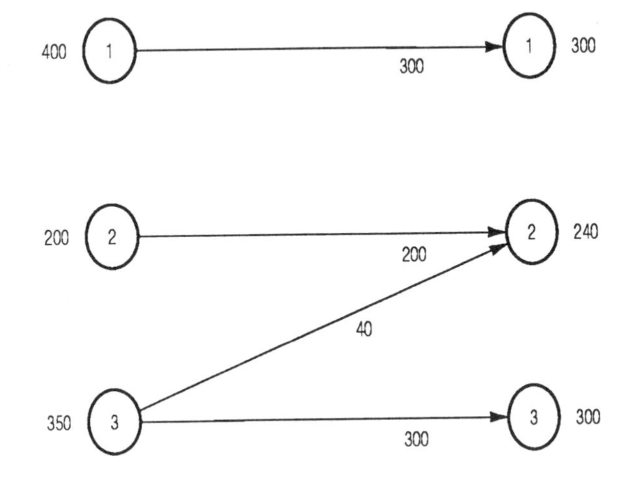

reservation price, below which the price of the primary good cannot fall. Rather than accepting a lower price, the owners of the primary good would instead prefer to hold back some of their good from the marketplace, so that there would be an excess supply that remains unsold.

What we have in mind for this more general case is not just a possible excess supply of labor in the presence of wages that are sticky downwards, but similar rigidities may also be present for other primary inputs. If freight rates for transporting goods by sea fall sufficiently, shipowners will lay up their ships in dry dock rather than operating them at a loss. The reason is that prices of real capital are rigid downwards and the owners are slow to accept the capital loss that has occurred. (If the price of a ship falls sufficiently, it may be possible for a new owner to buy the ship and to cover the costs of operating it even at the lower freight rates.) In a similar fashion, rigidities can be invoked to explain why a steel corporation facing falling steel prices will develop an excess supply of furnace capacity.

The notation to be used in the market for each primary good is now:

W_i total availability of primary good i.

$(Ax)_i$ demand for primary good i.

g_i^- possible excess supply of primary good i.

q_i market price of primary good i.

Q_i reservation price for primary good i, with $q_i \geq Q_i$.

For mathematical expediency, we simply assume that all primary goods have reservation prices. If necessary, a reservation price may always be put equal to zero. The market balancing condition for primary goods is

$$Ax + g^- = W \tag{19.5}$$

Thus prepared, consider the activity disequilibrium model

$$\begin{aligned} \text{Maximize} \quad & pd + Qg^- \\ \text{Subject to} \quad & d - Bx \leq 0 \\ & Ax + g^- = W \\ & x \leq X \\ & d, x, g^- \geq 0 \end{aligned} \tag{19.6}$$

The constraints of the model represent, as before, the markets for outputs and inputs respectively, and the capacity limits on all activities. You should compare this model with that in (17.1).

We are not yet ready to explain the full significance of the maximand appearing in program (19.6). For the time being, let us provisionally accept it as an "economic potential" function, designed to produce the desired price bounds on the dual side. For the dual reads

$$\begin{aligned} \text{Minimize} \quad & qW + sX \\ \text{Subject to} \quad & u \geq p \\ & -uB + qA + s \geq 0 \\ & q \geq Q \\ & u, s \geq 0 \end{aligned} \tag{19.7}$$

In addition to the dual constraints featured in equilibrium activity analysis [see (17.3)], there is a bounding condition on resource prices $q \geq Q$.

At the point of optimum:

(i) There is equilibrium in all output markets. But the input markets are in general in disequilibrium. If there is a positive excess supply of some primary input, the price of that input must have fallen to its lower bound. (If the price of an input stays above its lower bound, there is equilibrium in the input market.)

The resource price constraint and its complementary slackness condition are

$$q^* \geq Q, \qquad (q^* - Q)g^{-*} = 0. \tag{19.8}$$

(ii) The fixed output price of a final good cannot exceed its market price. If a positive quantity of the good is purchased, there is equality between the two.

(iii) If there is a capacity charge on an activity, that activity must be operated at capacity.

(iv) The net profit of operating any activity is nonpositive (the unit costs should include the capacity charge, if any). If an activity is operated, its profit is zero.

(v) The value of final demand equals the value of all income actually earned by the owners of primary inputs plus the capacity charges. Mathematically,

$$pd^* = q^*(W - g^{-*}) + s^*X. \tag{19.9}$$

We are now prepared to interpret the maximand of program (19.6). The first term is the value of final output which at the point of optimum will equal all income actually earned in the economy. The second term is the income foregone by all factors that are voluntarily unemployed. The sum equals the total income *ex ante* that all recipients of factor income collectively would have expected to receive. We know that not all of that income is going to be realized. But the mathematical program does not know it; the program only reflects the planning situation *ex ante* and the mutually inconsistent plans of the various economic factors. No information has been incorporated in the program regarding how such a possible discrepancy might be resolved *ex post*.

In brief, the disequilibrium activity model solves for the possible *ex ante* gaps in the markets for all primary inputs. But it does not tell us how such discrepancies between the planned supply of primary inputs and the planned demand for primary inputs are eventually resolved.

Example 2. Most U.S. observers seem to accept quite readily the phenomenon of unemployment in smokestack industries, such as in coal mining and in the steel industry. Most of these production facilities were built many years ago and represent technologies that are no longer competitive. Also, U.S. wages were for a long time propped up by expensive labor contracts. So, it might seem to be in the nature of things that these industries should gradually succumb to the competition from aggressive developing nations possessing advanced technology.

The U.S. public was shocked, however, when in the mid 1980s the pride of the nation, its computer industry ("Silicon Valley") ran into bad times, laying off computer engineers, systems analysts and other specialized labor. The programming models developed in the present chapter can be used to explain why this can happen, and why no category of labor can ever be shielded from the threat of unemployment.

The numerical example to be developed mimics these events. An activity analysis model of the computer industry is developed, featuring a limited supply of four categories of skilled labor: computer engineers ($i = 1$), systems analysts ($i = 2$), computer programmers ($i = 3$) and sales personnel ($i = 4$). The industry manufactures and delivers two main categories of output: personal computers, disk drives, printers and other hardware ($k = 1$) and computer software ($k = 2$). The market prices of these outputs are set in an arena of fierce international competition, and must be taken as fixed and given by the domestic industry. The computer industry had been booming during the 1970s because of strong prices. But eventually an international overcapacity developed, and the bottom fell out of the market for computer chips. In the face of lagging prices, the domestic computer industry contracted, causing layoffs.

This particular example also illustrates another interesting feature of the modern high technology economy: the rising importance of service industries. The computing boom brought with it a proliferation of computer consulting firms of all kinds. These consultants compete head-on with the large computer manufacturers, buying hardware from many different manufacturers and packing hardware and software to suit a specific customer. In the terminology of activity analysis, such services constitute intermediate goods.

There are four activities operated in the industry:

1. various hardware manufacturers distributing their products directly to the final customers ($j = 1$),
2. various software manufacturers distributing their products directly to final customers ($j = 2$),
3. software consulting firms selling their services to final customers ($j = 3$),
4. the software consulting firm selecting and developing the software that the customer requires ($j = 4$).

In reality, there might be as many different types of hardware configurations and software contracts as there are customers. To simplify the analysis, however, we shall imagine that all configurations and contracts are standardized; the unit level of operation of activity $j = 1$ is the sale and installation of a standard hardware configuration, the unit level of operation of activities $j = 2$ and $j = 4$ is a standard software contract, and the unit level of operation of activity $j = 3$ is a standard consulting contract.

The description of the activities listed can now be made more precise with reference to the input requirements and the outputs of each activity. The unit input requirements are listed in table below.

		Activities			
	Inputs of goods	$j=1$	$j=2$	$j=3$	$j=4$
Primary:	Engineers $i = 1$	20	0	0	0
	Systems analysts $i = 2$	0	4	0	4
	Programmers $i = 3$	0	24	0	26
	Sales personnel $i = 4$	2.4	12	0	6
Intermediate:	Software consulting	0	0	1	0

The top four lines of coefficients are the matrix A^P. The bottom line is A^I.

The figures show that two kinds of specialized labor are needed to sell and install hardware: computer engineers and sales personnel (first column). Three kinds of specialized labor are needed to design software: systems analysts, programmers and sales personnel (second column). When the consulting firm packages the services, some more programming hours are needed but the requirement of sales personnel is halved (fourth column).

The unit outputs are shown in table below. The top two lines are the matrix B^F. The bottom line is B^I.

		Activities			
	Outputs of goods	$j=1$	$j=2$	$j=3$	$j=4$
Final:	Hardware $k = 1$	1	0	0	0
	Software $k = 2$	0	1	1	0
Intermediate:	Software consulting	0	0	0	1

Let the given supplies of specialized labor be (in man years)

computer engineers	300
systems analysts	160
programmers	1000
sales personnel	400

and the reservation wages below which these persons will not accept employment:

computer engineers	37.5
systems engineers	70
programmers	25
sales personnel	25

measured in thousands of dollars per year.

The prices, or rather, unit valuations, of the final goods (in thousands of dollars) are

hardware	900
software	1800

The numerical example now being developed highlights the possible scarcity of specialized labor. All other inputs, including all hardware equipment, and real and financial capital, are assumed to be procured at fixed and known market prices. The unit valuations listed above are calculated net of the unit costs of such inputs. They therefore reflect only the costs of specialized labor sunk into each product.

The data box for program (19.6) is given below.

	d_1	d_2	x_1	x_2	x_3	x_4	g_1^-	g_2^-	g_3^-	g_4^-	
u_1^F	1		-1								≤ 0
u_2^F		1		-1	-1						≤ 0
u_1^I					1	-1					$= 0$
q_1			20				1				$= 300$
q_2				4		4		1			$= 160$
q_3				24		26			1		$= 1000$
q_4			2.4	12		6				1	$= 400$
	900	1800	0	0	0	0	37.5	70	25	24	

The optimal solution found by solving the program UNEMPL on page 338 is

$$d_1^* = 15, \qquad d_2^* = 38.46$$

$$x_1^* = 15, \qquad x_2^* = 0, \qquad x_3^* = x_4^* = 38.46$$

$$g_1^{-*} = 0, \qquad g_2^{-*} = 6.15, \qquad g_3^{-*} = 0, \qquad g_4^{-*} = 133.23.$$

Activity $j = 2$ will not be operated. The consulting firms are doing a better job of packaging the software services than that the customers are able to do by developing the required software designs and programs in-house.

There is some unemployment for systems analysts and sales personnel. So, unemployment is not always a low-wage phenomenon; quite on the contrary, it can affect people who have top pay, such as systems analysts. Why? Because the supply is not critical and they have a grossly inflated reservation wage.

The corresponding dual solution is

$$u_1^{F*} = 900, \qquad u_2^{F*} = 1800, \qquad u_2^{I*} = 1800$$

$$q_1^* = 42, \qquad q_2^* = 70, \qquad q_3^* = 52.69, \qquad q_4^* = 25$$

Note that the annual wages here obtained in all cases are less than or equal to the reservation wages, as stipulated. The optimal wage coincides with the reservation wage for two categories of labor: systems analysts and sales personnel. That is as it should be: there is less than full employment for these two categories, and the excess supply forces the wage down into equality with the reservation wage.

Foreign Trade and Economic Disequilibrium

Foreign trade can also affect the internal price structure of a country's industry, by setting upper and lower bounds on the prices of the products of that industry. This has become increasingly obvious as businesses become more and more internationalized. Examples of products of such industries that compete internationally are automobiles, computer chips, television sets, machine tools, etc.

We can easily set up a disequilibrium linear programming model to capture this idea. Let y^+ and y^- be m-dimensional column vectors of imports and exports of consumer goods, and let P^+ and P^- be m-dimensional row vectors of import and export prices. Then the activity model with imports and exports can be stated as a modification of (19.6) as

$$\begin{aligned} \text{Maximize} \quad & pd - P^+y^+ + P^-y^- \\ \text{Subject to} \quad & d - Bx - y^+ + y^- \leq 0 \\ & Ax \leq W \\ & x \leq X \\ & d, x, y^+, y^- \geq 0 \end{aligned} \tag{19.10}$$

The reader may recall the similar make-or-buy model of Chapter 6. The objective function can be interpreted as the maximization of current production less the costs of imports and plus the revenues from exports. The first constraint in (19.10) can be rewritten as

$$Bx + y^+ \geq d + y^- \tag{19.11}$$

which says that production plus imports must cover internal demand plus exports. The rest of the constraints in (19.10) are the same as those in (19.6).

One necessary assumption whose economic meaning is clear is

$$P_k^+ > P_k^- \qquad \text{for } k = 1, \ldots, r. \tag{19.12}$$

Figure 19.3

Price u_k of good k as a function of demand.

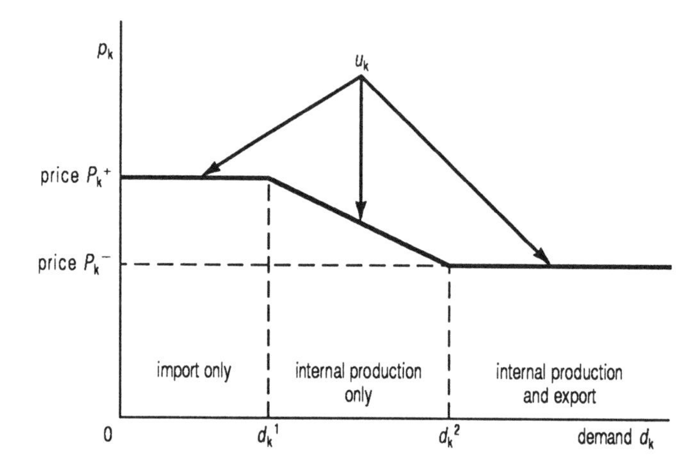

That is, the export price of each good must be smaller than its import price. From (19.12) we can easily conclude that

$$y_k^+ y_k^- = 0. \tag{19.13}$$

That is, it never pays to export and import the same good simultaneously, since doing so would cause a per unit loss to the country of $P_k^+ - P_k^- > 0$.

The dual problem for (19.10) is

$$\text{Minimize} \quad qW + sX \tag{19.14}$$

$$\begin{aligned} \text{Subject to} \quad & u \geq p \\ & -uB + qA + s \geq 0 \\ & -u \geq -P^+ \\ & u \geq P^- \\ & u, q, s \geq 0 \end{aligned}$$

Observe that three of the constraints in (19.14) involve upper or lower bounds on the price vector u. They are

$$u \geq p, \quad u \geq P^-, \quad \text{and} \quad u \leq P^+. \tag{19.15}$$

Noting that $u_k^* = p_k$ as long as demand comes out to be positive, it follows from (19.15) that the domestic price of good k must always be less than or equal to its import price, and greater than or equal to its export price. The effects of these constraints are illustrated in Figure 19.3. For low demands, $< d_k^1$, the demand for product k is covered by importing it at price P_k^+. There is no domestic production. Between d_k^1 and d_k^2, the country is self sufficient: all internal demand is covered by internal production, and there are neither exports nor imports of good k. Over this range, demand is given by the domestic demand curve. Finally, for demands d above d_k^2, the price has fallen to the point where the industry has become competitive with production in the outside world so that it exports good k at price P_k^-. The internal price of good k cannot drop further, even though the industry may become more efficient, because of the exports of the industry.

Exercises

1. Three chemical plants are located in a small town, manufacturing paint base. The production facilities vary somewhat between the three plants, and there are some differences in labor costs.

   There are three categories of labor

   1 male factory workers
   2 female factory workers
   3 laboratory staff.

   The unit labor requirements are as follows (in hours per barrel of paint base manufactured)

	labor category		
plant	*1*	*2*	*3*
1	0.20	0.10	0.03
2	0.15	0.10	0.03
3	0.10	0.08	0.04

   All labor is recruited locally; the total available workforce hours in the town is

labor category	*hours per day*
1	400
2	300
3	110

   The three plants have agreed to pay a minimum wage of $8.00 an hour to male factory workers and $5.00 an hour to female factory workers. No minimum wage has been specified for staff in the laboratories.

   The price of the finished paint base is $8.00 per barrel. The raw materials and capital charges are $4.80 per barrel.

   Construct a linear program that can be used to determine the optimal output and the optimal employment at each plant. Solve the linear program. Define and interpret the dual variables.

2. The personal computer industry produces three kinds of hardware:

	price in dollars
desktop personal computers	1500
portable personal computers for travel	2000
printers	1200

   The market is very large, both nationally and internationally, and the demand curves are approximately horizontal at the indicated price levels. Output is limited by the availability of scarce resources, primarily computer engineers, electronic chips, and installed capital. There is rapid product development and average costs are falling, but a recent study has resulted in the following estimates of the technical coefficients (= input requirements per unit of output):

	engineer hours	*chips*	*capital hours*
desktop units	4	10	300
portable units	6	8	250
printers	4	3	150

Total available inputs in the industry are:

engineer hours	800,000
chips	1,250,000
capital hours	40,000,000

The supply of chips listed above refers to chips of domestic origin. In addition, chips may be imported from abroad at a fixed price of $11.50 per chip.

Construct a linear program that can be used to determine the optimal manufacturing program in the industry, and optimal imports. Solve the linear program. Define the dual variables and interpret them.

3. In a country there are four integrated oil companies. The companies are engaged both in domestic drilling and pumping and in importing oil from abroad. The marginal cost functions of the companies are as follows (in U.S. dollars per barrel):

1	$10 + 0.010x_1$	*3*	$8 + 0.012x_2$
2	$12 + 0.008x_2$	*4*	$9 + 0.011x_4$

where x denotes the quantity pumped in millions of barrels.

Consumers have considerable brand loyalty and each company faces the following demand:

1	1200 million barrels	*3*	1000 million barrels
2	1500 million barrels	*4*	2000 million barrels

Oil can be imported from abroad at the world market price of $18.00 per barrel.

The government desires to limit total imports into the country to 500 million barrels. Construct a nonlinear programming problem that can be used to determine the optimal import duty on oil that would accomplish what is desired. (Hint: minimize total domestic production costs plus total import costs subject to the constraint that the total supply of each company meet demand, and that total imports do not exceed the set ceiling.) Define Lagrange multipliers and interpret them. Write down the Kuhn-Tucker conditions and interpret them.

Solution on a computer shows that $x_1^* = 1200$, $x_2^* = 1500$, $x_3^* = 1000$ and $x_4^* = 1500$. That is, companies 1–3 will satify their demand by domestic producton and all permitted imports will be allocated to company 4. Calculate the import duty that will be levied on the imports of company 4.

20

Input Output Economics

The concept of an input-output table was devised by W. Leontief as a way of representing the interdependencies among various productive sectors of an economy. A sector is an industry or group of industries such as steel, energy, transportation, etc. An input-output table is a square matrix whose entries indicate the inputs to each sector (products made by the same and other sectors) needed to make its own product. Given a final demand by the economy for the outputs of all sectors, it is desired to calculate for each sector the gross output necessary to cover both final demand and the corresponding internal demands arising from the other sectors.

To make this precise let us use the following notation:

$i, j = 1, \ldots, n$	indices of sectors.
$d = (d_1, \ldots, d_n)$	is the (column) vector of final demand, with all $d_i \geq 0$.
$x = (x_1, \ldots, x_n)$	is the (column) vector of gross output of sectors.
$M = \|m_{ij}\|$	is the $n \times n$ matrix of input-output coefficients; each coefficient m_{ij} denotes the quantity of deliveries from sector i required to support one unit of output of sector j, with $m_{ij} \geq 0$. (In practical input-output work, the coefficient m_{ij} is calculated as the value of purchases from sector i required to produce a dollar's worth of output of sector j.)
$p = (p_1, \ldots, p_n)$	is the (row) vector of prices or outputs.
$N = \|n_{ij}\|$	is the $n \times n$ matrix of unit labor requirements; each coefficient n_{ij} is the amount of labor from sector i required to support one unit of output of sector j; it is assumed that $n_{ij} = 0$ for $i \neq j$, i.e., the matrix N is diagonal.
$q = (q_1, \ldots, q_n)$	is the (row) vector of wage rates.

Using vector matrix notation with x being the production vector of the whole economy, it is easy to see that Mx is the internal (or inter-sector) demand, so that x must satisfy the following equation:

$$x = Mx + d. \tag{20.1}$$

In other words x must equal internal demand plus final demand. Rewriting (20.1) gives

$$(I - M)x = d. \tag{20.2}$$

where I is the $n \times n$ unit matrix (all elements on the main diagonal are one, all off-diagonal elements are zero). If the matrix $(I - M)$ has an inverse then the solution to (20.2) is

$$x = (I - M)^{-1}d. \tag{20.3}$$

If the inverse is nonnegative $(I - M)^{-1} \geq 0$ and if $d \geq 0$ it follows that $x \geq 0$. The latter result is obviously necessary in order that the solution have economic interpretations.

In order to find a condition under which we can be sure that the inverse of $(I - M)$ exists and is nonnegative we observe that the entries of Md can be interpreted as "one stage demands." Similarly, the entries of $M(Md) = M^2d$ can be interpreted as "two stage demands," etc., and the entries of M^kd can be interpreted as "k-stage demands." It is intuitively clear that in order for an economy to be able to function, the k-stage demands must tend to zero when k gets large. A sufficient condition for M^kd to tend to zero is

$$M^k \longrightarrow 0. \tag{20.4}$$

(This means each component of $M^k \longrightarrow 0$ as $k \longrightarrow \infty$.) It can be shown that condition (20.4) is a necessary and sufficient condition that the inverse of $(I - M)$ should exist and be nonnegative.

Typical applications of the Leontief system involve situations where one wants to compute the economic effects of some given change of the vector of final demand, such as a military buildup or an increased government welfare program. The initial stimulus will then be propagated throughout the economy as each producer places orders for increased inputs. This multiplicative expansion can be illustrated mathematically in the following fashion. Since total production must equal the sum of the final demands plus one-stage demands plus two-stage demands, etc., it follows that

$$\begin{aligned} x &= d + Md + M^2d + M^3d + \cdots \\ &= (I + M + M^2 + \cdots)d \end{aligned} \tag{20.5}$$

hence, comparing with (20.3), we see that

$$(I - M)^{-1} = I + M + M^2 + \cdots \tag{20.6}$$

These equations show how a change in demand can have a ripple effect throughout the whole economy.

Using the row vector p to represent the prices of the various products, we note that the output markets are in equilibrium when

$$p[(I - M)x - d] = 0. \tag{20.7}$$

We will shortly show how to calculate these prices.

One thing missing from the model so far is labor. Most Leontief tables include the unit labor requirements for each sector. It is assumed that each sector employs only one kind of labor (steel plants employ steel workers, mining companies employ miners, etc.). In other words, letting n_{ij} be the per unit requirements of labor for sectors $i = 1, \ldots, n$, one must have $n_{ij} = 0$ for $i \neq j$. The matrix $N = \|n_{ij}\|$ is then a diagonal matrix and the total labor required to generate gross output x is given by the product Nx.

If labor were the only factor of production, and if there were present excess labor (i.e., unemployment) in each category of labor, it would indeed be possible to step up gross output as shown in equation (20.5) without causing any pressure on wages and prices.

Let us now take a look at the implied assumptions of the conventional Leontief system. Let there be a horizontal supply curve for labor of each category. The row vector of given and fixed wage rates is denoted by q. The vector of total labor costs per unit of gross output is then obtained as qN. If labor is the only factor of production, these labor costs per unit of output must at least exhaust the value of net output ("value added") per unit of output, that is,

$$p(I - M) \leq qN. \tag{20.8}$$

Equilibrium in the labor markets require that

$$[p(I - M) - qN]x = 0 \tag{20.9}$$

i.e., for all goods and services which are being produced in positive quantities, there must be equality between value added and labor costs per unit of output; but if for some good, labor costs exceed the value added per unit of output, then production would occur at a loss, and output of that good would drop to zero.

The complete Leontief system consists of relations (20.2) and (20.7) through (20.9). As it so happens, the solution to this system can be obtained as the optimal solution to the following linear programming model:

$$\begin{aligned} &\text{Minimize} && (qN)x \\ &\text{Subject to} && (I - M)x \geq d \\ & && x \geq 0 \end{aligned} \tag{20.10}$$

To see this, consider also the corresponding dual program

$$\begin{aligned} &\text{Maximize} && pd \\ &\text{Subject to} && p(I - M) \leq (qN) \\ & && p \geq 0 \end{aligned} \tag{20.11}$$

From these two programs, relations (20.2) and (20.7) can be retrieved as the direct constraints and the conditions of complementary slackness in the direct program; relations (20.8) and (20.9) can be retrieved as the dual constraints and the conditions of complementary slackness in the dual program.

Furthermore, the duality theorem shows that, at the point of optimum

$$(qN)x^* = p^*d \tag{20.12}$$

i.e., the value of total final demand is exactly exhausted by all wage payments.

It is instructive to reflect on the nature of linear programming in the present application. There is no optimization formulation involved in the Leontief system as such; rather, the linear program is formed as a mathematical artifact designed to facilitate the solution of the given model (20.1) and (20.7) through (20.9). The solution emerges as if some central planning agency were charged with the task of minimizing total wage payments in the system (maximizing the value of final demand). In a capitalist economy, there is of course no such central planning agency. The workings of the competitive market mechanism accomplishes what the planning agency would be supposed to do.

Imbedding the Leontief System in a Framework of Scarce Labor Resources: Vertical Supply Curves for All Categories of Labor

Conventional Leontief calculations include the assumptions of constant wages and constant prices. At the going wage rates there is an infinite supply of labor of every category. But in the real world, the excess supply of at least some categories of labor eventually will be exhausted. Some wage rates will start rising, and prices will be pushed from the cost side. In order to study these phenomena, we shall proceed to imbed the Leontief model in a setting of scarce resources with given and known supply curves of labor and other factors. A given increase in final demand will then result in some increase in real outputs, and in some increase in output prices. In the extreme case, where there exists no excess of supply of resources at all, there will be no increase of gross output whatsoever. The entire effect of the initial stimulus of final demand will take the form of higher prices.

In order to achieve what is desired, we shall now give an explicit account of the wage formation for each category of labor.

We need the following additional notation:

$w = (w_1, \ldots, w_n)$ (column) vector of available labor.

$b = (b_1, \ldots, b_n)$ (row) vector of unit capital charges; b_j is the charge for interest payments, profit, and taxes per unit of output in sector i.

Equilibrium in the labor markets requires

$$Nx \leq w \tag{20.13}$$

$$q(Nx - w) = 0 \tag{20.14}$$

Clearly we have now gone beyond the scope of the original Leontief conception: we are imbedding the input-matrix in a setting of equilibrium that includes the determination of prices in the resource markets.

Second, we need to recognize that there are other resources (i.e., factors of production) than labor that are needed in order to maintain the production process; to wit: financial and real capital. The sum total of these charges assessed in the economy is bx. Relations (20.8) and (20.9) should then be amended to read

$$p(I - M) \leq qN + b \tag{20.15}$$

$$[p(I - M)p - qN - b]x = 0. \tag{20.16}$$

For all goods and services which are produced in positive quantities, there must be equality between value added and total factor payments per unit of output. If for some good the factor payments exceed the value added, production would occur at a loss, and output would drop to zero.

The complete system now consists of relations (20.1), (20.7), (20.15) and (20.16). The solution can be obtained as the optimal solution of the following linear program:

$$\begin{aligned} \text{Minimize} \quad & bx \\ \text{Subject to} \quad & (I - M)x \geq d \\ & -Nx \geq -w \\ & x \geq 0 \end{aligned} \tag{20.17}$$

The corresponding dual program is:

$$\begin{aligned} \text{Maximize} \quad & (pd - qw) \\ \text{Subject to} \quad & p(I - M) - qN \leq b \\ & p, q \geq 0 \end{aligned} \tag{20.18}$$

The original system can be retrieved from the direct and dual constraints, and from the relations of complementary slackness.

Example 1. In order to illustrate the above numerically, consider a developing country with three sectors: agriculture, mining, and construction. An input-output study has yielded the data shown below.

	Agriculture	*Mining*	*Construction*
Agriculture	0.1	0.3	0.25
Mining	0.25	0.15	0.18
Construction	0.2	0.2	0.12
Capital Charge	0.2	0.2	0.3
Labor Charge	0.25	0.15	0.15
Sums	1.0	1.0	1.0

The 3×3 matrix at the top is the input-output matrix M. The entries in each column show the dollar purchases required to sustain one dollar's worth of output in that sector. Correspondingly the entries in each row indicate the dollar sales by that sector to the other sectors.

The entries in rows 4 and 5 above show the payments to capital and labor. Each column displays all costs that a given sector will incur in producing one dollar's worth of output: first the inter sector purchases, then the capital charges, and the labor charges. The entries in each column sum to one.

The sum of the capital charge and labor cost is the "value added" per dollar of output. It consists of payments to capital (both interest and profit) and to labor (wages and salaries).

The input-output coefficients have been computed with reference to some base year. (In the U.S., the most recent input-output table refers to 1977. See *Survey of Current Business*, May 1984 for a summary with 85 sectors.) Suppose that the final demand (consumption demand, investment demand, government demand and exports) during the base year was: agriculture, 9 billion dollars; mining, 12 billion dollars; construction, 15 billion dollars.

In order to solve for the vector of gross outputs we now turn to program (20.10) and the data box below.

	x_1	x_2	x_3	
p_1	0.90	−0.30	−0.25	≥ 9
p_2	−0.25	0.85	−0.18	≥ 12
p_3	−0.20	−0.20	0.88	≥ 15
	0.45	0.35	0.45	

The solution gives gross outputs of

$$x_1^* = 27.85 \text{ billion dollars in agriculture}$$
$$x_2^* = 28.64 \text{ billion dollars in mining}$$
$$x_3^* = 29.88 \text{ billion dollars in construction}$$

and the dual solution is $p_1^* = p_2^* = p_3^* = 1$. The price level in each sector is a price index which for the base year equals unity.

When applying the input-output model one typically wants to find the effects on gross output of some proposed program of boosted final demand, caused, for instance, by the initiation of a large irrigation project. Examining the model above, we see that prices will stay the same and that gross output will expand as required.

It is common to compute and publish the unit labor requirement coefficients (the diagonal vector N) in conjunction with the input-output data. (For the U.S. unit labor coefficients, see *Survey of Current Business*, Nov. 1985). Let them be

	workers per $1000 of gross output
agriculture	$n_{11} = 0.150$
mining	$n_{22} = 0.100$
construction	$n_{33} = 0.200$

The labor coefficients were obtained by dividing the total employment in each sector by gross output in the sector. The employment figures in the base year were

	million workers
agriculture	4.177
mining	2.864
construction	5.976

The figures listed obviously constitute the demand for labor. But what can we say about the *supply* of labor; and how do we measure the supply of labor?

One statistical approach to the measurement of supply is to start out from demographic data about the number of men and women in ages 18–65, and then to multiply by labor force participation rates and employment rates. If the employment rate is 100%, one would end up with a figure equal to the actual employment. But if there is some unemployment, the supply figure would be greater than the actual employment.

Most countries collect data on unemployment rates. In the U.S., the Bureau of Labor Statistics defines an unemployed person as one who did not work during a survey week, but who was available for work except for temporary illness and had looked for jobs within the preceding 4 weeks. Persons who did not look for work because they were laid off or waiting to start new jobs within the next 30 days were also counted among the unemployed.

Suppose that the unemployment rate in each sector is 5%. Then the total supply of labor is obtained by dividing the employment figures by 0.95, giving

	million workers
agriculture	$w_1 = 4.397$
mining	$w_2 = 3.015$
construction	$w_3 = 6.275$

Program (20.17) now yields the data box below.

	x_1	x_2	x_3	
p_1	0.90	−0.30	−0.25	≥ 9
p_2	−0.25	0.85	−0.18	≥ 12
p_3	−0.20	−0.20	0.88	≥ 15
q_1	0.15			≤ 4.397
q_2		0.10		≤ 3.015
q_3			0.20	≤ 6.275
	0.20	0.20	0.30	

The three first constraints of the data box are the market balances for outputs of the three sectors. The corresponding dual variables are the prices; in the optimum solution they are all equal to unity. By complementary slackness, the three first constraints are then all tight at the optimum. Final demand is exactly satisfied.

The three latter constraints of the data box are the market constraints for labor. They turn out to be all slack at the optimum, with the slack being interpreted as the amount of unemployment in each sector.

But there is one problem with the program exhibited after its solution is found by solving `LEONTIEF` on page 339. The optimal wage rates, the duals of the labor market balances, have all dropped to zero. This result does not square with the statistical data. Actually, the wage rates in the three sectors in the base year can be computed as the ratio between the unit labor charge and the unit labor requirement

	$1000 per year
agriculture	1.67
mining	1.50
construction	0.75

Since these wage rates are being established in the face of a positive unemployment in each sector, these rates can be identified as the *reservation wages*. Amending the preceding mathematical program, and seeing to it that no market wage can fall below its reservation wage (see Chapter 19), we arrive at the data box below.

x_1	x_2	x_3	g_1^-	g_2^-	g_3^-	
0.90	−0.30	−0.25				≥ 9
−0.25	0.85	−0.18				≥ 12
−0.20	−0.20	0.88				≥ 15
0.15			1			$= 4.397$
	0.10			1		$= 3.015$
		0.20			1	$= 6.275$
0.20	0.20	0.30	−1.67	−1.5	−0.75	

The three new unknowns g_1^-, g_2^- and g_3^- represent unemployment in the three sectors. The optimal values found by solving the GAMS program `LEONTIEF1` on page 340 are:

	million workers
agriculture	0.220
mining	0.151
construction	0.299

which is precisely the difference between the earlier figures for supply and demand, respectively. The duals of the labor market constraints are:

	\$1000 per year
agriculture	$q_1 = 1.67$
mining	$q_2 = 1.50$
construction	$q_3 = 0.75$

as specified. In other words, since there is positive unemployment in each sector, the market wage has fallen to become equal to the reservation wage.

Consider the effects of the irrigation project mentioned before. Suppose that final demand is increased to

	billion dollars
agriculture	$d_1 = 9.6$
mining	$d_2 = 12.5$
construction	$d_3 = 15.5$

Optimal gross output now is

	billion dollars
agriculture	$x_1^* = 29.25$
mining	$x_2^* = 29.89$
construction	$x_3^* = 30.06$

and total employment has increased to

	million workers
agriculture	4.388
mining	2.989
construction	6.211

There is still unemployment in each sector; the wage rate in each sector still equals the reservation wage. But the reserve of unemployed persons is rapidly being exhausted. If final demand is increased somewhat more, say to

	billion dollars
agriculture	9.7
mining	12.5
construction	15.5

then an attempt to solve the linear program yields the result that no feasible solution exists. The existing labor supply does not permit the suggested expansion of final demand.

Exercises

1. Solve the numerical example in the data box on page 260 for the following final demand vectors, and show that the answers are as stated in the text.
   (a) $d = (9.6, 12.5, 15.5)$
   (b) $d = (9.7, 12.5, 15.5)$.

2. Analyze other proposed construction projects by solving the data box on page 260 for the following demand vectors:
   (a) $d = (11, 10, 14)$
   (b) $d = (11, 10, 15)$
   (c) $d = (8, 13, 11)$
   (d) Which group or groups of workers would like to see each of these projects be adopted?

3. The input-output table of a small developing nation has been consolidated into three sectors

   $i = 1$ agriculture
   $i = 2$ manufacturing
   $i = 3$ services

   The matrix of input-output coefficients $M = \|m_{ij}\|$ $(i, j = 1, 2, 3)$ reads

$$M = \begin{bmatrix} 0.20 & 0.15 & 0.20 \\ 0.15 & 0.10 & 0.05 \\ 0.10 & 0.05 & 0.15 \end{bmatrix}$$

   where m_{ij} denotes the value of purchases from sector i required to produce a dollar's worth of output of sector j. Final demand is $d = (3000, 2000, 1000)$.

(a) Introducing suitable additional unknowns, write down the Leontief equations.

(b) Write a linear program minimizing the sum total of all value added in this economy, subject to the requirement that net output in each sector must suffice to cover final demand. Solve it.

(c) Write the corresponding dual program, interpret and solve it.

PART IV

Portfolios & Financial Planning

INTRODUCTION

An economist makes a distinction between real capital (such as a plant or machinery) and financial capital (such as a demand deposit). Financial capital is a claim issued by a debtor. The claim is a debt or a liability of the issuer, and a financial asset of the party who holds the asset. A demand deposit is a debt of the issuing bank and an asset of the person or the firm which holds the deposit.

Financial claims can be bought and sold in financial markets. Federal funds are overnight debt issued by commercial banks in the United States and held by other commercial banks (in Great Britain, Federal funds are called interbank funds). In effect, it is an overnight loan from one bank (the holder of the funds) to another (the issuer). Some banks need overnight cash and others have a surplus of liquidity. The market for Federal funds is made up of all banks demanding overnight funds or supplying overnight funds. The market rate or interest rate on Federal funds is the price that the borrowers have to pay and that the lenders will collect.

Often an original issue of debt is resold by the first purchaser and transacted in a *secondary market*. The secondary market for government debt (United States Treasury bonds or Treasury bills) is the market in which holders of such paper, desiring to sell, meet investors desiring to buy. The seller (say a private person having bought some government bonds one year ago) is not the same as the issuer (the Treasury). Neither may the buyer (a commercial bank, say) need to be the same party which eventually, at the time of redemption, collects the nominal sum of the original debt.

Cash is financial capital because it is a claim on the central bank.

The liquidity of an asset refers to the *exchangeability* of that asset into cash. Liquid assets, such as a cashier's check drawn on a large local bank or an American Express travellers check or a Unites States government Treasury bill can be converted into cash quickly and at little or no cost. The market for such assets is broad and the price is very close to unity (a nominal dollar held in the asset can be converted to a dollar of cash). Other assets, such as an out-of-town check drawn on a small bank, a corporate bond, or a trade bill drawn on a foreign importer, may have a quite low liquidity, which means that the market for the asset is thin and that it will take time and cost money to convert the asset into cash. The market price is substantially below the nominal price.

The *return* on an asset is the sum of the interest paid and possible price appreciation of the asset. The return on a government bond is the sum of the coupon and the appreciation of the bond over the period of time considered. The rate of return is the return divided by the initial market value.

Most financial capital is *risky* in that there is a risk that the value of the claim might deteriorate. The value of a claim may depreciate for two reasons: because the price of the claim may actually fall in the market, and/or because the issuer of the claim may fail to meet his obligations (fail to pay the stipulated interest in a timely manner and/or fail to pay back the principal when coming due.) The first kind of risk is called price risk, the second kind of risk is default risk.

Because of the presence of risk, the return on an asset is actually subject to random variation. It is stochastic. If the price appreciates and if the issuer of the claim meets his obligations, there might be a good return on the asset. But if the price in the market falls, and/or if there are repayment irregularities, the net return after default cost may be low or even negative.

Financial markets typically offer the possibility of a trade-off between liquidity, expected return, and risk. If you choose to invest your savings in liquid low-risk financial capital, say in United States government bonds, you will have to remain content with a comparatively low expected return. If you are prepared to forego some liquidity and willing to accept a somewhat higher risk, like investing in a corporate bond, you should be able to expect a higher return.

Common stock is not financial capital. It is not a claim, it is equity, i.e., it is real capital.

The word "securities" is commonly employed to cover both claims (such as a corporate bond) and common stock. A *portfolio* is a collection of securities held by some economic entity, such as the portfolio of a private investor, a corporation, or a bank.

The theoretical treatment of financial capital and of common stock is quite similar. An investor typically is looking for a balanced portfolio, which includes both financial capital and common stock. Financial capital is held to provide liquidity and some expected return. Common stock is less liquid, is riskier than financial capital, but often has the potential of a greater return (= dividends + price appreciation).

Portfolio Selection

The art of allocating a given sum of money among alternative holdings of securities is called investing, or portfolio selection. By diversification it is possible to reduce the overall risk content of a portfolio while still maintaining its yield. For instance, buying some corporate stock issued by oil companies and some stock issued by aircraft manufacturers will result in a lower overall risk than placing all funds in just one of these two alternatives.

The Nobel prize in economics in 1990 went to Harry Markowitz, William Sharpe, and Merton Miller. The trio led a revolution in finance that began in the 1950s and by now has changed the world of investment brokers, bankers, and financial consultants. Markowitz defined the risk of owning securities as variance, a statistical concept, and rigorously developed the principles governing the way that portfolio variance, or risk, is affected by adding and/or subtracting individual securities from a portfolio. The major lesson implied by this procedure is that a portfolio can offer a superior return for given risk (variance) than can an individual security. This may sound like a pretty obvious proposition, but it was contrary to the accepted wisdom of an earlier era which was preoccupied with efforts to pick winners on Wall Street.

The emphasis on diversification and portfolio management is at the heart of practical investment management today. Recent innovations such as options, index funds, and program trading were all developed to heighten the efficiency of portfolio management.

Notes on Literature Relevant to Part IV

The purpose of the cash management procedure to be dealt with in Chapter 21 is to plan for the cash receipts and cash disbursement of an individual firm. Mathematically, the plan takes the form of an optimal time path of holdings of cash and short term assets, and short term borrowings, as required. A pioneering paper in this field is due to Charnes, Cooper, and Miller [1]. In a simple warehouse model, these authors added a deterministic liquidity constraint that places lower limits on the cash balances that the owner of the warehouse deems necessary to hold in each time period. To satisfy this requirement, the operator is permitted to engage in borrowing and lending in short term financial investments. The credit flows over time were illustrated by an intertemporal network.

Building similar network formats, Rutenberg [5] analyzed the cash management problem in the setting of a multinational company. This paper also included the spatial aspect of cash management, as encountered in the optimal use of tax havens and bilateral tax agreements, and the optimal short term investment and borrowing strategy in several different countries.

Chapter 22 takes the reader to the classical field of portfolio selection. In his original 1952 paper [2], Harry Markowitz defined the concept of risk diversification. The goal of the portfolio manager should be to minimize portfolio risk for any level of expected returns. Such a portfolio was called efficient. The locus of efficient portfolios was called the efficiency frontier.

In 1956 Markowitz developed a computer algorithm known as the critical line method which solved for various portfolios along the efficiency frontier [3]. In 1959, he published a large applied study sponsored by the Cowles Commission [4].

Harry Markowitz and William Sharpe worked together at Rand Corporation in the late 1950s and early 1960s. Sharpe developed a simplified model for portfolio analysis, featuring his "beta" measure of risk [6].

Sharpe has also been a leading figure in converting these early academic concepts into practical computer packages used in the financial community. His "ATT Asset Allocation Tool" [7] includes algorithms and extensive financial data bases.

References

1. Charnes, A., W. W. Cooper and M. H. Miller, "Application of Linear Programming to Financial Budgeting and the Costing of Funds," *Journal of Business of the University of Chicago*, Vol. 32, Jan. 1959, pp. 20–46.

2. Markowitz, H. M., "Portfolio Selection," *Journal of Finance*, Vol. 7, March 1952, pp. 77–91.
3. Markowitz, H. M., "The Optimization of a Quadratic Function Subject to Linear Constraints," *Naval Research Logistics Quarterly*, Vol. 3, March and June 1956, pp. 111–133.
4. Markowitz, H. M., *Portfolio Selection: Efficient Diversification of Investment*, Cowles Commission Monograph No. 16, Wiley, New York 1959.
5. Rutenberg, D. P., "Maneuvering Liquid Assets in a Multi-National Company: Formulations and Deterministic Solution Procedures," *Management Science*, Vol. 16, No. 10, June 1970, pp. B671–684.
6. Sharpe, W. F., "A Simplified Model for Portfolio Analysis," *Management Science*, Vol. 9, Jan. 1963, pp. 277–93.
7. Sharpe, W. F., *AAT Asset Allocation Tools*, The Scientific Press, Redwood City, Calif. 1985, 2nd ed. 1987.

21

Cash Management

Consider the short term cash management problem faced by the financial officer of a small corporation. The corporation receives payments from customers at certain times, and must make payments to suppliers at other times. The officer can invest excess cash in short term paper, such as corporate certificates of deposit and treasury notes, and can borrow for short periods of time from banks. We can represent investments as payments, with interest, to the corporation at a future time. Similarly, borrowing can be represented as payments from the corporation's future cash account to the present, less necessary interest charges.

There are many aspects to a cash management problem. One is the question of determining the optimal geographical location of lock-boxes at which customers of a bank or company can make deposits or pay bills. Another is the issue of finding an optimal portfolio that balances cash on hand and short-term investments. Here we shall focus on yet another problem: the optimal maturity structure of a portfolio containing both short term claims and short term debt.

In order to highlight the problem of maturity structure we assume that any purchase of a claim remains perfectly illiquid until it matures (is redeemed). It can not be converted into cash before that time. At maturity, the claim is paid together with accumulated interest. Similarly, any contracted debt cannot be shifted or sold but remains on the books of the debtor until maturity. The interest for the entire borrowing period is deducted up front so that the net cash proceeds at the time of the borrowing equal the principal minus the total interest that will be charged. At the time of maturity, the original principal is to be paid back.

To formulate the problem we use the following notation:

$s, t = 1, \ldots, n$	indices of time periods, n is the last period (the planning horizon).
x_{st} with $s < t$	purchase of claim (lending) in time period s, maturing in time period t.

r_{st} with $s < t$	rate of interest obtained from investment x_{st}, $s < t$ (calculated over $t - s$ time periods).
x_{st} with $s > t$	issue of debt (borrowing) in time period t falling due in period s.
r_{st} with $s > t$	rate of interest charged on debt issued in period t and falling due in period s (calculated over $s - t$ periods).
a_t	cash receipts in period t.
b_t	cash outlays in period t.
P, L	P is the total buildup of cash available in period n (P = "profit"); a negative accumulation of cash is denoted L (L = "loss").

The intertemporal maturity management problem aims to maximize the total buildup of cash at the planning horizon. There is a budget constraint in each time period which states that the total sum of the cash funds coming available (cash receipts a_t, maturing claims redeemed, and debt issued) must equal the sum of the cash needs (cash outlays b_t, repayment of maturing debt, and new purchases of investments). Mathematically,

$$\text{Maximize} \quad P - L$$

$$\text{Subject to} \quad \sum_{s=1}^{t-1} (1 + r_{st})x_{st} + \sum_{s=t+1}^{n} (1 - r_{st})x_{st} - \sum_{s=1}^{t-1} x_{ts} - \sum_{s=t+1}^{n} x_{ts} = -a_t + b_t, \quad t = 1, \ldots, n-1 \tag{21.1}$$

$$\sum_{s=1}^{n-1} (1 + r_{sn})x_{sn} - \sum_{s=1}^{n-1} x_{ns} - P + L = -a_n + b_n$$

$$x_{st} \geq 0, \qquad s, t = 1, \ldots, n$$

$$P, L \geq 0.$$

Note that this is a network flow with gains model similar to the personnel model of Chapter 12.

The network flow model for a simple four period problem is shown in Figure 21.1. In the figure one can see that the corporation expects payments of $300 at times 1 and 4, and must make payments of $100 and $400 at times 2 and 3, respectively. The various interest factors for lending and borrowing are shown in the triangles on each arc. Clearly long term lending is more profitable than short term lending. For instance, a loan for one period yields 4 percent, while a loan for three periods yields 16 percent. Similarly, short term borrowing costs less than long term, since borrowing for one period cost 5 percent, while borrowing for two or three periods costs 11 and 18 percent, respectively. The two arcs attached to node 4 marked P and L are included to make the sum of inflows and outflows add to zero at that node.

Using the network flow diagram of Figure 21.1, we can derive the data box shown below. Observe that the objective function is to maximize profits if there are any, and

Figure 21.1

Network flow model for cash management example.

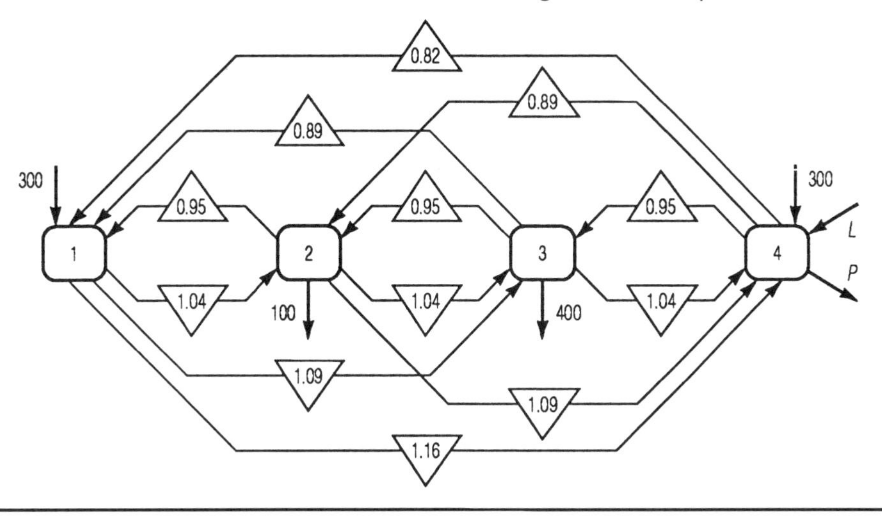

otherwise to minimize losses. It is easy to see that the model can not simultaneously have both profits and losses.

	lending arcs						*borrowing arcs*								
	x_{12}	x_{13}	x_{14}	x_{23}	x_{24}	x_{34}	x_{21}	x_{31}	x_{41}	x_{32}	x_{42}	x_{43}	P	L	
u_1	−1	−1	−1	0	0	0	0.95	0.89	0.82	0	0	0	0	0	= −300
u_2	1.04	0	0	−1	−1	0	−1	0	0	0.95	0.89	0	0	0	= 100
u_3	0	1.09	0	1.04	0	−1	0	−1	0	−1	0	0.95	0	0	= 400
u_4	0	0	1.16	0	1.09	1.04	0	0	−1	0	−1	−1	1	−1	= −300
	0	0	0	0	0	0	0	0	0	0	0	0	+1	−1	

The problem above was solved using the program CASHMAN on page 341. The primal solution is shown graphically in Figure 21.2. Note that the \$300 received in period 1 are immediately invested long term for three periods while short term borrowing is used to pay bills of \$100 and \$400 at periods 2 and 3, respectively. Profits of \$116.14 is obtained, of which \$100 comes from the excess of receipts over expenditures and \$16.14 comes from the excess of the interest received over the interest paid.

The dual solution variables have been entered on the left of the data box above. There is one dual variable u_t for each node in the graph corresponding to time periods. The optimal solution is

$$u_1^* = 1.160, \qquad u_2^* = 1.108, \qquad u_3^* = 1.053, \qquad u_4^* = 1.000.$$

The interpretation of these dual variables is easy. They are the net rates of return that can be obtained from having an additional dollar to invest at each time period; i.e., 16 percent at time 1, 10.8 percent at time 2, 5.3 percent at time 3, and 0 percent at time 4.

Figure 21.2

Solution for cash management example.

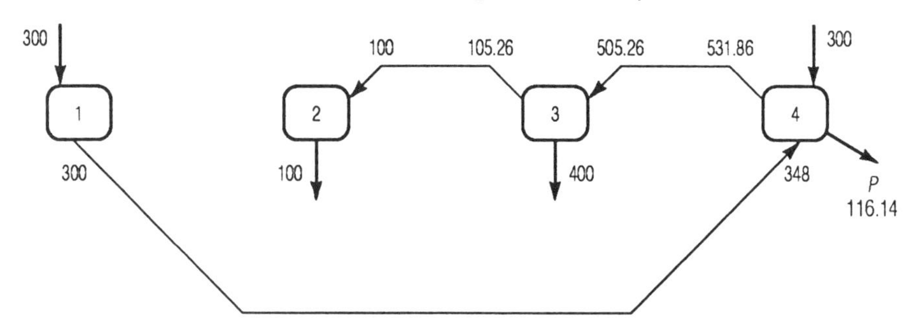

Exercises

1. Solve the numerical example shown in Figure 21.1 when only \$100 is received at time 1 instead of \$300. Now there is a net loss of \$115.86 instead of a profit. The difference between this loss and the previous profit is \$232 of which \$200 is the reduction in receipts and \$32 is reduction in interest earned. The dual solution remains the same.
2. Solve a cash management problem with the following data: $n = 5$, and

t	*rate (%) lending*	*rate (%) borrowing*	*receipts*	*payments*
1	2	4	1000	—
2	5	9	500	2000
3	8	14	1500	—
4	11	19	—	1700
5	14	24	500	—

   The rates displayed are for the maturities indicated. For any maturity, rates are assumed to remain constant over time. Receipts and payments are for the time periods indicated. Discuss interpretations for values of the primal and dual variables.

3. Consider the problem in Figure 21.1 again, and assume that management has imposed an upper limit of \$300 on the total amount of debt that it is willing to contract at any time. Solve the new problem. Interpret the dual variable of the new constraint.

4. Devise a model for the management of the maturities of foreign debt for a developing country. At the beginning of the first time period, there is an initial debt portfolio with given maturities. In each time period there are cash receipts (= exports) and cash expenditures (= imports). A target horizon debt is set. In each time period, the country's treasury can invest funds and/or contract new debt. Construct a small numerical example and solve it.

22

Common Stock Portfolios

The problem of selecting an optimal portfolio of common stocks was originally solved by H. Markowitz (see the bibliographic notes). As we shall see, his analysis leads to the formulation of a quadratic programming problem with linear constraints.

Consider an investor who has available a given sum of money to be invested in $i = 1, \ldots, n$ different stocks. The stocks are risky in that the price p_i of each stock to be quoted at the end of the planning period is unknown and random.

Let the investor buy x_i shares of stock i. The value of the entire stock portfolio is then

$$\sum_{i=1}^{n} p_i x_i$$

Since the prices p_i are random, the value of the portfolio is also random.

Total return on a stock can take two forms: dividends and a possible appreciation of price. Both forms of return will be covered by the analysis to follow, since we assume that the stock price is quoted to include dividends paid.

At this point we need some simple results from probability theory. For background material the reader may wish to consult an introductory text in statistics.

We need the concepts of mathematical expectation, variance and covariance. The operator E is used to denote mathematical expectation so that Ep_i is the expected price of stock i. It is defined as

$$Ep_i = (\sum p_i)/N.$$

The summation is to be carried out over a number N of price observations over time. To simplify notation, the index of these observations is not shown explicitly. For instance, we may have recorded the price of the stock during a 52 week period, and the expected price is then the average price during the entire year.

Suppose a portfolio contains n stocks, with x_i being the number of shares of stock i owned, and p_i its price. Then to compute its expected value, we note that the operator E obeys the following simple additive rule:

$$E\left(\sum_{i=1}^{n} p_i x_i\right) = \sum_{i=1}^{n} (Ep_i) x_i . \tag{22.1}$$

The expected value of the entire portfolio equals the sum of the expected values of the holdings of each stock.

Next, the operator Cov will be used to denote covariance. The covariance between the price of stock i and the price of stock j is defined as

$$\text{Cov } (p_i, p_j) = [\Sigma \, (p_i - Ep_i)(p_j - Ep_j)]/N$$

where again the summation is to be carried out over the number of price observations over time. In particular, the variance of the price of a stock is defined to be the covariance of the price of the stock with itself, i.e.,

$$\text{Var } p_i = [\Sigma \, (p_i - Ep_i)^2]/N.$$

The operator Var obeys the rule

$$\text{Var}\left(\sum_{i=1}^{n} p_i x_i\right) = \sum_{i=1}^{n} \sum_{j=1}^{n} \text{Cov } (p_i, p_j) x_i x_j \tag{22.2}$$

which means that the variance of the entire portfolio depends upon the covariances of all the price pairs.

The expected value of a given portfolio and the variance of the portfolio, as calculated, reflect the current and past variablility of prices. Hence they reflect historic risk. But will these calculations present a fair representation of the expected future course of prices, and the inherent future risk in the portfolio?

If the underlying probabilistic structure of stock prices remains unchanged over time, it would indeed in principle be possible to extrapolate future risk from historic risk. But prices on the stock exchange also are affected by the interpretation by stock investors of a continuous stream of new information about investments concerning such things as new technologies and new market potentials. This new information may not, even implicitly, be contained in past information. If so, there will arise systematic errors if we try to deduce future risk from past risk.

We shall later explain some more sophisticated methods of forecasting the expected return and expected risk. At the moment, we shall stick to the historic risk estimates E and the variance V.

The complete notation to be used in our model is listed below:

$i, j = 1, \ldots, n$	are indices of stocks.
$x = (x_1, \ldots, x_n)$	the (column) vector of the number of shares of each stock held, to be determined.
$p = (p_1, \ldots, p_n)$	the (row) vector of stock prices at the end of the planning period, random.
$p^0 = (p_1^0, \ldots, p_n^0)$	current stock prices.
M	sum of money available for investments.
λ	parameter, indicating the unwillingness of the investor to assume risk.

Figure 22.1

Feasible region of portfolios.

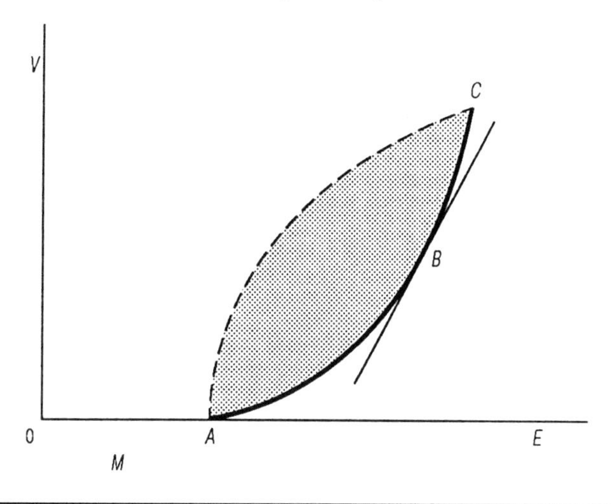

The budget constraint of the investor may then be written

$$\sum_{i=1}^{n} p_i^0 x_i \leq M. \tag{22.3}$$

The inequality sign in (22.3) may be changed to an equality sign if it is understood that there is always available one risk free investment alternative, say for index $i = n$, which may be taken to be holding cash.

For any given vector of stock holdings x one may compute E and V as given by (22.1) and (22.2), respectively. The set of all x that satisfies the budget constraint (22.3) and the nonnegativity condition $x \geq 0$ is the set of *feasible portfolios*.

The set of all feasible portfolios defines a feasible region in (E, V) space that is illustrated schematically in Figure 22.1 (shaded area). Point A represents the alternative at which the entire portfolio is placed in cash. Its mathematical expectation is then M, and its risk measured by V is zero. If some part of M is placed in common stock, there will be positive risk. The mathematical expectation may increase if the choice of stocks is made wisely and if there is at least one stock that offers the prospect of its price rising. The highest mathematical expectation can be achieved by investing the entire sum M in the one stock which holds the promise of the greatest appreciation; presumably this alternative will also entail the greatest risk (point C in Figure 22.1).

Using terms analogous to those introduced in Chapter 16, we shall say that a point (E^1, V^1) in (E, V) space *dominates* (E, V) if $E^1 \geq E$ and $V^1 \leq V$ with at least one inequality being strict. The set of all points (E^1, V^1) that dominate point (E, V) is shown geometrically in Figure 22.2. Observe that any point (E^1, V^1) located to the "south-east" of (E, V) (but still in the positive orthant) is in the dominating set. Points in the dominating set of (E, V) are clearly preferred to (E, V), because they have the same or higher expected return with the same or lower variance.

Figure 22.2

Dominating set for (E, V).

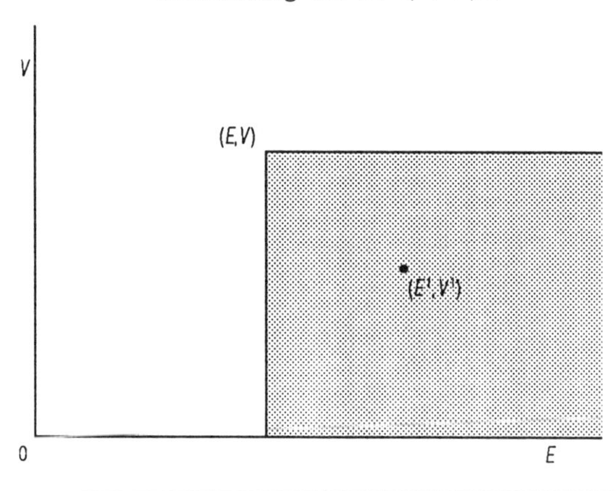

Returning to Figure 22.1, we observe that all points along the frontier indicated by a dark line are undominated. The set of such portfolios is called the *efficiency frontier* and they are *efficient portfolios*. Clearly, the investor will want to choose one of the portfolios on the efficiency frontier rather than one that is dominated.

For a portfolio to be efficient there cannot be any other portfolio which produces a higher expected return but has the same variance, or which produces a given expected return with a lower variance.

We shall use a technique similar to the "spiral method" in Chapter 16 to determine the locus of efficient portfolios. Define the economic potential function $E - \lambda V$ where λ is a positive parameter, $\lambda > 0$. Alternatively, we can look at $E - \lambda V$ as a simple utility function for the investor, the utility being calculated as the expected return on the portfolio minus an allowance for risk (measured by the variance). The coefficient λ, then, measures the investors attitude toward risk, a large positive λ indicating substantial aversion against risk and a small λ indicating only small aversion against risk.

The expression $E - \lambda V$ is linear in E and V. The equation $E - \lambda V = \text{constant}$ represents a straight line in (E, V) space with slope $1/\lambda$. As the constant λ is varied, that equation will trace an entire map of iso-potential or iso-utility lines (the Greek prefix "iso" means constant or unchanged). The potential becomes numerically greater as that line moves parallel to itself to the southeast in the diagram.

The optimal solution to the problem

$$\begin{aligned} &\text{Maximize} \quad E - \lambda V \\ &\text{Subject to} \quad \sum_{i=1}^{n} p_i^0 x_i \leq M, \\ &\qquad\qquad x_i \geq 0, \qquad i = 1, \ldots, n \end{aligned} \tag{22.4}$$

where E and V are defined by (22.1) and (22.2) respectively, will be an efficient portfolio. For the optimal solution must be feasible, i.e., it must lie in the feasible region (see

Figure 22.1) and to reach the highest iso-potential level, we must clearly travel on the efficient frontier *ABC* shown darkened in that figure.

By varying λ parametrically, the optimal solution to the program will trace the locus of all efficient portfolios, i.e., *ABC* itself in Figure 22.1. For small positive values of λ, the slope of the iso-potential line will be quite steep and corresponds to an optimal point close to C. As λ becomes numerically greater, the slope becomes flatter, and the optimal point moves along *CBA* toward A.

Inserting (22.1) and (22.2) into the objective function of (22.4) one gets the following quadratic programming problem

$$\text{Maximize} \quad z = \sum_{i=1}^{n} (Ep_i)x_i - \lambda \sum_{i=1}^{n} \sum_{j=1}^{n} \text{Cov}\,(p_i, p_j)x_i x_j \tag{22.5}$$

$$\text{Subject to} \quad \sum_{i=1}^{n} p_i^0 x_i \leq M$$

$$x_i \geq 0, \qquad i = 1, \ldots, n$$

The first term of the maximand z is linear, and the second term of z is a so-called quadratic form. In the ensuing discussion attention will be restricted to the case when the quadratic form $\sum \sum \text{Cov}\,(p_i, p_j)x_i x_j$ is convex. The second term of the maximand is then concave, and the entire maximand is concave. The constraint set is linear.

Observe that the objective function of (22.5) is separable only if the matrix $\text{Cov}(p_i, p_j)$ is a *diagonal* matrix which rarely happens. Hence our discussion of the Kuhn-Tucker condition in Chapter 4 is not applicable. In order to proceed we digress to discuss the Kuhn-Tucker conditions in a more general setting.

Kuhn-Tucker Conditions for the Nonseparable Case

In Chapter 4 we listed the Kuhn-Tucker conditions for the case of a programming problem having a separable concave objective function and linear constraints. Here we have no longer separability and so the conditions are slightly more involved.

Consider a nonlinear programming problem

$$\text{Maximize} \quad f(x_1, \ldots, x_n)$$

$$\text{Subject to} \quad Ax \leq b$$

$$x \geq 0$$

where f is concave and $A = [a_{ij}]$ $(i = 1, \ldots, n)$ and $b = [b_j]$ $(j = 1, \ldots, n)$. The Kuhn-Tucker conditions will involve the partial derivatives

$$\frac{\partial f}{\partial x_1}, \ldots, \frac{\partial f}{\partial x_n}.$$

The partial derivative $\partial f/\partial x_1$ is calculated by taking the derivative of f with respect to x_1 while keeping all the other independent variables constant. The other partial derivatives are defined in an analogous manner. (For details, see any introductory textbook on calculus.)

Defining the row vector of Lagrange multipliers $u = (u_1, \ldots, u_m)$, the Kuhn-Tucker conditions are

$$u_1^* a_{11} + \cdots + u_m^* a_{m1} \geq \frac{\partial f^*}{\partial x_1}$$

$$\vdots$$

$$u_1^* a_{1n} + \cdots + u_m^* a_{mn} \geq \frac{\partial f^*}{\partial x_n}$$

$$u_1^*, \ldots, u_m^* \geq 0$$

As always, the asterisk indicates that the value should be calculated at the optimal point. Also

$$\left(u_1^* a_{11} + \cdots + u_m^* a_{m1} - \frac{\partial f^*}{\partial x_1}\right) x_1^* = 0$$

$$\vdots$$

$$\left(u_1^* a_{1n} + \cdots + u_m^* a_{mn} - \frac{\partial f^*}{\partial x_n}\right) x_n^* = 0$$

The final two sets of Kuhn-Tucker conditions are the same as before

$$A^* x^* \leq b, \qquad x^* \geq 0$$

$$u^*(b - Ax^*) = 0.$$

Note that the mnemonic rule for writing down the Kuhn–Tucker conditions explained in Chapter 4 still works, if the ordinary derivatives of the separate functions making up the separable optimand in that chapter are replaced by the corresponding partial derivatives.

We return to the solution of the problem in (22.5)

Let u denote the Lagrange multiplier of the constraint in (22.5). The optimal u^* is obviously the imputed rate of return on the entire portfolio. (It measures the incremental return that can be obtained if an additional dollar of initial capital is optimally invested.) The Kuhn-Tucker conditions stated above are the following:

$$u^* p_i^0 \geq Ep_i - 2\lambda \sum_{j=1}^{n} \text{Cov}(p_i, p_j) x_j^* \qquad i = 1, \ldots, n \qquad (22.6)$$

$$\left[u^* p_i^0 - Ep_i + 2\lambda \sum_{j=1}^{n} \text{Cov}(p_i, p_j) x_j^*\right] x_i^* = 0, \qquad i = 1, \ldots, n \qquad (22.7)$$

In order to interpret these results let us assume, as already stated, that the last investment medium is risk-free (cash). Then $p_n^0 = 1$ and all the entries Cov (p_i, p_n) vanish. Hence, (22.6) and (22.7) read, for $i = n$

$$u^* \geq 1$$

$$(u^* - 1) x_n^* = 0$$

so that if the investor invests in cash at all, $u^* = 1$.

Next, dividing (22.6) and (22.7) by p_i^0, the current price of stock i, and rearranging we obtain

$$u^* + (2\lambda/p_i^0)\sum_{j=1}^{n-1} \mathrm{Cov}(p_i, p_j)x_j^* \geq (Ep_i/p_i^0), \qquad i = 1, \ldots, n-1 \tag{22.8}$$

$$\left[u^* + (2\lambda/p_i^0)\sum_{j=1}^{n-1} \mathrm{Cov}(p_i, p_j)x_j^* - (Ep_i/p_i^0)\right]x_i^* = 0, \qquad i = 1, \ldots, n-1 \tag{22.9}$$

Looking first at relation (22.8), the right hand side (Ep_i/p_i^0) is the expected rate of return on stock i. The left hand side is the sum of the imputed rate of return on the portfolio and an allowance for risk (a "risk discount"). If the risk allowance turns out to be excessive so that the left hand side of (22.8) is greater than the expected return, the investor will not buy stock i. But if the investor buys stock i, relation (22.8) must hold as an equality.

Summing (22.7) over all i and also using $u^*(M - \sum p_i^0 x_i^*) = 0$ one finds that

$$u^* = (E^* - 2\lambda V^*)/M \tag{22.10}$$

The imputed return on the entire portfolio can therefore be written as the expected *average* return minus an allowance for risk.

Example. Consider an investor who has available the sum of $15,000 for investment, and is considering the purchase of some of each of three stocks: Kodak, IBM, and Ford. The prices of these stocks during the last 12 months are exhibited in the table below.

	month											
	1	*2*	*3*	*4*	*5*	*6*	*7*	*8*	*9*	*10*	*11*	*12*
Kodak	40	42	44	40	46	48	50	41	48	38	40	40
IBM	120	118	120	116	122	115	123	124	117	119	118	116
Ford	60	61	58	52	54	49	55	37	38	40	39	45

The prices shown are the closing prices on the last business day of each month. It is now the afternoon of that last business day of the twelfth month and the stock market is still open. Determine the locus of efficient portfolios.

Based on the price data supplied, it is a routine matter to calculate the mathematical expectations of stock prices Ep_i for $i = 1, 2, 3$ as

Kodak	$(i = 1)$	43.1
IBM	$(i = 2)$	119.0
Ford	$(i = 3)$	49.0

and also the covariance matrix

$$[\mathrm{Cov}(p_i, p_j)] = \begin{bmatrix} 14.6 & 1.4 & 5.7 \\ 1.4 & 7.7 & 1.8 \\ 5.7 & 1.8 & 73.2 \end{bmatrix}$$

We shall use the expected prices as forecasts. Note that the current prices ($40, $116, and $45 respectively) all are less than the expected prices so that investment in any stock will yield an expected capital gain. However, the risks are not equal, with IBM being the least risky stock (as measured by the variance) and Ford the most risky.

The holding of cash is denoted x_4. The portfolio problem to be solved then is

Maximize

$$43.1x_1 + 119.0x_2 + 49.0x_3 + x_4 - \lambda(14.6x_1^2 + 1.4x_1x_2 + 5.7x_1x_3 + 1.4x_2x_1 + 7.7x_2^2 + 1.8x_2x_3 + 5.7x_3x_1 + 1.8x_3x_2 + 73.2x_3^2)$$

Subject to $40x_1 + 116x_2 + 45x_3 + x_4 = 15000$

$$x_1, x_2, x_3, x_4 \geq 0$$

where the risk parameter λ is to be varied parametrically.

The results of a series of parametric experiments for various values of λ are given below. They were obtained by running the program PORTFOLIO on page 342.

	Optimal Solution						
	Kodak	*IBM*	*Ford*	*Cash*	*E*	*V*	*dual u**
0.0005	140.6	69.1	30.3	0	15,761	475,463	1.019
0.0006	118.9	78.4	25.5	0	15,704	368,790	1.017
0.0007	103.4	85.1	22.0	0	15,662	304,470	1.016
0.0008	91.8	90.1	19.4	0	15,631	262,724	1.014
0.0009	82.8	94.0	17.4	0	15,607	234,103	1.012
0.0010	75.5	97.1	15.8	0	15,587	213,630	1.011
0.0015	53.9	106.5	10.9	0	15,529	165,143	1.002
0.0020	41.1	88.3	8.3	2,747	15,425	106,137	1.000

Under all scenarios the investor holds a balanced portfolio, with Kodak and IBM being the favored portfolio choices. When λ is small, meaning a small aversion to risk, the purchases of the riskiest stock (Ford) are large. When λ is large, meaning a greater aversion to risk, the purchases of Ford are small. Also, the greater the aversion against risk, the heavier reliance will be placed on IBM (the stock having the lowest risk).

For $\lambda \leq 0.0015$ the investor is still fully invested, i.e., he doesn't hold cash. But for $\lambda = 0.0020$ the investor becomes wary of the risk and holds some proportion of his available funds in cash.

Note that the return of the portfolio (u^*) drops as one moves from more risky to less risky alternatives.

Finally, the relationship between E and V is shown in Figure 22.3.

Sharpe's Diagonal Model

The original Markowitz formulation requires information about the covariance matrix of all stock prices, i.e., the complete matrix $[\mathrm{Cov}(p_i, p_j)]$. In applied work the sheer size

Figure 22.3

Efficiency frontier in the example. Both the expectation and variance are measured in thousands of dollars.

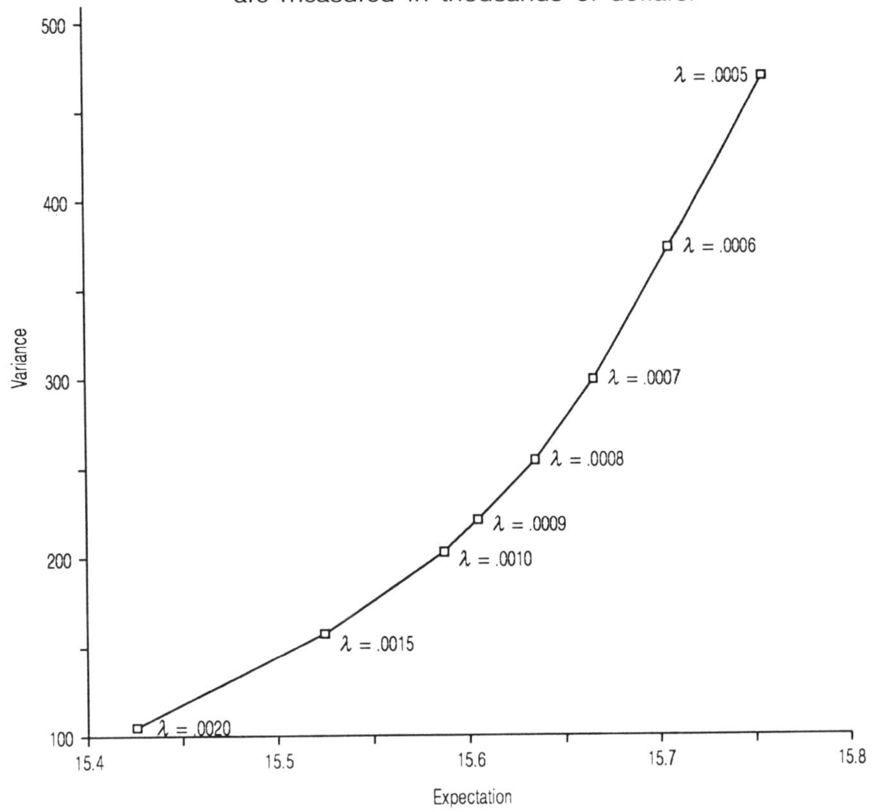

of this matrix can easily create difficulties. To analyze 100 stocks one would need to compute a covariance matrix with $100 \times 100 = 10{,}000$ entries. Similarly, to analyze 1,000 stocks requires a covariance matrix with 1,000,000 entries.

To deal with this task Sharpe designed his "diagonal model," which is a method of compressing the information held by the entire covariance matrix into a much smaller number of parameters, one of which is the "beta" coefficient of each stock (which measures the degree of covariability of the price of the stock with the Dow Jones stock index or some other suitable index). In the case of 100 stocks the entire covariance matrix can then be expressed in terms of 201 parameters only: the beta coefficient for each stock, the variance of the error term for each stock, and the variance of the Dow Jones index.

Sharpe assumed that each stock price p_i can be written as a least squares linear regression

$$p_i = \alpha_i + \beta_i I + \epsilon_i \tag{22.11}$$

where I is some general stock price index (such as the Dow Jones index), α_i and β_i are parameters to be estimated and ϵ_i is the so-called regression residual. The regression is defined so that $E\epsilon_i = \text{Cov}(\epsilon_i, I) = 0$. In words, (i) the prediction $\alpha_i + \beta_i I$ should be "unbiased" in the sense that $Ep_i = E(\alpha_i + \beta_i I)$; (ii) the residual ϵ_i should be uncorrelated with the explanatory factor. In addition, the Sharpe diagonal method assumes that the residuals ϵ_i and ϵ_j for any pair of stocks (i, j) will be uncorrelated with each other, $\text{Cov}(\epsilon_i, \epsilon_j) = 0$ for $i, j = 1, \ldots, n$.

What these assumptions mean is that the various stock prices are related to each other only through a common basic underlying factor, the common stock index I. The price of any stock is therefore determined solely by random factors and the stock index.

If one collects historical data and estimates the regression (22.11) for each stock, there is no reason to expect that $\text{Cov}(\epsilon_i, \epsilon_j)$ will always vanish for each pair of stocks (i, j). But that observation is beside the point. The Sharpe assumption is that the *subjective* expectations of investors obey this condition.

One can now calculate

$$Ep_i = E(\alpha_i + \beta_i I + \epsilon_i) = \alpha_i + \beta_i EI \tag{22.12}$$

and

$$\begin{aligned} \text{Cov}(p_i, p_j) &= \text{Cov}(\alpha_i + \beta_i I + \epsilon_i, \alpha_j + \beta_j I + \epsilon_j) \\ &= \text{Cov}(\beta_i I + \epsilon_i, \beta_j I + \epsilon_j) = \begin{cases} \beta_i \beta_j \text{ Var } I & \text{for } i \neq j \\ \beta_i^2 \text{ Var } I + \text{Var } \epsilon_i & \text{for } i = j \end{cases} \end{aligned} \tag{22.13}$$

These formulas are due to Sharpe.

Returning to the numerical example already discussed, assume the value of the Dow Jones index during the 12 months is given below.

	month											
	1	*2*	*3*	*4*	*5*	*6*	*7*	*8*	*9*	*10*	*11*	*12*
Dow Jones (I)	1950	1960	1965	1980	1985	2010	2050	2020	2010	1980	1940	1900

Estimation of the regressions (22.10) gives

Kodak $(i = 1)$	$p_1 = -87.9 + 0.07I + \epsilon_1$	with Var $\epsilon_1 = 8.1$
IBM $(i = 2)$	$p_2 = 55.7 + 0.03I + \epsilon_2$	with Var $\epsilon_2 = 6.1$
Ford $(i = 3)$	$p_3 = 87.8 - 0.02I + \epsilon_3$	with Var $\epsilon_3 = 72.6$

Also, Var $I = 1486.8$.

By inspecting the beta coefficients, we see that Kodak and IBM covary positively with the Dow Jones Index. Ford covaries negatively with the Dow Jones.

Application of the formulas (see Exercise 2) supplied in (22.13) then gives the approximate values

$$[\text{Cov}(p_i, p_j)] = \begin{bmatrix} 14.6 & 3.1 & -1.9 \\ 3.1 & 7.7 & -0.9 \\ -1.9 & -0.9 & 73.2 \end{bmatrix}$$

Note that the approximation along the main diagonal agrees exactly with the covariance matrix. (This will always be the case.)

Clearly the above example is too small to be realistic. One really needs price statistics over a much longer time period in order to establish the covariability of prices over the business cycle. Also, the beta coefficients that are published in newspapers are typically calculated from logarithmic data, so that the beta coefficient measures the *relative* covariability of the price of a stock with the Dow Jones index. Perfect percentage covariability then yields a beta equal to 1.

Exercises

1. (This example is due to A. S. Manne.) A certain investor is interested in investing a fixed sum of money S in four different investments: a computer hardware firm, a computer software firm, a firm that finances Broadway shows, and Treasury bills. The mean annual return on each of these investments is 8, 9, 12, and 7 respectively. The covariance matrix is:

	Hardware	*Software*	*Show-biz*	*T-bills*
Hardware	4	3	−1	0
Software	3	6	1	0
Show-biz	−1	1	10	0
T-bills	0	0	0	0

Determine the relative fraction of the fixed sum S to be put into each of the four investments if the investor has a target goal of making 10 percent expected return on his portfolio. [Hint: Rather than constructing the entire efficiency frontier, you are asked to find only one point on the frontier. The point can be found by replacing (22.4) by the problem: minimize V, subject to $\sum p_i^0 x_i \leq 1$, $E \geq 1.10$, $x \geq 0$, where x_i is the fraction of S invested in investment i.]

2. Use the GAMS program `DIAGONAL` on page 343 to calculate the approximate covariance matrix given on page 282. Explain how the program works and why the program has no `SOLVE` statement.

3. A United States dealer in foreign exchange, headquartered in New York, desires to invest the sum of $500,000 over a time period of three months. The current exchange rates ("spot rates") and the rates of interest to be obtained from three months investments are exhibited in the table below:

		exchange rate h_i^0 (*purchase*)	*nominal rate of interest* r_i (*converted to annual yield*)
Deutsche mark	($i = 1$)	0.5307	6.63%
French francs	($i = 2$)	0.1571	8.81%
Pound sterling	($i = 3$)	1.6862	13.06%
U.S. Dollar	($i = 4$)	1.0000	10.06%

The interest rate to be obtained in different currencies depends on the particular investment made; the alternatives listed above refer to three month Treasury bills in each currency (short term debt issued by the Treasury in each country).

The effective rate of return on an investment in a foreign currency depends upon the future exchange rate three months from now. Suppose for instance that the rate for Deutsche mark turns out to be 0.5350. The rate of return is then $(0.5350/0.5307) \times 1.0663 - 1.0000 = 7.49\%$. In this numerical example the effective rate of return would be higher than the local nominal rate. The effective rate consists of a nominal interest part and a capital gain due to the rising value of the foreign currency.

But future exchange rates 3 months from now (h_i, say) are uncertain. Hence, expected effective rates of return $(h_i/h_i^0)(1 + r_i) - 1$ are also uncertain.

Applying the model in the main text, the "price" (= value) of currency i expected to obtain at the end of the planning period is $p_i = (h_i/h_i^0)(1 + r_i)$. Note that $p_4 = 1.1006$.

Assumptions about the future course of exchange rates can be made in different ways. One common assumption is the "random walk" hypothesis, according to which expected future exchange rates are identical to the last observed exchange rates $Eh_i = h_i^0$. Then the expected rates $Ep_i = 1 + r_i$.

Further, statistical analysis of foreign exchange data has yielded the estimates of the covariance matrix $\text{Cov}(p_i, p_j)$ displayed below:

	$i = 1$	$i = 2$	$i = 3$	$i = 4$
$i = 1$	685.39×10^{-4}	607.78×10^{-4}	510.85×10^{-4}	0.0
$i = 2$		549.90×10^{-4}	450.54×10^{-4}	0.0
$i = 3$			901.20×10^{-4}	0.0
$i = 4$				0.0

(only the northeast part of the matrix has been filled in. The southwest part mirrors the northeast part.)

Determine the efficient portfolios.

(A commercial data package named CUMIX is used by the foreign exchange community. It contains data and programs for the necessary calculations. See C. M. Schilbred, *Managing Short Term Currency Risk*, Tano Publishers, Oslo 1990.)

APPENDICES

A

A Brief Introduction To GAMS

GAMS stands for General Algebraic Modeling System and is fully described in the book *GAMS: A User's Guide*, by A. Brooke, D. Kendrick, and A. Meeraus, The Scientific Press, 1988. We give a brief introduction to the use of GAMS and illustrate each point considered here in one or more of the sample GAMS programs included in Appendix B. Further information on the use of GAMS can be found in the book cited above.

How to Install GAMS in Your Computer

Your instructor may provide you with access to a computer which already has GAMS installed on it. If so you can skip the rest of this section.

The computer programs needed to run GAMS are included on the high density diskette attached to the back cover of this book. (If your computer cannot read high density diskettes, contact the publisher to obtain the proper kind.)

There are two methods of installing GAMS. The first requires you to edit your `AUTOEXEC.BAT` file. If you are not comfortable making this change, you should follow the single directory procedure, otherwise use the "Editing AUTOEXEC.BAT" installation procedure.

The procedures below use drives C and A. If you are installing GAMS on a drive other than C or from a drive other than A, substitute the appropriate drive letters.

Installation Procedure—Editing AUTOEXEC.BAT

1. Make sure there is enough space on your hard disk: the GAMS system will need approximately two megabytes.

2. To create a GAMS system directory, `C:\GAMS`, and to make it the current directory, enter the commands:

```
C:> mkdir \gams
C:> cd \gams
```

3. To copy the GAMS system files from the diskette to this directory, first put your diskette in drive A and then enter the comand:

```
C:\GAMS> copy a:\gams\*.*
```

4. To create a directory for the example models, and then to go to that directory, enter the commands:

```
C:\GAMS> mkdir models
C:\GAMS> cd models
```

5. To copy the model examples from the diskette, enter the command:

```
C:\GAMS\MODELS> copy a:\models\*.*
```

6. Edit your `AUTOEXEC.BAT` file to include the GAMS system directory (`C:\GAMS`) in its path statement. An example of such a path statement is:

```
PATH = C:\;C:\DOS;C:\UTILS;C:\WP
```

   Use an editor to include the GAMS system in the path, by adding `;C:\GAMS` at the end of the path statement so that it looks like:

```
PATH = C:\;C:\DOS;C:\UTILS;C:\WP;C:\GAMS
```

   (If you don't know how to use an editor, ask someone to help on this step.)

7. Reboot the computer to make sure that the new path is being used. To reboot, push the CTRL, ALT, and DEL keys simultaneously.

8. To test the system, go to the `MODELS` directory and run the `TRANS.GMS` model by entering the commands:

```
C:\> cd gams\models
C:\GAMS\MODELS> gams trans
```

   The output that appears on your screen should be similar to Figure A-1.

9. If you see this output on your screen, the installation of GAMS on your computer is complete.

Installation Procedure—Single Directory

1. Make sure there is enough space on your hard disk: the GAMS system will need approximately two megabytes.

2. To create a GAMS system directory, `C:\GAMS`, and to make it the current directory, enter the commands:

```
C:> mkdir \gams
C:> cd \gams
```

Figure A-1

Sample GAMS output to test installation.

```
GAMS 2.25X (c) Copyright 1988-91 GAMS Development Corp. All rights reserved
Licensee: GAMS DEMONSTRATION SYSTEM FOR USE WITH          G911008-1243AX-TP5
          THOMPSON AND THORE, "COMPUTATIONAL ECONOMICS"
--- Starting compilation
--- TRANS.GMS(45)
--- Starting execution
--- TRANS.GMS(3)
--- Generating model TRANS
--- TRANS.GMS(45)
---     7 rows, 10 columns, and 28 non-zeroes.
--- Executing MINOS5
 GAMS/MINOS5 is running in demonstration mode
 Estimate work space needed    --     39 Kb
 Work space allocated          --    144 Kb
 Reading data...

   Itn  Nopt  Ninf  Sinf,Objective
     1     1     3  2.82842712E+00

 Itn     6 -- Feasible solution.  Objective =   1.390000000E+03


 EXIT -- OPTIMAL SOLUTION FOUND

 Major, Minor itns              1            8
 Objective function       1.0500000000000E+03
 Degenerate steps               0          .00
 Norm X,      Norm PI    3.26E+00     1.30E+03
 Norm X,      Norm PI    6.36E+02     1.45E+01  (unscaled)
--- Restarting execution
--- TRANS.GMS(45)
--- Reading solution for model TRANS
--- All done
```

3. To copy the GAMS system files from the diskette to this directory, first put your diskette in drive A and then enter the comand:

```
C:\GAMS> copy a:\gams\*.*
```

4. To copy the model examples from the diskette, enter the command:

```
C:\GAMS> copy a:\models\*.*
```

5. To test the system, run the TRANS.GMS model by entering the command:

```
C:\GAMS> gams trans
```

   The output that appears on your screen should be similar to Figure A-1.

6. If you see this output on your screen, the installation of GAMS on your computer is complete.

How to Write a GAMS Program

In order to solve a problem with GAMS the first step is to create an ASCII file that states your problem in the GAMS language. Any word processor (such as Word Perfect) can be used as well as any resident editor (such as EMACS or Epsilon) that you may have on your computer. The resulting file name must end with .GMS if you are using a personal computer. Thus if you are writing a program called TEST you should create a file called TEST.GMS. Here are some hints as to how to write your program.

1. Never use the TAB key since doing so will create an error message. Instead fill in blanks with the space bar.
2. Always push the ENTER key when you want to go to the next line.
3. Use arrows to move the cursor to the location of a mistake in order to correct it.
4. Use spaces and blank lines freely to make your program readable.
5. Comments may be added freely as documentation within the program. Such comments will be used later by GAMS to help in the documentated program listings. Comments may not take more than one line and must not use reserved words or symbols, see Figure A-1, unless they are surrounded by quotation marks.
6. Any line that begins with an "*" is treated as a comment and is ignored by the computer. It is a good practice to start each program with one or more comment lines which indicate such things as: the purpose of the program, the name of author, the date the program was created, etc.
7. GAMS is not case sensitive. In the programs in this book the GAMS commands are entered in upper case, and comments are in lower case. You can use this or other conventions as you wish.

GAMS programs are written in free format; that is, you may arrange for indenting and blank lines as desired. In the program listings the following conventions have been followed: upper case entries constitute the instructions to the computer, using reserved words, which tell it how to solve the program. Lower case entries as used here are explanations and documentation. You may use some other convention such as writing everything in upper case (or everything in lower case) if you prefer.

A GAMS program consists of several sections, each terminated with a semicolon (;). These sections are discussed in order, using the program TRANS as the main example.

SETS Section

Here should be listed all the sets of indices to be employed in writing the model equations. Indices are alpha-numeric expressions. For instance, in program TRANS below, the section SETS lists warehouses indicated by the index I and markets indicated by the index J. The GAMS program is looking for a name of each index. For easy recognition, the warehouses are called WAREHOUSE1, WAREHOUSE2, WAREHOUSE3 and the markets are called MARKET1, MARKET2, MARKET3. Any names containing up to ten characters (with the first one being a letter) may be used. Imbedded blanks are not permitted, so that multiple

Figure A-2

Some reserved words and symbols.

ACRONYM	EPS	LE	NEGATIVE	PROD	VARIABLE
ALIAS	EQ	LOOP	NO	SCALAR	XOR
ALL	EQUATION	LT	NOT	SET	YES
AND	FREE	MAXIMIZING	OPTION	SOLVE	=
ASSIGN	GE	MINIMIZING	OR	SUM	,
BINARY	GT	MODEL	ORD	SYSTEM	;
CARD	INF	NA	PARAMETER	TABLE	/
DISPLAY	INTEGER	NE	POSITIVE	USING	

word names such as New York should be written New-York. The elements of the set should be enclosed within slashes, like this:

```
I warehouses /WAREHOUSE1, WAREHOUSE2, WAREHOUSE3/
```

Alternatively, the following format which contains comments is also permitted:

```
I warehouses

/WAREHOUSE1 this is the first warehouse
 WAREHOUSE2 this is the second warehouse
 WAREHOUSE3 this is the third warehouse/
```

In these (and later) statements the words in lower case letters are comments or documentation and have no effect on the running of the program. They will be used by GAMS for documentation purposes when it prints its solution report.

There is a neat shorthand way of defining a set of consecutive elements, using the asterisk symbol. For instance, the three warehouses could be defined as

```
SET I /WAREHOUSE1*WAREHOUSE3/
```

which produces

```
SET I /WAREHOUSE1, WAREHOUSE2, WAREHOUSE3/
```

It is also possible to use just numbers as indices. As example the instruction

```
SET I /1*8/
```

produces the following

```
SET I /1 2 3 4 5 6 7 8/
```

see, for instance, programs NETWORK and CAPBUD.

Sometimes it is necessary to use two different set names to denote the same set. This is done using the ALIAS command. For instance, the command

```
ALIAS (I,K);
```

introduces the alternate name K to I. This is needed, for instance, when you are writing a double summation over the same set. See programs ELECTRIC and LEONTIEF.

It is also possible that one of the index sets is a subset of another. For use of subsets, see examples in programs PURINVEN and PERSONNEL.

PARAMETERS Section

In GAMS parameters are fixed known vectors and the values of the parameters are declared as data in this section. In order to declare its values the index set of the vector must have been previously defined in the SETS section.

In the example of the program TRANS, under PARAMETERS the available supplies and market demands for each of the elements in their respective sets are listed. Each PARAMETER is given a name; the vector of supplies is called A; the vector of demands is called B. In the TRANS program the vector A has one numerical value for each member of the set I, which is indicated as follows:

```
A(I) supplies at each warehouse I
    /WAREHOUSE1   70
     WAREHOUSE2  100
     WAREHOUSE3   30/
```

The values of A(I) cannot be asserted until set I and parameter A(I) have been declared, see TRANS. Failure to do so will result in an error message. The vector B of market demand in TRANS is introduced in an analogous fashion.

If there are several vectors of data to be entered in a program, they may be listed, one after another, in the same PARAMETERS section. Do *not* put a semicolon after each parameter data statement because that will lead to an error.

TABLE Section

The next section of the program lists TABLE. In GAMS a fixed known matrix is called a TABLE and the values of the table are declared as data in this section. For example in TRANS, the matrix of unit shipping costs is defined as follows:

```
TABLE
  C(I,J) unit transportation costs
                      MARKET1   MARKET2   MARKET3
    WAREHOUSE1           5         3         5
    WAREHOUSE2          15         6        10
    WAREHOUSE3           2        11        12 ;
```

Notice that the values of C(I,J) are given only after C(I,J) has been declared.

Only one matrix may be entered in each TABLE section and it must be terminated with a semicolon. To enter several different matrices of data, several TABLE sections are required, one for each matrix. (See for instance CAPTRANS.)

Sometimes it is useful, especially during the debugging phase of the use of GAMS, to ask the computer to DISPLAY data that has been entered. That can be done as follows:

```
DISPLAY A, C;
```

This causes PARAMETER A and the TABLE C to be printed. Note that only the names of the vectors and matrices should be entered when using this command, not the names of the individual elements. For an example of the use of display see the program DIAGONAL.

Vectors and matrices of data can also be entered by "assignment." For instance, in the program TRANS, vector A(I) may alternatively be defined in the following fashion:

```
A(I) supplies at each warehouse I;
  A("WAREHOUSE1") = 70;
  A("WAREHOUSE2") = 100;
  A("WAREHOUSE3") = 30;
```

Note that in these assignment statements individual elements are addressed by enclosing them between quotation marks, and their values are indicated using an ordinary equals sign "=." For another example of data entry by assignment, see the program CAPBUD.

VARIABLES Section

In the VARIABLES section are listed the unknowns of the problem. Variables can be a scalar (i.e., it has no domain), a vector (having a single domain), a two dimensional matrix (having two domains), a three dimensional matrix (having three domains), etc. One of the variables must be the objective function itself listed as a separate unknown, it must be a scalar and it must not be constrained. Nonnegative (and nonpositive) variables are listed separately. In the GAMS language "nonnegative" variables are listed as being "POSITIVE" variables. Similarly, "nonpositive" variables are listed as being "NEGATIVE".

Variables can also be BINARY, that is they may be required to take on only the values 0 or 1, (BINARY programming). For examples of BINARY variables see programs CAPBUD and NEWLAND.

EQUATIONS Section

The next section called EQUATIONS declares the names of the objective function and the various constraints of the problem. Inequalities as well as equations appear in this section. In the case of program TRANS, the name OBJECTIVE is chosen to signify the expression defining the minimand. The name WHOUSEBAL(I) is chosen for the warehouse balances (stating that the total delivery from each warehouse cannot exceed the available supply). Note that the domain (I) at the end of WHOUSEBAL(I) means that an inequality is to be defined for each member of the domain I. Thus the same statement defines the problem whether the number of warehouses is 3, 30, 300, etc. The name MARKETBAL(J) is chosen for the market balances (stating that the total shipments to a market cannot fall short of the demand). It defines an equation for each member of set J. Any name having up to ten characters (and beginning with a letter) can be used.

Next, each equation is entered. The rules are simple. First type the name of the equation, followed by two periods (..). Then the algebraic definition of the constraint is written using notation that is quite close to standard mathematical notation, see the list of standard GAMS functions given in Figure A-3, which provides a list of some standard functions that can be used in GAMS. Multiplication is indicated by an asterisk, i.e., 2.50*X. Division is denoted by the slash sign, as in X/2.50. Exponentiation is denoted by **, as in X**2 (read: X squared); for an example, see program SUPPLY. Single

Figure A-3

Some standard functions.

Name	*Description*	*Definition*
ABS	Absolute value	$\|arg\|$
COS	Cosine	cos(arg); argument in radians
EXP	Exponential	exp(arg)
LOG	Natural logarithm	log base e of arg
LOG10	Common logarithm	log base 10 of arg
MAX	Largest value	max(arg1, arg2, arg3, . . .)
MIN	Smallest value	min(arg1, arg2, arg3, . . .)
NORMAL	Normal random	random number normally ditributed with mean arg1 and standard deviation arg2
ROUND	Rounding	round(arg) round to the nearest integer
SIGN	Sign	$\text{sign(arg)} = \begin{cases} +1 \text{ if arg} > 0 \\ -1 \text{ if arg} < 0 \\ 0 \text{ if arg} = 0 \end{cases}$
SIN	Sine	sin(arg); argument in radians
SQR	Square	arg*arg
SQRT	Square root	sqrt(arg)

and double summations are denoted as shown in Figure A-4, which provides a list of standard algebraic statements in GAMS followed by the same statements in standard mathematical notation.

Thus the equation declarations and equation definitions for TRANS are as follows:

```
EQUATIONS
  OBJECTIVE        objective function
  WHOUSEBAL(I)     goods balance for warehouse I
  MARKETBAL(J)     goods balance for market J;

OBJECTIVE..        COSTS =E= SUM((I,J),C(I,J)*X(I,J));
WHOUSEBAL(I)..     SUM(J,X(I,J)) =L= A(I);
MARKETBAL(J)..     SUM(I,X(I,J)) =G= B(J);
```

The two periods at the end of each equation name are required and their ommission will cause error messages to be printed. The final semicolon is also required.

It is important that the symbol " =" not be used for "=E=" in these GAMS statements. Attempts to do so will lead to error messages. Similar remarks hold for "=G=" and "=L=."

In GAMS there is a shorthand way of writing simple upper bound, lower bound, and equality constraints involving a single variable as follows:

GAMS	*Standard mathematical notation*
X =L= 10.0	$X \leq 10.0$
X =G= 10.0	$X \geq 10.0$
X =E= 10.0	$X = 10.0$

Figure A-4

Standard algebraic statements.

GAMS	*Ordinary Mathematical Notation*
SUM(I,)	$\sum_{i \in I}$
SUM((I,J),)	$\sum_{i \in I} \sum_{j \in J}$
=E=	$=$
=G=	$\geq$
=L=	$\leq$

Rather than defining and entering such constraints in the EQUATIONs section, they may instead be entered separately at the end of the program, as follows:

```
X.UP = 10.0;
X.LO = 10.0;
X.FX = 10.0;
```

Here the acronyms UP, LO, FX stand for "upper limit," "lower limit," and "fixed value," respectively. See for example programs PAPERCO and WAREHOUSE.

Sometimes it is necessary to address individual elements of a vector (PARAMETER) or matrix (TABLE) which can be done by enclosing the name of the element between quotation marks. For examples, see PROPPROD and PAPERCO (showing how to address a single element when writing an EQUATION) and ELECTRIC (showing how to address a single element when defining the data of a vector or matrix by assignment).

MODEL and SOLVE Section

In the last section of the program the model is given a name having up to eight characters permitted in the student version of GAMS. Up to ten characters are permitted in the main frame version. For the transportation problem the name TRANS was chosen.

In GAMS the word "model" means a set of GAMS equations, one of which is the objective function. For instance the penultimate line of the computer program TRANS is

```
MODEL TRANS / ALL /;
```

which tells the computer that ALL equations previously listed should be included in TRANS. One could also have written

```
MODEL TRANS/OBJECTIVE,WHOUSEBAL, MARKETBAL/;
```

to achieve the same effect. Or one could write

```
MODEL TRANS/OBJECTIVE, WHOUSEBAL /;
```

if only the first set of constraints were to be imposed.

The last line in the GAMS program

```
SOLVE TRANS USING LP MINIMIZING COSTS;
```

instructs the computer to solve TRANS using the linear programming (LP) code resident in its program library, minimizing the variable defined as COSTS. Usually GAMS programs have a solve statement so that GAMS will do something. It is not an error to omit the solve statement, but GAMS will then just check the program for errors and stop without printing output. For an example of a program not having a solve statement see DIAGONAL which uses GAMS to compute and display some data tables without doing any optimization.

In some examples, nonlinear programming (NLP) will be used, see programs SUPPLY and MASTER1. When the program at hand involves both ordinary (unconstrained or nonnegative) variables and BINARY or INTEGER variables, so called "mixed integer programming" (MIP) is required. See programs CAPBUD and NEWLAND.

In other programs such as SUPPLY the objective function is nonlinear. In this case GAMS is instructed to use its nonlinear programming code to solve the problem as follows:

```
SOLVE SUPPLY USING NLP MINIMIZING COST;
```

This completes the description of a typical GAMS program.

How to Run a GAMS Program

When GAMS was installed on your computer a directory called MODELS was created in some cases. If you do not have a MODELS subdirectory, skip steps 1 and 2.

1. Copy your file TEST.GMS into the MODELS directory.
2. Enter the command CD MODELS.
3. Enter the command GAMS TEST or GAMS TEST.GMS.

This instructs the computer to solve your GAMS problem. After it finds the solution it prints a solution report in a file called TEST.LST. Use your editor to examine this file, or print it out. The first time you run a new program it will probably contain errors which are marked with four asterisks (****) to the left of a line. To debug the program see the section on debugging below.

Assuming that your program has no errors you will find several parts to the TEST.LST printout. The first is an Echo Print of your program. Next is a map of all the symbols used in the program and references to each of them in the program. This may be of use if you are making changes in the program. Next is a listing of symbols with their explanatory text. Next is a listing of several instances of each type of equation written in full without using summations, and with the variables substituted in the proper places. You can control the number of such equations listed by changing LIMROW and LIMCOL as explained on page 298. Next comes the solve summary which lists detail about the solution process.

Finally comes the solution summary which contains most of the information you will need. The solution summary begins with four hyphens "----", and you can use them as a marker for this section. For the program TRANS.GMS the solution summary is:

```
---- EQU WHOUSEBAL GOODS BALANCE FOR WAREHOUSE I

                   LOWER    LEVEL     UPPER    MARGINAL

  WAREHOUSE1       -INF    70.000    70.000    -5.000
  WAREHOUSE2       -INF   100.000   100.000      .
  WAREHOUSE3       -INF    30.000    30.000    -8.00

---- EQU MARKETBAL    GOODS BALANCE FOR MARKET J

                LOWER       LEVEL       UPPER   MARGINAL

  MARKET1     70.000      70.000       +INF     10.000
  MARKET2     90.000      90.000       +INF      6.000
  MARKET3     40.000      40.000       +INF     10.000
                          LOWER       LEVEL       UPPER     MARGINAL

----  VAR COSTS            -INF      1050.000     +INF          .

   COSTS          TOTAL TRANSPORTATION COSTS

----  VAR X            QUANTITY SHIPPED FROM WAREHOUSE I TO MARKET J

                         LOWER        LEVEL        UPPER       MARGINAL

WAREHOUSE1.MARKET1         .         40.000          +            .
WAREHOUSE1.MARKET2         .            .          +INF        2.000
WAREHOUSE1.MARKET3         .         30.000        +INF           .
WAREHOUSE2.MARKET1         .            .          +INF        5.000
WAREHOUSE2.MARKET2         .         90.000        +INF           .
WAREHOUSE2.MARKET3         .         10.000        +INF           .
WAREHOUSE3.MARKET1         .         30.000        +INF           .
WAREHOUSE3.MARKET2         .            .          +INF       13.000
WAREHOUSE3.MARKET3         .            .          +INF       10.000
```

The first part of the solution summary gives the equations solutions. The main thing needed here are the entries listed under the column MARGINAL. These are, in fact, the values of the optimal dual variables, one for each equation. Thus,

```
u(WAREHOUSE1)=-5, u(WAREHOUSE2)=0, u(WAREHOUSE3)=-8,
v(MARKET1)=10, v(MARKET2)=6, v(MARKET3)=10.
```

The second part of the solution summary includes the optimal objective function value costs which is equal to 1050, and then the optimal values of the primal variables, which are listed under the column labeled level. Thus X(WAREHOUSE1,MARKET1)=40, X(WAREHOUSE1,MARKET2)=0, etc.

When you first solve a problem, GAMS will print out the full solution report discussed above, which is quite long. That is a good idea at the beginning and will help during the debugging phase. However, later on you may wish to reduce the number of pages printed. In order to do this add the command

```
OPTION LIMROW = 0, LIMCOL = 0;
```

at the beginning of your problem file. See programs TRANS and CORN for how this is done. Instead of making the limits both 0, they can be made larger (say 10 or 15) in order to check for possible data entry errors. Making the limits larger will also give a more complete written statement of the model which may be desirable when showing the output to other, possibly less experienced, users.

Another useful series of commands which will limit the total number of pages printed out is:

```
$OFFUPPER  OFFSYMXREF  OFFSYMLIST  OFFUELLIST  OFFUELXREF
```

These commands have the following effects:

$OFFUPPER	makes the program printout stay in the case in which you typed it (for instance with comments in lower case)
$OFFSYMXREF	and $OFFSYMLIST turn off the production and printing of symbol cross references.
$OFFUELLIST	and $OFFUELXREF turn off the printing of symbols listed both by GAMS entry and in alphabetical order, and also the complete cross reference list by line number.

The above commands are called "dollar control directives" and permit the user to change the amount of information to be printed during the course of debugging and later making production runs of a GAMS program.

Both of these command lines are included as comments at the beginning of the TRANS program. Try removing the asterisks at the beginning of one or both lines to see what effects they have on the solution printout. You can add them to other programs if you wish.

How to Debug a GAMS Program

The use of any software program requires trial and error practice runs for the user to gain experience. Fortunately GAMS is quite easy to debug since its compiler prints out elaborate error messages. A single error can produce several error messages, some of which are irrelevant or hard to interpret. However the cardinal rule is *find the first error and concentrate on removing it before going on to the second error.*

The first step is to examine the file TEST.LST to look for errors. TEST.LST contains a listing of the program exactly as it was written in TEST.GMS. Any statement that contains such an error is followed in the next one or two lines by an error message line that begins with four asterisks "****" and contains a "$" placed directly below where the compiler thinks the error is. The "$" is followed by a numerical error code number. At the end of the program, explanations for each of the numerical error codes are given. Some of these error messages will be relevant and some not, because the compiler may or may not make a correct guess as to the actual location and cause of the error. However, usually at least one will be relevant.

Example 1. Consider the following incorrect modification of the TRANS program as it appears in TRANS.LST after complilation:

```
  10  PARAMETERS
  11     A(I)    SUPPLY AT EACH WAREHOUSE
  12             /WAREHOUSE1     70
  13              WAREHOUSE2    100
  14              WAREHOUSE3     30/;
  15
  16     B(J)    DEMAND IN EACH MARKET J
****     $140          $35
```

Two error numbers 140 and 35 are found. At the end of the program another error number, 257 is also found. These three errors are explained in later error messages as follows:

```
 35  '='  OPERATOR EXPECTED
140  UNKNOWN SYMBOL, ENTERED AS A PARAMETER
257  SOLVE STATEMENT NOT CHECKED BECAUSE OF PREVIOUS ERRORS
```

Error message 35 does not seem to be particularly relevant. But error message 140 is exactly correct. The additional extraneous semicolon at the end of statement 14 is followed by an undefined vector B(J), which confuses the compiler which expects to see a GAMS instruction word following a semicolon. The last error message, 257, is clear and self explanatory. Removal of the semicolon at the end of statement 14 makes the program be correct and will also remove all three error statements from the next TRANS.LST listing.

Example 2. Here is another fragment of a TRANS.LST listing that contains an error.

```
  21  TABLE
  22     C(I,J)  UNIT TRANSPORTATION COSTS
  23                  MARKET1    MARKET2    MARKET3
  24     WAREHOUSE1      5          3          5
  25     WAREHOUSE2     15          6         10
  26     WAREHOUSE3      2         11                        12;
****                                                          $225
```

There is also a $257 error message at the end of the program. The error messages printed later are:

```
225  FLOATING ENTRY IGNORED
257  SOLVE STATEMENT NOT CHECKED BECAUSE OF PREVIOUS ERRORS
```

The error is clear; the last entry of the matrix in statement 26 which is 12 has been shifted so far to the right that it is no longer under MARKET3. Hence the compiler does not know how to interpret it. The solution is simply to remove enough of the spaces before 12 so that it is aligned with the 10 in the previous line.

Example 3. Here is an example of an error in the TRANS program that produces a total of eight error messages!

```
    39  OBJECTIVE..      COSTS = SUM((I,J),C(I,J)*X(I,J));
                                 $36,12,118$188$93,148,35
  ****
```

Shown are seven error numbers, and there is another one, $257, found at the end of the program. The corresponding error messages are:

```
 12  ';' EXPECTED
 35  '=' OPERATOR EXPECTED
 36  '=L=' OPERATOR EXPECTED
 93  A SET MUST HAVE ONE OR MORE DIMENSIONS
118  UNRECOGNIZED STATEMENT
148  DIMENSION DIFFERENT
188  ASSIGNING TO SET USED AS DOMAIN
257  SOLVE STATEMENT NOT CHECKED BECAUSE OF PREVIOUS ERRORS
```

Clearly the compiler knows that an error has been committted and is floundering around trying to guess what the error is. The problem, of course, is that to define COSTS as a double summation in the GAMS language requires the use of the GAMS equals symbol "=E=" instead of "=". Making this change removes all eight error statements.

Example 4. The next example shows what happens when the two periods ". . " are omitted after the name of an equation when the equation is being defined in the program TRANS.

```
    40  WHOUSEBAL(I)..   SUM(J,X(I,J)) =L= A(I);
    41  MARKETBAL(J)     SUM(I,X(I,J)) =G= B(J);
  ****                   $35
```

The resulting error messages are:

```
 35  '=' OPERATOR EXPECTED
257  SOLVE STATEMENT NOT CHECKED BECAUSE OF PREVIOUS ERRORS
```

The error message 35 is not particularly relevant, but it does bring the user's attention to the place where the error is. Comparison of statements 40 and 41 make the missing periods be quite apparent and inserting them removes the error messages.

Example 5. Our next example shows what will happen if the MODEL statement is removed from the program TRANS.

```
    41  MARKETBAL(J)..   SUM(I,X(I,J)) =G= B(J);
    42
    43  SOLVE TRANS USING LP MINIMIZING COSTS;
  ****              $240,241                  $257
```

The corresponding error messages are:

```
240  UNKNOWN IDENTIFIER, ENTERED AS BEST GUESS
241  MODEL HAS NOT BEEN DEFINED
257  SOLVE STATEMENT NOT CHECKED BECAUSE OF PREVIOUS ERRORS
```

Here the error message 241 is exactly correct, and tells the user to insert the model definition statement.

Example 6. Our last example shows what will happen if the user forgets to put a solve statement at the end of a GAMS program. We use the example TRANS. There are no error message and the last two lines of TRANS.LST are:

```
          43  SOLVE TRANS USING LP MINIMIZING COSTS;
      COMPILATION TIME       =          0.079 MINUTES
```

In other words, the GAMS compiler compiles the program and stops without trying to solve the model! This should not be surprising since it was not instructed to do anything more. The program DIAGONAL does not have a solve statement because all it does is preliminary computation whose results are displayed, and that is all that it is intended to do.

This has been only a brief introduction to the GAMS language, but it should be adequate to work the examples and exercises in this book. For further information the reader is referred to the GAMS user's guide book referred to in the first paragraph of this appendix.

List of GAMS Programs with Appendix Page Number and Referenced to Text Chapters

B

GAMS Programs

TRANS

Program TRANS solves the first example in Chapter 1. Note that each program begins with a comment line identifying the program.

```
*Program TRANS solves the first example in Chapter 1.

*OPTION LIMROW=0, LIMCOL = 0;
*$OFFUPPER OFFSYMXREF OFFSYMLIST OFFUELLIST OFFUELXREF

SETS
  I       warehouses   /WAREHOUSE1,WAREHOUSE2,WAREHOUSE3/
  J       markets      /MARKET1,MARKET2,MARKET3/;

PARAMETERS
  A(I)   supply at each warehouse I
         /WAREHOUSE1    70
          WAREHOUSE2   100
          WAREHOUSE3    30/

  B(J)   demand in each market J
         /MARKET1    70
          MARKET2    90
          MARKET3    40/;

TABLE
  C(I,J) unit transportation costs
              MARKET1   MARKET2   MARKET3
  WAREHOUSE1     5         3         5
  WAREHOUSE2    15         6        10
  WAREHOUSE3     2        11        12;

VARIABLES
  COSTS    total transportation costs
```

```
POSITIVE VARIABLES
  X(I,J)   quantity shipped from warehouse I to market J;

EQUATIONS
  OBJECTIVE       objective function
  WHOUSEBAL(I)    goods balance for warehouse I
  MARKETBAL(J)    goods balance for market J;

OBJECTIVE..       COSTS =E= SUM((I,J),C(I,J)*X(I,J));
WHOUSEBAL(I)..    SUM(J,X(I,J)) =L= A(I);
MARKETBAL(J)..    SUM(I,X(I,J)) =G= B(J);

MODEL TRANS / ALL /;

SOLVE TRANS USING LP MINIMIZING COSTS;
```

CAPTRANS

```
* CAPTRANS solves the capacitated transportation problem given in
* Chapter 1.  XCEILING is the matrix of upper bounds.

SETS
  I      warehouses  /WAREHOUSE1,WAREHOUSE2,WAREHOUSE3/
  J      markets     /MARKET1,MARKET2,MARKET3/;

PARAMETERS
  A(I)   supply at each warehouse I
         /WAREHOUSE1    70
          WAREHOUSE2   100
          WAREHOUSE3    30/

  B(J)   demand in each market J
         /MARKET1    70
          MARKET2    90
          MARKET3    40/;

TABLE
  C(I,J) unit transportation costs
              MARKET1    MARKET2    MARKET3
  WAREHOUSE1     5          3          5
  WAREHOUSE2    15          6         10
  WAREHOUSE3     2         11         12

TABLE
  XCEILING(I,J) upper limit on each quantity shipped from I to J
              MARKET1    MARKET2    MARKET3
  WAREHOUSE1    40         40         40
  WAREHOUSE2    35         35         35
  WAREHOUSE3    50         50         50;

VARIABLES
  COSTS    total transportation costs

POSITIVE VARIABLES
  X(I,J)   quantity shipped from warehouse I to market J;

EQUATIONS
  OBJECTIVE       objective function
  WHOUSEBAL(I)    goods balance for warehouse I
  MARKETBAL(J)    goods balance for market J
  CAPACITY(I,J)   capacitating condition on shipment from I to J;
```

```
OBJECTIVE..        COSTS =E= SUM((I,J),C(I,J)*X(I,J));
WHOUSEBAL(I)..     SUM(J,X(I,J)) =L= A(I);
MARKETBAL(J)..     SUM(I,X(I,J)) =G= B(J);
CAPACITY(I,J)..    X(I,J) =L= XCEILING(I,J);

MODEL CAPTRANS / ALL /;

SOLVE CAPTRANS USING LP MINIMIZING COSTS;
```

TULIP

```
*  Program TULIP solves the tulip auction problem of Chapter 2.

SETS
  I     sellers/SELLER1,SELLER2/
  J     buyers/BUYER1,BUYER2,BUYER3,BUYER4/;

PARAMETERS
  A(I)    supply of each seller I
          /SELLER1   100
           SELLER2   140/

  B(J)    demand of each buyer J
          /BUYER1     30
           BUYER2     60
           BUYER3     80
           BUYER4     70/;

TABLE
  C(I,J)    bids
            BUYER1     BUYER2     BUYER3     BUYER4
  SELLER1     22         18         21         25
  SELLER2     25         23         22         20;

VARIABLES
  POTENTIAL  TOTAL BID VALUE

POSITIVE VARIABLES
  X(I,J)     quantity sold by seller I to buyer J;

EQUATIONS
  OBJECTIVE  defines the objective function
  SELBAL(I)  balance relation for each seller I
  BUYBAL(J)  balance relation for each buyer J;

SELBAL(I)..   SUM(J,X(I,J)) =L= A(I);
BUYBAL(J)..   SUM(I,X(I,J)) =L= B(J);

MODEL TULIP/ALL/;

SOLVE TULIP USING LP MAXIMIZING POTENTIAL;
```

RESERVE

```
* Program RESERVE solves the tulip problem with reservation prices of
* Chapter 2.  LOPRICE is the matrix of reservation seller prices.

SETS
  I     sellers/SELLER1,SELLER2/
  J     buyers/BUYER1,BUYER2,BUYER3,BUYER4/;
```

```
PARAMETERS
  A(I)    supply of each seller I
          /SELLER1   100
           SELLER2   140/

  B(J)    demand of each buyer J
          /BUYER1    30
           BUYER2    60
           BUYER3    80
           BUYER4    70/

LOPRICE(I)  reservation price of each seller I
          /SELLER1  22
           SELLER2  23/;

TABLE
  C(I,J)    bids
            BUYER1     BUYER2     BUYER3     BUYER4
  SELLER1     22         18         21         25
  SELLER2     25         23         22         20 ;

VARIABLES
  POTENTIAL  total bid value plus value of all buy-backs

POSITIVE VARIABLES
  X(I,J)     quantity sold by seller I to buyer J
  Y(I)       buy-backs of seller I ;

EQUATIONS
  OBJECTIVE  defines the objective function
  SELBAL(I)  balance relation for each seller I
  BUYBAL(J)  balance relation for each buyer J;

OBJECTIVE..   POTENTIAL =E= SUM((I,J),C(I,J)*X(I,J))
                           +SUM(I,LOPRICE(I)*Y(I));
SELBAL(I)..   SUM(J,X(I,J))+Y(I) =E= A(I);
BUYBAL(J)..   SUM(I,X(I,J)) =L= B(J);

MODEL RESERVE/ALL/;

SOLVE RESERVE USING LP MAXIMIZING POTENTIAL;
```

EQUILIB

Program EQUILIB below solves the equilibrium example in Chapter 3. It is an instance of quadratic programming. The OBJECTIVE function contains a term involving supply S(I) raised to the second power, denoted by S(I)**2. The last line of the GAMS program instructs the computer to solve EQUILIB using the nonlinear programming (NLP) code resident in its program library, minimizing the variable termed COST.

```
* Program EQUILIB solves the text example in Chapter 5.

SETS
  I     plants /PLANT1, PLANT2, PLANT3/
  J     retailing regions /REGION1, REGION2, REGION3/;
```

```
PARAMETERS
  GAMMA(I)   supply price intercepts
             /PLANT1     42
              PLANT2     35
              PLANT3     50 /
  DELTA(I)   supply price coefficients
             /PLANT1    0.30
              PLANT2    0.25
              PLANT3    0.50 /
  B(J)       demands
             /REGION1    300
              REGION2    150
              REGION3    200 /;

TABLE
 C(I,J)   unit shipment costs
               REGION1  REGION2  REGION3
    PLANT1        0        1        1.5
    PLANT2        1        0        2.0
    PLANT3        1.5      2.0      0   ;

VARIABLES
  COST      total operating cost

POSITIVE VARIABLES
  X(I,J)    quantity shipped from plant I to region J
  S(I)      supply at plant I;

EQUATIONS
  OBJECTIVE   objective function defined
  SUPBAL(I)   commodity balance at each plant I
  DEMBAL(J)   commodity balance at each retailing region J ;

OBJECTIVE..  COST =E= SUM(I,GAMMA(I)*S(I)) + 0.5*SUM(I,DELTA(I)*
                     S(I)**2) + SUM((I,J),C(I,J)*X(I,J));
SUPBAL(I)..  SUM(J,X(I,J)) - S(I) =L= 0;
DEMBAL(J)..  SUM(I,X(I,J)) =G= B(J);

MODEL EQUILIB/ALL/;

SOLVE EQUILIB USING NLP MINIMIZING COST;
```

FURNITURE

```
* The program FURNITURE solves the first text example in Chapter 5.
* If you have student GAMS change the name to FURNITUR.

SETS
  I   machines
      /SAW,CARPENTER,PAINT/

  J   outputs
      /VICTORIAN,BOHEMIAN,MODERN/;

PARAMETERS
  B(I) availabilities of machine hours
       /SAW       400
        CARPENTER 625
        PAINT     200/
```

```
      P(J) output prices
           /VICTORIAN 2780
            BOHEMIAN  3225
            MODERN    2450/

      H(J) unit requirements of labor
           /VICTORIAN 16
            BOHEMIAN  20
            MODERN    10/

      C(J) raw material costs
           /VICTORIAN 800
            BOHEMIAN  625
            MODERN    950/ ;

    TABLE
      A(I,J)  unit machine requirements
                VICTORIAN   BOHEMIAN   MODERN
      SAW           2           3         2
      CARPENTER     5           4         1.5
      PAINT        1.5         1.25       0.75 ;

    VARIABLES
      REVENUE  revenue net of cost of labor and raw materials

    POSITIVE VARIABLES
      X(J)     quantity of output obtained;

    EQUATIONS
      OBJECTIVE   defining the objective function
      MACHBAL(I)  availability of machine hours of machine I;

    OBJECTIVE..  REVENUE =E= SUM(J,P(J)*X(J)-30.0*H(J)*X(J)-C(J)*X(J));
    MACHBAL(I).. SUM(J,A(I,J)*X(J)) =L= B(I);

    MODEL FURNITURE /ALL/;

    SOLVE FURNITURE USING LP MAXIMIZING REVENUE;
```

PROPROD

Program PROPPROD below belongs to Chapter 5, section "Proportional production." This example features a constraint named PROPORTION spelling out the requirement that six chairs and one table form a dining set. Note that an individual element in a variable is addressed by enclosing the name of the element within quotation marks. The notation X("CHAIRS") thus is the particular value of the variable X(J) for which J = CHAIRS.

```
    * Program PROPPROD solves the proportional production example given
    * in Chapter 5.

    SETS
      I   machines
          /SAW,CARPENTER,PAINT/

      J   outputs
          /CHAIRS,TABLES/;
```

```
PARAMETERS
  B(I) availability of machines
      /SAW       80
       CARPENTER 200
       PAINT     60/;

TABLE
  A(I,J)  unit machine requirement
              CHAIRS    TABLES
  SAW          0.25      0.5
  CARPENTER    0.6       1.4
  PAINT        0.2       0.3 ;

VARIABLES
  QUANTITY  number of tables produced

POSITIVE VARIABLES
  X(J)     quantity of outputs ;

EQUATIONS
  OBJECTIVE  defining the objective function
  MACHBAL(I) availability of machine hours
  PROPORTION 6 chairs and 1 table make a dining set;

OBJECTIVE..   QUANTITY =E= X("TABLES");
MACHBAL(I)..  SUM(J,A(I,J)*X(J)) =L= B(I);
PROPORTION..  X("CHAIRS") - 6*X("TABLES") =E= 0;

MODEL PROPPROD /ALL/;

SOLVE PROPPROD USING LP MAXIMIZING QUANTITY;
```

KANTOROVICH

```
* Program KANTOROVICH solves the optimal machine loading problem
* discussed in Chapter 5. If you have student GAMS change the
* name to KANTOROV before running this program.

SETS
  I   machines
      /MACHINE1,MACHINE2,MACHINE3/

  J   produced parts
      /PART1,PART2/;

PARAMETERS
  B(I) availability of machines
      /MACHINE1  9
       MACHINE2  9
       MACHINE3  3/

TABLE
  A(I,J)  production by each machine of each product
             PART1     PART2
  MACHINE1    10        20
  MACHINE2    20        30
  MACHINE3    30        80

VARIABLES
  QUANTITY  number of parts produced
```

```
POSITIVE VARIABLES
  X(I,J)   number of hours spent producing part j on machine i
  Z        number of units of each part produced

EQUATIONS
  OBJECTIVE   defining the objective function
  MACHBAL(I)  machine hours balance for machine I
  LOADING(J)  calculating the output of part J;

OBJECTIVE..   QUANTITY =E= Z;
MACHBAL(I)..  SUM(J,X(I,J))          =L= B(I);
LOADING(J)..  SUM(I,A(I,J)*X(I,J))-Z =E= 0;

MODEL KANTOROV /ALL/;

SOLVE KANTOROV USING LP MAXIMIZING QUANTITY;
```

AIRPLANE

```
* Program AIRPLANE is set up to solve the first linear program for
* the data envelopment analysis of the airline companies discussed
* in Chapter 6.  The other linear programs needed to complete
* the analysis are easily found by modifying this program.

SETS
    I  inputs /SERVICE, FUEL/

    J  airplanes /A, B, C, D, E, F/;

TABLE
  X(J,I)  unit input requirements
               SERVICE       FUEL
        A         29         2800
        B         26         2000
        C         23         2400
        D         38         2500
        E         22         3400
        F         32         3500 ;

VARIABLES
  EFFICIENCY    efficiency measure
  THETA         factor shrinking inputs I

POSITIVE VARIABLES
  LAMBDA(J)     weight of airplane J;

EQUATIONS
  OBJECTIVE     defining THETA
  OUTPUTBAL     checking the output of airplane A
  INPUTBAL(I)   checking the inputs of airplane A;

OBJECTIVE..   EFFICIENCY =E= THETA;
OUTPUTBAL..   SUM(J, LAMBDA(J)) =G= 1.0;
INPUTBAL(I).. X("A", I)*THETA - SUM(J, X(J, I)*LAMBDA(J)) =G= 0;

MODEL AIRPLANE /ALL/;

SOLVE AIRPLANE USING LP MINIMIZING THETA;
```

CHICKEGG

```
* This is program CHICKEGG.GMS which solves Example 2 in Chapter 6.
* Note that it has 3 inputs and 2 outputs, and that the outputs are
* also inputs. The program is set up to check efficiency of farmer A.
* It must be slightly modified to do the same for the other farmers.

SETS
  I  inputs
     /CHICKIN chickens as inputs
      EGGIN   eggs as inputs
      FEED    chicken feed/
  J   farmers
      /A,B,C,D,E,F/
  K   outputs
      /CHICKOUT chickens as outputs
       EGGOUT   eggs as outputs/;

TABLE X(J,I) unit input requirements
          CHICKIN   EGGIN   FEED
      A      20       40      80
      B      22       36      95
      C      18       32      70
      D      17       36      65
      E      25       50     110
      F      21       45      92 ;

TABLE Y(J,K) unit outputs
          CHICKOUT EGGOUT
      A      70      120
      B      58      125
      C      50      105
      D      52      110
      E      78      125
      F      80      122 ;

VARIABLES
  EFFICIENCY  efficiency measure
  THETA       factor shrinking all inputs;

POSITIVE VARIABLES
  LAMBDA(J)   weight of farmer J;

EQUATIONS
  OBJECTIVE      defining theta
  OUTPUTBAL(K)   checking the outputs of farmer A
  INPUTBAL(I)    checking the inputs of farmer A;

OBJECTIVE..      EFFICIENCY =E= THETA;
OUTPUTBAL(K)..   SUM(J,Y(J,K)*LAMBDA(J)) =G= Y("A",K);
INPUTBAL(I)..    X("A",I)*THETA - SUM(J,X(J,I)*LAMBDA(J)) =G= 0;

MODEL CHICKEGG /ALL/;

SOLVE CHICKEGG USING LP MINIMIZING THETA;
```

MASTER

Program MASTER solves the master of the decentralization problem discussed in Chapter 7. To simplify the writing of the program, all numerical coefficients appearing in the

OBJECTIVE function and in the constraints have been entered directly in the EQUATIONS section (rather than defined as PARAMETERS).

```
* The program MASTER solves the decentralization problem given in
* Chapter 7.

SETS
 I   city / A,B,C /;

PARAMETERS
  XUP(I)   divisional demand for first product
         / A  200
           B  100
           C  100 /

  YUP(I)   divisional demand for second product
         / A  300
           B  180
           C   90 /

  WORKSTAT(I)  number of work stations
         / A  240
           B  160
           C  160 / ;

VARIABLES
  REVENUE

POSITIVE VARIABLES
  X(I)   quantity of first product sold
  Y(I)   quantity of second product sold;

EQUATIONS
  OBJECTIVE      defining the objective function as gross revenue
  XBAL(I)        balance for first product at each location I
  YBAL(I)        balance for second product at each location I
  WORKSTABAL(I)  balance for workstation hours at each location I
  CONSULTHR      availability of management consultant hours;

OBJECTIVE..      REVENUE =E= SUM(I,21.50*X(I) + 7.25*Y(I));
XBAL(I)..        X(I) =L= XUP(I);
YBAL(I)..        Y(I) =L=YUP(I);
WORKSTABAL(I).. 0.75*X(I) + 0.50*Y(I) =L= WORKSTAT(I);
CONSULTHR..      SUM(I,0.5*X(I) + 0.2*Y(I)) =L= 250;

MODEL MASTER /ALL/;

SOLVE MASTER USING LP MAXIMIZING REVENUE;
```

DECOMP

```
* Program DECOMP is the decomposed version of MASTER. The CONSULTHR
* constraint has been removed and the coefficients of the objective
* function have been "corrected".

SETS
  I   city / A,B,C / ;
```

```
PARAMETERS
  XUP(I)   divisional demand for first product
         / A  200
           B  100
           C  100 /
  YUP(I)   divisional demand for second product
         / A  300
           B  180
           C   90 /
  WORKSTAT(I)  number of work stations
         / A  240
           B  160
           C  160 / ;
VARIABLES
  REVENUE
POSITIVE VARIABLES
  X(I)   quantity of first product sold
  Y(I)   quantity of second product sold;
EQUATIONS
  OBJECTIVE      defining the corrected objective function
  XBAL(I)        balance for first product at location I
  YBAL(I)        balance for second product at location I
  WORKSTABAL(I)  balance for workstation hours at location I;
OBJECTIVE..      REVENUE =E= SUM(I,3.375*X(I));
XBAL(I)..        X(I) =L= XUP(I);
YBAL(I)..        Y(I) =L=YUP(I);
WORKSTABAL(I).. 0.75*X(I) + 0.50*Y(I) =L= WORKSTAT(I);
MODEL DECOMP /ALL/;
SOLVE DECOMP USING LP MAXIMIZING REVENUE;
```

MASTER1 and DECOMP1

The next two programs MASTER1 and DECOMP1 deal with the nonlinear decomposition model discussed in Chapter 7, in the section titled "Decentralization in a nonlinear world: coherent decentralization by prices alone."

```
* Program MASTER1 solves the nonlinear master model in
* Chapter 7.
SETS
  I   CITY / A,B,C / ;
PARAMETERS
  XUP(I)   divisional demand for first product
         / A  200
           B  100
           C  100 /
  YUP(I)   divisional demand for second product
         / A  300
           B  180
           C   90 /
```

```
  WORKSTAT(I)  number of work stations
              / A  240
                B  160
                C  160 / ;

VARIABLES
  REVENUE

POSITIVE VARIABLES
  X(I)   quantity of first product sold
  Y(I)   quantity of second product sold;

EQUATIONS
  OBJECTIVE      defining the nonlinear master objective
  XBAL(I)        balance for first product at location I
  YBAL(I)        balance for second product at location I
  WORKSTABAL(I)  balance for workstation hours at location I
  CONSULTHR      availability of management consultant hours;

OBJECTIVE.. REVENUE =E= SUM(I,27*X(I)-.06*X(I)**2+7.5*Y(I)-.01*Y(I)**2);
XBAL(I)..        X(I) =L= XUP(I);
YBAL(I)..        Y(I) =L=YUP(I);
WORKSTABAL(I).. 0.75*X(I) + 0.50*Y(I) =L= WORKSTAT(I);
CONSULTHR..      SUM(I,0.5*X(I) + 0.2*Y(I)) =L= 250;

MODEL MASTER1/ALL/;

SOLVE MASTER1 USING NLP MAXIMIZING REVENUE;


* This is the program DECOMP1 which is the decomposed version of the
* nonlinear program MASTER1.

SETS
  I   city / A,B,C / ;

PARAMETERS
  XUP(I)   divisional demand for first product
          / A  200
            B  100
            C  100 /

  YUP(I)   divisional demand for second product
          / A  300
            B  180
            C   90 /

  WORKSTAT(I)  number of work stations
              / A  240
                B  160
                C  160 / ;

VARIABLES
  REVENUE

POSITIVE VARIABLES
  X(I)   quantity of first product sold
  Y(I)   quantity of second product sold;
```

```
EQUATIONS
  OBJECTIVE        defining the corrected nonlinear objective function
  XBAL(I)          balance for first product at location I
  YBAL(I)          balance for second product at location I
  WORKSTABAL(I)    balance for workstation hours at location I;

OBJECTIVE..       REVENUE =E= SUM(I,16.5306*X(I)-.06*X(I)**2+3.31224*Y(I)
                         -.01*Y(I)**2);
XBAL(I)..         X(I) =L= XUP(I);
YBAL(I)..         Y(I) =L= YUP(I);
WORKSTABAL(I).. 0.75*X(I) + 0.50*Y(I) =L= WORKSTAT(I);

MODEL DECOMP1/ALL/;

SOLVE DECOMP1 USING LP MAXIMIZING REVENUE;
```

PUMPOIL

```
* Program PUMPOIL solves the oil pumping example for Chapter 8.
* Note the abbreviated listing of the elements of the set I. The set
* consists of the elements {1, 2, 3, 4, 5, 6}.

SETS
  I   nodes/1*6/
  K   arcs /13,14,23,24,35,36,45,46/;

PARAMETERS
  B(I)  supplies (negative entries) or demands (positive entries)
        /1  -150
         2  -200
         3     0
         4     0
         5   175
         6   175/

  C(K)  unit shipping costs along arc K
        /13    8
         14    6
         23    9
         24   11
         35   21
         36   18
         45   22
         46   15/;

TABLE
  M(I,K)  incidence matrix
      13  14  23  24  35  36  45  46
  1   -1  -1   0   0   0   0   0   0
  2    0   0  -1  -1   0   0   0   0
  3    1   0   1   0  -1  -1   0   0
  4    0   1   0   1   0   0  -1  -1
  5    0   0   0   0   1   0   1   0
  6    0   0   0   0   0   1   0   1;
```

```
VARIABLES
  MINCOST  total shipping costs to be minimized

POSITIVE VARIABLES
  X(K)     flow along arc K;

EQUATIONS
  OBJECTIVE       defines objective functions as sum of shipping costs
  NODECONSTR(I) oil flow conservation condition at node I;

OBJECTIVE..       MINCOST =E= SUM(K,C(K)*X(K));
NODECONSTR(I).. SUM(K,M(I,K)*X(K)) =E= B(I);

MODEL PUMPOIL/ALL/;

SOLVE PUMPOIL USING LP MINIMIZING MINCOST;
```

PAPERCO

Program PAPERCO is the text example in Chapter 9. For a large network problem like this it is still perfectly possible to define the incidence matrix and to write all node conservation conditions of the network with the help of the incidence matrix. An alternative approach, shown here, is to list the node conservation equations one by one. The advantage of the latter method is that it will not become much longer as the size of the problem increases.

There is a feature in this program that you encounter here for the first time: the abbreviated notation of equations entered at the end of the program. The statement X.UP("10TOO") = 25 sets an upper limit equal to 25 for the variable X("10TOO"). The statement X.LO("10TOO")= 18 sets a lower limit equal to 18 for the same variable.

```
* Program PAPERCO solves the paper company example in Chapter 9.

SETS
  I activities
      /1T03  company logs
       2T03  farmers logs
       3T04  logs to grinder
       3T05  logs to chipper
       4T06  wood to pulper1
       4T07  wood to pulper2
       5T06  chips to pulper1
       5T07  chips to pulper2
       6T08  pulp1 to storage
       7T09  pulp2 to storage
      8T010  pulp1 to kraft paper mill
      8T011  pulp1 to newsprint mill
      8T012  pulp1 to book paper mill
      9T010  pulp2 to craft paper mill
      9T011  pulp2 to newsprint mill
      9T012  pulp2 to book paper mill
      10T00  kraft paper to sales1
      11T00  newsprint to sales2
      12T00  book paper to sales3
       0T08  pulp1 purchases
       8T00  pulp1 sales
       0T09  pulp2 purchases
       9T00  pulp2 sales     /;
```

```
PARAMETERS
  A(I)   unit revenue (pos) or unit cost (neg)
      /1T03  -65
       2T03  -65
       3T04  -18
       3T05  -16
       4T06  -40
       4T07  -55
       5T06  -40
       5T07  -55
       6T08    0
       7T09    0
      8T010  -40
      8T011  -60
      8T012  -70
      9T010  -55
      9T011  -50
      9T012  -45
      10T00  265
      11T00  275
      12T00  310
       0T08 -120
       8T00  120
       0T09 -140
       9T00  140   /;

VARIABLES
  PROFIT    net revenue above costs

POSITIVE VARIABLES
  X(I)   quantity processed by activity I, in tons;

EQUATIONS
  DEFPROFIT      profit computed
  NODECONS3      node3 conservation of flow
  NODECONS4      node4 conservation of flow
  NODECONS5      node5 conservation of flow
  NODECONS6      node6 conservation of flow
  NODECONS7      node7 conservation of flow
  NODECONS8      node8 conservation of flow
  NODECONS9      node9 conservation of flow
  NODECONS10     node10 conservation of flow
  NODECONS11     node11 conservation of flow
  NODECONS12     node12 conservation of flow
  RATIO6         ratio constraint at node 6
  RATIO7         ratio constraint at node 7
  RATIO10        ratio constraint at node 10
  RATIO11        ratio constraint at node 11
  RATIO12        ratio constraint at node 12;

DEFPROFIT..    PROFIT =E= SUM(I, A(I)*X(I));
NODECONS3..    -X("1T03")- X("2T03")+ X("3T04")+ X("3T05") =E= 0 ;
NODECONS4..    -0.97* X("3T04")+ X("4T06")+ X("4T07") =E= 0 ;
NODECONS5..    -0.97* X("3T05")+ X("5T06")+ X("5T07") =E= 0 ;
NODECONS6..    -X("4T06")- X("5T06")+ X("6T08") =E= 0 ;
NODECONS7..    -X("4T07")- X("5T07")+ X("7T09") =E= 0 ;
```

```
NODECONS8..    -X("6TO8")+ X("8TO10")+ X("8TO11")+ X("8TO12")
               - X("0TO8")+ X("8TO0")=E= 0;
NODECONS9..    -X("7TO9")+ X("9TO10")+ X("9TO11")+ X("9TO12")
               - X("0TO9")+ X("9TO0")=E= 0;
NODECONS10..   -X("8TO10")- X("9TO10")+ X("10TO0") =E= 0;
NODECONS11..   -X("8TO11")- X("9TO11")+ X("11TO0") =E= 0;
NODECONS12..   -X("8TO12")- X("9TO12")+ X("12TO0") =E= 0;
RATIO6..       0.4* X("4TO6")- 0.6* X("5TO6") =E= 0;
RATIO7..       0.7* X("4TO7")- 0.3* X("5TO7") =E= 0;
RATIO10..      0.32* X("8TO10")- 0.68* X("9TO10") =E= 0;
RATIO11..      0.55* X("8TO11")- 0.45* X("9TO11") =E= 0;
RATIO12..      0.75* X("8TO12")- 0.25* X("9TO12") =E= 0;

X.UP("10TO0") = 25;
X.LO("10TO0") = 18;
X.UP("11TO0") = 15;
X.LO("11TO0") = 12;
X.UP("12TO0") = 7;
X.UP("0TO8")  = 0;
X.UP("8TO0")  = 0;
X.UP("0TO9")  = 0;
X.UP("9TO0")  = 0;

MODEL PAPERCO /ALL/;

SOLVE PAPERCO USING LP MAXIMIZING PROFIT;
```

PURINVEN

PURINVEN solves the first example for Chapter 10. This is the first multiperiod model that we have encountered. There are five time periods T = 1, 2, 3, 4, 5. In addition, we need notation for the opening stock at time T = 0 and for the terminal stock at time T = 5. To handle the notation of these different periods, the set T = {0, 1, 2, 3, 4, 5} is introduced, together with the subsets INDEX(T) = {1, 2, 3, 4, 5}, OPENING(T) = {0} and TERMINAL(T) = {5}.

Note that the inventory constraint is written as INVBAL(T-1) rather than just INVBAL(T). The purpose is to get the very first constraint right, which reads

```
XMINUS(1) - XPLUS(1) + I(1) - I(0) =E= 0;
```

The statement I.UP(T) = 500 at the end of the program sets an upper limit equal to 500 for the variable I(T) for all values of the index T. The statement I.FX(OPENING) = 300 sets the variable I equal to 300 for the index OPENING.

```
* Program PURINVEN solves the pure inventory model in Chapter 10.

SETS
  T    time periods/0,1,2,3,4,5/
  INDEX(T)         / 1,2,3,4,5/
  OPENING(T)       /0          /
  TERMINAL(T)      /          5/;
```

```
PARAMETERS
  P(INDEX)      market price
                /1   75
                 2   65
                 3   89
                 4   77
                 5   80/ ;
VARIABLES
  PROFIT

POSITIVE VARIABLES
  XMINUS(T)   quantity sold at time T
  XPLUS(T)    quantity bought at time T
  I(T)        inventory held at time T;

EQUATIONS
  OBJECTIVE   calculating net profit
  INVBAL(T)   inventory balance in period T;

OBJECTIVE..     PROFIT =E= SUM(INDEX,(P(INDEX)-2.0)*XMINUS(INDEX)
                -(P(INDEX)+2.0)*XPLUS(INDEX)-I(INDEX-1));
INVBAL(T-1)..   XMINUS(T)-XPLUS(T)+I(T)-I(T-1) =E= 0;

I.UP(T)         = 500;
I.FX(OPENING)   = 300;
I.FX(TERMINAL)  = 300;

MODEL PURINVEN/ALL/;

SOLVE PURINVEN USING LP MAXIMIZING PROFIT;
```

INVENDEMAN

```
* The program INVENDEMAN solves an inventory problem with demand in
* Chapter 10. If you have student GAMS change the name to INVENDEM.

SETS
  T    time periods/0,1,2,3,4,5/
  INDEX(T)        /  1,2,3,4,5/
  OPENING(T)      /0         /
  TERMINAL(T)     /         5/;

PARAMETERS
  P(INDEX)      market price
                /1   75
                 2   65
                 3   89
                 4   77
                 5   80/

  D(T)          market demand
                /0    0
                 1    0
                 2  200
                 3  300
                 4  400
                 5    0/;
```

```
VARIABLES
  PROFIT

POSITIVE VARIABLES
  XMINUS(T)   quantity sold at time T
  XPLUS(T)    quantity bought at time T
  I(T)        inventory held at time T;

EQUATIONS
  OBJECTIVE   calculating net profit
  INVBAL(T)   inventory balance at time T;

OBJECTIVE..   PROFIT =E= SUM(INDEX,(P(INDEX)-2.0)*XMINUS(INDEX)
              -(P(INDEX)+2.0)*XPLUS(INDEX)-I(INDEX-1));
INVBAL(T-1).. XMINUS(T)-XPLUS(T)+I(T)-I(T-1) =E= -D(T);

I.UP(T)        = 500;
I.FX(OPENING)  = 300;
I.FX(TERMINAL) = 300;

MODEL INVENDEMAN/ALL/;

SOLVE INVENDEMAN USING LP MAXIMIZING PROFIT;
```

INVENDAMP

```
* INVENDAMP solves the market problem discussed in the section
* "Inventories dampen price swings" in Chapter 10.  If you have
* student GAMS, change the name to INVENDAM.

SETS
  T    time periods/0,1,2,3,4,5/
  INDEX(T)          /  1,2,3,4,5/
  OPENING(T)        /0         /
  TERMINAL(T)       /         5/;

SCALARS
  BETA      demand price coefficient /0.75/
  DELTA     supply price coefficient /2/
  STORCOST  unit inventory holding cost /0.8/;

PARAMETERS
  ALPHA(INDEX) demand price intercept
               /1  40
                2  42
                3  44
                4  46
                5  48/

  GAMMA(INDEX) supply price intercept
               /1  -30
                2  -25
                3  -20
                4  -15
                5  -10/;

VARIABLES
  PROFIT
```

```
POSITIVE VARIABLES
  D(T)   quantity demanded at time T
  W(T)   quantity supplied at time T
  I(T)   inventory held at time T;

EQUATIONS
  OBJECTIVE   defining the nonlinear potential function
  MARKBAL(T)  market balance in period T;

OBJECTIVE..      PROFIT =E= SUM(INDEX,ALPHA(INDEX)*D(INDEX)
                 -0.5*BETA*D(INDEX)**2-GAMMA(INDEX)*W(INDEX)
                 -0.5*DELTA*W(INDEX)**2-0.8*I(INDEX-1));
MARKBAL(T-1)..   D(T)-W(T)+I(T)-I(T-1) =E= 0;

I.UP(T)         = 310;
I.FX(OPENING)   = 300;
I.FX(TERMINAL)  = 300;

MODEL INVENDAMP/ALL/;

SOLVE INVENDAMP USING NLP MAXIMIZING PROFIT;
```

CAPBUD and CAPBUD1

The next two programs belong to Chapter 11, Capital Budgeting, and employ 0–1 programming. Notice that the `PARAMETER NPV(I)` is introduced in a manner that you have not seen before; rather than listing the elements, the vector is defined by assignment. For the assignment statement, the standard algebraic notation is employed. The equality sign is written "=".

The expression `ORD(J)` which appears in the definition of `NPV(I)` (it is defined by assignment) requires explanation. When GAMS reads the elements of the set `J`, it reads them as labels, not as numbers. The elements can therefore not be manipulated algebraically. Instead, we form `ORD(J)` which produces the order of element `J`. Thus, in the present instance,

```
ORD("1") = 1
ORD("2") = 2
```

etc.

The 0–1 programming feature is accomplished by defining the `X(I)` variables as being `BINARY`, i.e., they can only take on the values 0 or 1. The `SOLVE` statement at the end instructs the computer to use the programming code MIP (mixed integer programming) resident in its memory.

There are effective budget constraints only in the first two time periods. An arbitrary large number (9999) has been entered for the amount of `CASHONHAND` in later periods.

Alternatively, it is also possible to enter only the two first budget constraints, like this:

```
SUM(I, -CASHFLOW("1", I)*X(I)) =L= 300;
SUM(I, -CASHFLOW("2", I)*X(I)) =L= 375;
```

Try both alternatives!

```
* Program CAPBUD solves the capital budgeting problem in Example 3
* of Chapter 11.
```

```
SETS
  I   projects / A1, A2, B1, B2, C1, C2/
  J   TIME PERIODS / 1, 2, 3, 4, 5/

TABLE
  CASHFLOW(J,I)  cash flow in period J from project I
            A1       A2       B1       B2       C1       C2
      1   -200        0     -300        0     -250        0
      2    125     -200      175     -300      150     -250
      3    125      125      175      175      150      150
      4    125      125      175      175      150      150
      5      0      125        0      175        0      150 ;

PARAMETER
  CASHONHAND(J)  budget constraint in period J
         /1    300
          2    375
          3   9999
          4   9999
          5   9999 /

  NPV(I)    net present value of project I;
    NPV(I) = SUM(J, CASHFLOW(J,I) /(1.1**(ORD(J)-1))) ;

VARIABLES
  VALUE   total net present value

BINARY VARIABLES
  X(I)  project acceptance variables;

EQUATIONS
  OBJECTIVE     defining total net present value
  CONSTRAINT(J) budget constraint in time period J;

OBJECTIVE..       VALUE =E= SUM(I, NPV(I)*X(I));
CONSTRAINT(J)..   SUM(I, -CASHFLOW(J, I)*X(I)) =L= CASHONHAND(J);

MODEL CAPBUD /ALL/;

SOLVE CAPBUD USING MIP MAXIMIZING VALUE;
```

CAPBUD1 is a slightly expanded capital budgeting problem discussed in Example 4 in Chapter 11. Rather than listing the entire GAMS program here, it will be sufficient to point out that the program can be obtained by adjoining to CAPBUD the following three new constraints:

```
ADDCONSTR1     additional constraint no 1
ADDCONSTR2     additional constraint no 2
ADDCONSTR3     additional constraint no 3
```

written as follows:

```
ADDCONSTR1..   X("1") - X("2") =L= 0;
ADDCONSTR2..   -X("5") + X("6") =L= 0;
ADDCONSTR3..   X("2") + X("4") - 2*X("5") =L= 0;
```

The rest is left to the reader.

PERSONNEL

Program PERSONNEL is for Chapter 12. The organization of SETS and subsets over the time span is analogous to the one we have
already employed in WAREHOUSE.

```
* The program PERSONNEL solves the personnel problem in Examples 1
* and 2 of Chapter 12, and with minor modifications also Examples 3
* and 4.  If you have student GAMS change the name to PERSONL.

SETS
  T        time periods/0,1,2,3,4/
  INDEX(T)             /1,2,3,4/
  OPENING(T)           /0       /
  TERMINAL(T)          /       4/ ;

PARAMETER
  R(INDEX)  personnel requirements
               /1   5100
                2   4750
                3   5060
                4   5000/

  A(T)  gain factors
               /0   1.00
                1   0.97
                2   0.96
                3   0.95
                4   1.00/ ;

VARIABLES
  COSTS

POSITIVE VARIABLES
  H(T)   workers hired at time T
  F(T)   workers fired at time T
  N(T)   workers at time T;

EQUATIONS
  OBJECTIVE           calculating total costs
  LABORBAL(T)         labor balance in period T
  LABORREQ(INDEX)     labor supply must cover demand;

OBJECTIVE.. COSTS =E= SUM(INDEX,0.2*H(INDEX)+0.4*F(INDEX)+5.0*N(INDEX));
LABORBAL(T-1)..  -H(T)+F(T)+N(T) -A(T-1)*N(T-1) =E= 0;
LABORREQ(INDEX).. N(INDEX) =G= R(INDEX);

N.FX(OPENING)  = 5000;
N.FX(TERMINAL) = 5000;

MODEL PERSONNEL /ALL/;

SOLVE PERSONNEL USING LP MINIMIZING COSTS;
```

CORN

Program CORN solves the first text example of Chapter 13. Notice the OPTION statement at the end of the program (it can appear anywhere in the program). This statement suppresses the portions of the output listing rows and columns, and may be used as desired to compress the volume of output.

```
* Program CORN solves Example 1 of Chapter 13.

SETS
  K    outputs /CORN,WHEAT/
  J    activities /GROWCORN,GROWWHEAT/
  I    resources /LAND,FERTILIZER,MACHINERY/;

PARAMETERS
  Q(I)   prices of resources
         /LAND        25
          FERTILIZER  95
          MACHINERY  500/
  D(K)   demands
         /CORN        50000
          WHEAT      120000/
  CEILING(J)  upper bounds on activities
              /GROWCORN   600
               GROWWHEAT 1500/;

TABLE  A(I,J)   unit resource requirements
                GROWCORN     GROWWHEAT
  LAND             1             1
  FERTILIZER      2.5           1.75
  MACHINERY       0.5           0.60
TABLE  B(K,J)   unit outputs
                 GROWCORN     GROWWHEAT
  CORN             120            0
  WHEAT              0           85 ;

VARIABLES
  COST    total input costs
POSITIVE VARIABLES
  X(J)    activity levels;

EQUATIONS
  OBJECTIVE       calculating total cost
  DEMANDBAL(K)    market balance for output K
  CAPACITY(J)     capacity constraint for activity J;

OBJECTIVE..     COST =E= SUM((I,J),Q(I)*A(I,J)*X(J));
DEMANDBAL(K).. SUM(J,B(K,J)*X(J)) =G= D(K);
CAPACITY(J)..   X(J) =L=CEILING(J);

OPTION LIMROW = 0, LIMCOL = 0;

MODEL CORN /ALL/;

SOLVE CORN USING LP MINIMIZING COST;
```

HOGS

Program HOGS solves the second farming example in Chapter 13. There are now two intermediate goods: corn and wheat for hog feed. The program shown here is slightly simplified compared to the data box in the main text; the two activities X1 and X3 in the text have been pooled to form the activity GROWCORN (both for sale and for hog feed), and the two activities X2 and X4 in the text have been pooled to form the activity GROWWHEAT (both for sale and for hog feed). It is of course also perfectly possible to spell out these individual activities separately, as in the text.

```
* Program HOGS solves Example 2 of Chapter 13.
SETS
  K     outputs /CORN,WHEAT,HOGS/
  J     activities /GROWCORN,GROWWHEAT,RAISEHOG/
  I     resources /LAND,FERTILIZER,MACHINERY/;
PARAMETERS
  Q(I)    prices of resources
        /LAND          25
         FERTILIZER  95
         MACHINERY  500/
  D(K)    demands
        /CORN          50000
         WHEAT        120000
         HOGS          10000/;
TABLE
  A(I,J)    unit resource requirements
                      GROWCORN      GROWWHEAT      RAISEHOG
    LAND                  1             1              0
    FERTILIZER          2.5          1.75              0
    MACHINERY           0.5          0.75              0
TABLE
  B(K,J)    unit outputs
                      GROWCORN      GROWWHEAT      RAISEHOG
    CORN                120             0            -18
    WHEAT                 0            85             -7
    HOGS                  0             0              1  ;
VARIABLES
  COST    total input costs
POSITIVE VARIABLES
  X(J)    activity levels ;
EQUATIONS
  OBJECTIVE         calculating total cost
  DEMANDBAL(K)      demand balance for output K;
OBJECTIVE..     COST =E= SUM((I,J),Q(I)*A(I,J)*X(J)) + 50*X("RAISEHOG");
DEMANDBAL(K).. SUM(J,B(K,J)*X(J)) =G= D(K);
MODEL HOGS /ALL/;
SOLVE HOGS USING LP MINIMIZING COST;
```

FARMTOCITY

Program FARMTOCITY solves the special farming example of Chapter 14. To simplify the GAMS program, no index sets are defined for farms and cities; instead, relations for each farm and for each city are listed separately.

```
* Program FARMTOCITY solves Example 1 of Chapter 14.  If you have
* student GAMS shorten the name to FARMCITY.

SETS
  K    outputs /CORN,WHEAT/
  J    activities /GROWCORN,GROWWHEAT/
  I    resources /LAND,FERTILIZER,MACHINERY/;

PARAMETERS
  QFARM1(I)   prices of resources
              /LAND        25
               FERTILIZER  95
               MACHINERY  500/

  QFARM2(I)   /LAND        30
               FERTILIZER 100
               MACHINERY  470/

  DCITY1(K)   demands
              /CORN        50000
               WHEAT      120000/

  DCITY2(K)   /CORN        70000
               WHEAT      140000/

  DCITY3(K)   /CORN        60000
               WHEAT      135000/;

TABLE
  A(I,J)   unit resource requirements
                     GROWCORN     GROWWHEAT
    LAND                 1             1
    FERTILIZER          2.5          1.75
    MACHINERY           0.5          0.75

TABLE
  BFARM1(K,J)   unit outputs
                     GROWCORN     GROWWHEAT
    CORN               120            0
    WHEAT                0           85

TABLE
  BFARM2(K,J)
                     GROWCORN     GROWWHEAT
    CORN               135            0
    WHEAT                0           75 ;

VARIABLES
  COST    total input costs

POSITIVE VARIABLES
  XFARM1(J)    activity levels at farm 1
  XFARM2(J)    activity levels at farm 2
  T11(K)       quantities shipped from farm 1 to city 1
  T12(K)       quantities shipped from farm 1 to city 2
  T13(K)       quantities shipped from farm 1 to city 3
  T21(K)       quantities shipped from farm 2 to city 1
  T22(K)       quantities shipped from farm 2 to city 2
  T23(K)       quantities shipped from farm 2 to city 3 ;
```

```
EQUATIONS
  OBJECTIVE      calculating total cost
  FARM1BAL(K)    balance at farm 1 for output K
  FARM2BAL(K)    balance at farm 2 for output K
  CITY1BAL(K)    balance at city 1 for output K
  CITY2BAL(K)    balance at city 2 for output K
  CITY3BAL(K)    balance at city 3 for output K
  ACRESFARM1     land balance for farm 1
  ACRESFARM2     land balance for farm 2 ;

OBJECTIVE..     COST =E= SUM((I,J),QFARM1(I)*A(I,J)*XFARM1(J))+
                SUM((I,J),QFARM2(I)*A(I,J)*XFARM2(J))-.1*SUM(K,T11(K))
                -.3*SUM(K,T12(K))-.2*SUM(K,T13(K))-.2*SUM(K,T21(K))
                -.30*SUM(K,T22(K))-.1*SUM(K,T23(K));
FARM1BAL(K)..   SUM(J,BFARM1(K,J)*XFARM1(J))-T11(K)-T12(K)-T13(K) =E= 0;
FARM2BAL(K)..   SUM(J,BFARM2(K,J)*XFARM2(J))-T21(K)-T22(K)-T23(K) =E= 0;
CITY1BAL(K)..   T11(K)+T21(K) =G= DCITY1(K);
CITY2BAL(K)..   T12(K)+T22(K) =G= DCITY2(K);
CITY3BAL(K)..   T13(K)+T23(K)=G= DCITY3(K);
ACRESFARM1..    SUM(J,XFARM1(J)) =L= 4000;
ACRESFARM2..    SUM(J,XFARM2(J)) =L= 3500;

MODEL FARMTOCITY /ALL/;

SOLVE FARMTOCITY USING LP MINIMIZING COST;
```

PINEAPPLE

PINEAPPLE solves the text example in Chapter 14, "The distribution of agricultural harvest to processing plants."

```
* Program PINEAPPLE solves Example 2 of Chapter 14. If you have
* student shorten the name to PINEAPPL.

SETS
  H   regions /ONE,TWO,THREE/
  J   activities /NEWPLANT,OLDPLANT/
  I   inputs with fixed price   /LABOR,CAPITAL/

PARAMETER
  Q(I)       prices of fixed price inputs
             /LABOR   1.25
              CAPITAL  .40/

PARAMETER
  SUPPLY(H) supply of pineapples in region H
             /ONE    4000
              TWO    5000
              THREE  6000/

TABLE    C(H,J)  unit transportation costs
            NEWPLANT    OLDPLANT
   ONE         0.02        0.04
   TWO         0.01        0.03
   THREE       0.04        0.01
```

```
TABLE    A(I,J)  unit requirement of fixed price inputs
                 NEWPLANT     OLDPLANT
  LABOR            0.04         0.08
  CAPITAL          2.00         1.45

VARIABLES
  RETURN           net return after costs

POSITIVE VARIABLES
  X(J)             level of plant activities
  T(H,J)           quantity transported from region H to plant J

EQUATIONS
  OBJECTIVE        calculating net returns
  HARVESTBAL(H)    balance for pineapples in each harvesting region H
  PLANTBAL(J)      balance for pineapples at each plant J;

OBJECTIVE..      RETURN =E= 12.50*SUM(J,X(J)) -SUM((H,J),C(H,J)*T(H,J))
                            -SUM((I,J),Q(I)*A(I,J)*X(J));
HARVESTBAL(H).. SUM(J,T(H,J))-SUPPLY(H) =L= 0;
PLANTBAL(J)..   16*X(J)-SUM(H,T(H,J)) =L= 0;

MODEL PINEAPPLE /ALL/;

SOLVE PINEAPPLE USING LP MAXIMIZING RETURN ;
```

STEEL

Program STEEL solves the goal programming example discussed in Chapter 15 when the price of steel equals $200 per ton. To solve the same program for the various different prices listed in the text, you need to change the entry NPENALTY("STEEL") and to solve the program anew.

```
* Program STEEL solves the steel production problem of Chapter 15.
SETS
  I    goals / STEEL,SLAG,WASTE,SMOKE /;

PARAMETERS
  MPENALTY(I)  penalties for excess achievements
               /STEEL    0
                SLAG     4
                WASTE   15
                SMOKE   18/
  NPENALTY(I)  penalties for deficit achievements
               /STEEL  200
                SLAG     0
                WASTE    0
                SMOKE    0/
  B(I)         output per ton of steel manufactured
               /STEEL    1
                SLAG   0.25
                WASTE   15
                SMOKE   10/
  GOAL(I)      goals
               /STEEL  100
                SLAG    20
                WASTE 1200
                SMOKE  900/ ;
```

```
VARIABLES
  COSTS        total penalty costs

POSITIVE VARIABLES
  X            steel output
  GPLUS(I)     excess relative to goal
  GMINUS(I)    deficit relative to goal ;

EQUATIONS
  OBJECTIVE       calcalating total panety costs
  DEFGOAL(I)      defining each goal I;

OBJECTIVE..  COSTS =E= SUM(I,MPENALTY(I)*GPLUS(I)+NPENALTY(I)
                       *GMINUS(I));
DEFGOAL(I).. B(I)*X-GPLUS(I)+GMINUS(I) =E= GOAL(I);

MODEL STEEL /ALL/;

SOLVE STEEL USING LP MINIMIZING COSTS;
```

RESGOAL

Problem RESGOAL (for "resource goals") solves Example 1 in Chapter 15, involving the growing of rice in a developing country. You have encountered the notation on the two last lines of the program

```
X.UP("LOYIELD") = 1.0 ;
X.UP("HIYIELD") = 0.4 ;
```

before, see, e.g., program PERSONNEL.

```
* Program RESGOAL solves Example 1 in Chapter 15.

SETS
  I  resources  /WATER, LABOR, LAND, FERTILIZER, PESTICIDES /
  J  activities /LOYIELD, HIYIELD /;

PARAMETERS
  Q(I)  resource prices
      /WATER          1.5
       LABOR          2
       LAND           6
       FERTILIZER    12
       PESTICIDES    20/

  GOAL(I) resource goals
      /WATER         11
       LABOR          0
       LAND           0
       FERTILIZER     0
       PESTICIDES     0.0025/

  M(I)   penalties for over-use
      /WATER        111
       LABOR          0
       LAND           0
       FERTILIZER     0
       PESTICIDES   999/
```

```
  N(I)   penalties for under-use
       /WATER          0
        LABOR          0
        LAND           0
        FERTILIZER     0
        PESTICIDES     0/ ;
TABLE
  A(I, J) unit input requirements
                      LOYIELD        HIYIELD
        WATER           10              6
        LABOR            0.77           0.43
        LAND             0.67           0.33
        FERTILIZER       0.01           0.04
        PESTICIDES       0              0.01   ;
VARIABLES
  COST     total cost including penalties
POSITIVE VARIABLES
  X(J)       activity levels in millions of tons grown
  GPLUS(I)   excessive use of resource I
  GMINUS(I)  deficit use of resource I ;
EQUATIONS
  OBJECTIVE   calculating total costs
  RICEBAL     balance for rice
  DEFGOAL(I)  defining each goal I ;
OBJECTIVE..   COST =E= SUM((I,J), Q(I)*A(I,J)*X(J))
                  +SUM(I,M(I)*GPLUS(I)+N(I)*GMINUS(I));
RICEBAL..     SUM(J, X(J)) =G= 1.2;
DEFGOAL(I)..  SUM(J, A(I, J)*X(J)) - GPLUS(I) + GMINUS(I) =E= GOAL(I);
X.UP("LOYIELD") = 1.0;
X.UP("HIYIELD") = 0.4;
MODEL RESGOAL /ALL/ ;
SOLVE RESGOAL USING LP MINIMIZING COST;
```

STRIPMINE

```
* Program STRIPMINE solves Example 2 in Chapter 15 which is
* nonlinear.  If you have student GAMS change the name to STRIPMIN.
SETS
  I origins      /REGION1, REGION2/
  J destinations /UTILITY1, UTILITY2/;
PARAMETERS
  GAMMA(I)     supply price coefficient team
       /REGION1        100
        REGION2         60 /
  DELTA(I)     supply price coefficients
       /REGION1         20
        REGION2         26 /
```

```
    DEMAND(J)     demand in tons
         /UTILITY1        3200
          UTILITY2        2400 /

    GOAL(I)    goals
         /REGION1         2000
          REGION2         4500 /

    MPENALTY(I)  penalty for excessive mining
         /REGION1         9999
          REGION2          999 /

    NPENALTY(I)  penalty for mining below limit
         /REGION1            0
          REGION2            0 /;
VARIABLES
    COST      supply cost plus penalties
POSITIVE VARIABLES
    W(I)      supply at region I
    X(I, J)   quantity shipped from I to J
    GPLUS(I)  excessive mining in region I
    GMINUS(I) mining below limit in region I ;

EQUATIONS
    OBJECTIVE     calculating COST
    REGIONBAL(I)  balance in each region I
    DEMBAL(J)     balance at each utility J
    DEFGOAL(I)    defining each goal I ;

OBJECTIVE..     COST =E= SUM(I, GAMMA(I)* W(I) + 0.5*DELTA(I)*W(I)**2)
                + SUM(I, MPENALTY(I)*GPLUS(I) + NPENALTY(I)*GMINUS(I)) ;
REGIONBAL(I).. SUM(J, X(I, J)) - W(I) =L= 0 ;
DEMBAL(J)..     SUM(I, X(I, J)) =G= DEMAND(J) ;
DEFGOAL(I)..   W(I) - GPLUS(I) + GMINUS(I) =E= GOAL(I) ;

MODEL STRIPMINE /ALL/ ;

SOLVE STRIPMINE MINIMIZING COST USING NLP ;
```

NEWLAND

Program NEWLAND solves the land investment problem discussed in Chapter 16. The program listed below solves the more general Example 2 of the text. To solve for Example 1, only two changes are required: first, change the data in the TABLE D(T,K), entering the given expected demand for both crops in each of the three planning periods; second, change the data in TABLE P(T,K), entering zeroes throughout.

NEWLAND is an instance of mixed integer programming (MIP). The variables Y(T, J) are BINARY.

There are some methods of data entry and data manipulation here that you have not seen before. A fixed and known value of a parameter may be entered as a SCALAR. The format is

```
SCALAR
GAMMA    fixed change costs /40000/ ;
```

Note that SCALAR is defined by "assignment," the format being

```
SCALAR
  RATE    discount rate;
  RATE = 1.100 ;
```

a regular equality sign is used. For the notation ORD(T), see CAPBUD.

```
* Program NEWLAND for solving Examples 1 and 2 of Chapter 16.
SETS
  K  outputs/CORN, WHEAT/
  J  activities/GROWCORN, GROWWHEAT/
  I  resourses/LAND, FERTILIZER, MACHINERY/
  T  time periods/PERIOD1, PERIOD2, PERIOD3/
  ALIAS(T,T1) ;
PARAMETERS
  Q(I) prices of resources( (same in all periods)
      /LAND        25
       FERTILIZER  95
       MACHINERY  500/
  INITCAP(J)  initial capacity to operate activity J
      /GROWCORN   600
       GROWWHEAT 1500/;
TABLE  A(I,J)  unit resource requirements
                          GROWCORN          GROWWHEAT
        LAND                 1                 1
        FERTILIZER           2.5               1.75
        MACHINERY            0.5               0.60 ;
TABLE  B(K,J)  unit outputs
                          GROWCORN          GROWWHEAT
        CORN                120                0
        WHEAT                 0               85   ;
SCALARS
  GAMMA    fixed charge capacity costs/ 40000 /
  DELTA    variable capacity costs/ 100 /
  CRF      capital recovery factor
  RATE     discount rate ;
RATE=  1.100;
CRF = ((RATE-1)*(RATE**10))/((RATE**10)-1.0);
DISPLAY CRF;
TABLE  Unitmatrix(T,T1) lower triangular unit matrix
               PERIOD1      PERIOD2         PERIOD3
    PERIOD1       1            0               0
    PERIOD2       1            1               0
    PERIOD3       1            1               1 ;
TABLE  D(T,K) demands in period T
                 CORN         WHEAT
    PERIOD1      50000        120000
    PERIOD2          0             0
    PERIOD3          0             0  ;
```

```
TABLE P(T,K) market output price in period T
              CORN         WHEAT
    PERIOD1     0            0
    PERIOD2     4.3          5.9
    PERIOD3     4.5          7     ;

VARIABLES
  PROFIT  net profit;

POSITIVE VARIABLES
  X(T,J)        level of operation in period T of activity J
  INCRCAP(T,J) increased capacity in period T of activity J ;

BINARY VARIABLES
  Y(T,J)   equals unity if there is positive addition to capacity in
           period T to operate activity J, else zero;

EQUATIONS
  DEFPROFIT          defining net profit
  DEMANDBAL(T,K)     balance in period T for output K
  CAPACITY(T,J)      capacity limit in period T for activity J
  YBINARY(T,J)       binary variable in period T for activity J ;

DEFPROFIT..          PROFIT=E= SUM((T,K,J),P(T,K) * B(K,J)*X(T,J)
                           /(RATE**ORD(T)))-SUM((T,I,J), Q(I)* A(I,J)
                           * X(T,J)/(RATE**ORD(T)))- SUM((T,T1,J),
                           CRF*UNITMATRIX(T,T1)* (GAMMA*Y(T1,J)
                           + DELTA*INCRCAP(T1,J))/(RATE**ORD(T)));
DEMANDBAL(T,K)..     SUM(J,B(K,J) *X(T,J)) =G= D(T,K);
CAPACITY(T,J)..      X(T,J) - SUM(T1,UNITMATRIX(T,T1)* INCRCAP(T1,J))
                     =L= INITCAP(J);
YBINARY(T,J)..       INCRCAP(T,J)=L=  1000*Y(T,J);

MODEL NEWLAND /ALL/;

SOLVE NEWLAND  USING MIP MAXIMIZING PROFIT;
```

KOOPMANS

Program KOOPMANS solves the text example discussed in Chapter 17. The prices of FOOD and GOODS are 36 and 29.2 respectively. To conduct the numerical experiment discussed in the main text, change these two prices parametrically as required.

```
*Program KOOPMANS solves Example 1 of Chapter 17.

SETS
  K      final goods
       /FOOD  food products
        GOODS manufactures goods/

 INTER intermediate goods
       /TRANSP transportation services /

 I     primary goods
       /LAND   land resources
        ENERGY electricity, coal, oil
        CAPITAL capital goods /
```

```
 J     activities
       /AGRI   agriculture
        TRUCK  transportation by truck
        RAIL   transportation by railroad
        MANUF  manufacturing / ;

PARAMETERS
  P(K) prices of final goods
       /FOOD    36
        GOODS   29.2 /

  W(I) endowments of primary goods
       /LAND       100
        ENERGY     357.5
        CAPITAL    227.5 /

TABLE
  AP(I,J) unit requirements of primary goods
             AGRI    TRUCK    RAIL    MANUF
    LAND      2        0        0       0
    ENERGY   4.5      12       10      0.5
    CAPITAL   3        4        6      1.5   ;

TABLE
  AI(INTER,J) unit requirements of intermediate goods
              AGRI    TRUCK    RAIL    MANUF
    TRANSP     0        0        0       0.4   ;

TABLE
  BF(K,J) unit outputs of all final goods
             AGRI    TRUCK   RAIL    MANUF
    FOOD      1        0       0       0
    GOODS     0        0       0       1    ;

TABLE
  BI(INTER,J) unit outputs of intermediate goods
              AGRI    TRUCK    RAIL    MANUF
    TRANSP     0        1        1       0 ;

VARIABLES
  OBJ

POSITIVE VARIABLES
  D(K) quantities of final goods demanded
  X(J) levels of operations of activities ;

EQUATIONS
  OBJECTIVE         total value of final goods
  FINALBAL(K)       market balance for final goods
  INTERBAL(INTER)   market balance for intermediate goods
  PRIMBAL(I)        market balance for primary goods;

OBJECTIVE..        OBJ =E= SUM(K,P(K)*D(K));
FINALBAL(K)..      D(K) =L= SUM(J,BF(K,J)*X(J));
INTERBAL(INTER).. SUM(J,AI(INTER,J)*X(J)) - SUM(J,BI(INTER,J)*X(J)) =L= 0;
PRIMBAL(I)..       SUM(J,AP(I,J)*X(J)) =L= W(I);

MODEL KOOPMANS /ALL/;

SOLVE KOOPMANS USING LP MAXIMIZING OBJ;
```

ENERGY

```
* Program ENERGY solves the first text example in Chapter 18.

SETS
  I nodes /NODE1, NODE2, NODE3, NODE4, NODE5/
  J arcs  /1TO3, 2TO3, 2TO4, 3TO5, 4TO5/ ;

PARAMETERS
  B(I)  influxes (neg) and effluxes (pos)
        /NODE1      -200
         NODE2       -80
         NODE3         0
         NODE4         0
         NODE5       120 /

  C(J)  UNIT COSTS
        /1TO3        4.5
         2TO3        6
         2TO4        6
         3TO5       19
         4TO5       12 / ;

TABLE
  M(I, J)    incidence matrix
               1TO3   2TO3   2TO4    3TO5    4TO5
    NODE1       -1     0      0       0       0
    NODE2        0    -1     -1       0       0
    NODE3        0.9   0.8    0      -1       0
    NODE4        0     0      0.9     0      -1
    NODE5        0     0      0       0.6     0.6 ;

VARIABLES
  COST      total costs

POSITIVE VARIABLES
  X(J)      flow along each arc J ;

EQUATIONS
  OBJECTIVE      defining costs
  NODECONSTR(I)  flow conservation condition for each node I ;

OBJECTIVE..      COST =E= SUM(J, C(J)*X(J)) ;
NODECONSTR(I).. SUM(J, M(I, J)*X(J)) =G= B(I) ;

MODEL ENERGY /ALL/ ;

SOLVE ENERGY MINIMIZING COST USING LP ;
```

ELECTRIC

Program `ELECTRIC` solves the electricity generation problem in Chapter 18. Note the specification of data for the two sparse matrices `C(H, K, S)` and `G(H, K)`. The matrices are named as `PARAMETERS`. First, all entries of each matrix are put equal to zero by assignment. Next the given nonzero values are superimposed, also by assignment. To check that these two matrices indeed have been formed as desired, they are `DISPLAY`ed.

```
* Program ELECTRIC solves the generation problem in Chapter 18.

SETS
  H   regions /REGION1,REGION2/
  S   fuels /COAL,OIL/
  ALIAS (H,K);

PARAMETERS
  D(H)  demand by region
       /REGION1  170
        REGION2  135/

TABLE
  F(H,S)  supply of fuels
              COAL     OIL
    REGION1   1.75     0.9
    REGION2   0.65     1.2

TABLE
  A(H,S)  unit input requirements
              COAL     OIL
    REGION1  0.01144  0.011
    REGION2  0.01070  0.012

TABLE
  B(H,S)  unit operating costs
              COAL     OIL
    REGION1   350      280
    REGION2   420      310

TABLE
  XUP(H,S)  generation upper limits
              COAL     OIL
    REGION1   120       80
    REGION2    95       55

PARAMETERS
  C(H,K,S)  unit transportation cost
  G(H,K)    transmission losses;

  C(H,K,S) = 0;
  C("REGION1","REGION2","COAL") = 0.2;
  C("REGION2","REGION1","COAL") = 0.2;
  C("REGION1","REGION2","OIL") = 0.1;
  C("REGION2","REGION1","OIL") = 0.1;
  G(H,K) = 0;
  G("REGION1","REGION2") = 22.5;
  G("REGION2","REGION1") = 22.5;

  DISPLAY C,G;

VARIABLES
  COST

POSITIVE VARIABLES
  X(H,S)    kwh of electricity generated
  T(H,K,S)  fuels transported from H to K
  W(H,K)    electricity transported from H to K
```

```
EQUATIONS
  OBJECTIVE    defining the objective as total costs
  ELECBAL(H)   electricity balance in region H
  FUELBAL(H,S) fuel balance in region H for fuel S
  GENCAP(H,S)  generation capacity in region H burning fuel S ;

OBJECTIVE..    COST =E= SUM((H,S),B(H,S)*X(H,S))+SUM((H,K),G(H,K)*W(H,K))
                        +SUM((H,K,S),C(H,K,S)*T(H,K,S));
ELECBAL(H)..   SUM(S,X(H,S))+SUM(K,(W(K,H)-W(H,K))) =G= D(H);
FUELBAL(H,S).. A(H,S)*X(H,S)-SUM(K,(T(K,H,S)-T(H,K,S))) =L= F(H,S);
GENCAP(H,S)..  X(H,S) =L= XUP(H,S);

MODEL ELECTRIC /ALL/;

SOLVE ELECTRIC USING LP MINIMIZING COST;
```

RETRAIN

```
* Program RETRAIN solves Example 1 in Chapter 19.

SETS
  I  occupations
     /HEALTH
      PROGRAMMER
      MECHANIC /
  ALIAS(I, J);

PARAMETERS
  A(I)  available workers
     /HEALTH        400
      PROGRAMMER    200
      MECHANIC      350 /

  B(J)   demand
     /HEALTH         300
      PROGRAMMER     240
      MECHANIC       300 /

  RESWAGE(I)   reservation wage in thousands of dollars
     /HEALTH          35
      PROGRAMMER      36
      MECHANIC        34 / ;

TABLE
  C(I, J)   unit retraining cost
                   HEALTH        PROGRAMMER       MECHANIC
     HEALTH          0              2.5              0.8
     PROGRAMMER      0.3            0                1.0
     MECHANIC        1.2            3.0              0   ;

VARIABLES
  POTENTIAL    total retraining costs minus wage sum foregone

POSITIVE VARIABLES
  X(I, J)    number of workers transiting from I to J
  GMINUS(I)  unemployment in occupation I ;
```

```
EQUATIONS
  OBJECTIVE     defining the potential function
  SUPPLYBAL(J)  balance for labor of occupation J
  DEFGOAL(I)    employment goal in occupation I ;

OBJECTIVE..     POTENTIAL =E= SUM((I, J), C(I, J)*X(I, J))
                              - SUM(I, RESWAGE(I)*GMINUS(I)) ;
SUPPLYBAL(J).. SUM(I, X(I, J)) =G= B(J) ;
DEFGOAL(I)..    SUM(J, X(I, J)) + GMINUS(I) =E= A(I) ;

MODEL RETRAIN /ALL/ ;

SOLVE RETRAIN USING LP MINIMIZING POTENTIAL ;
```

UNEMPL

```
* The program UNEMPL solves Example 2 of Chapter 19.  The general
* structure of the program has been brought from KOOPMANS.

SETS
  K  final goods
     /HARD   hardware
      SOFT   software/

  INTER intermediate goods
     /CONSULT   software consulting services/

  I  primary goods
     /ENGIN    computer engineers
      ANALYSTS system analysts
      PROGRAM  computer programmers
      SALES    sales personnel/

  J  ACTIVITIES
     /HARDBUY    buyer coordinating hardware purchase himself
      SOFTBUY    buyer coordinating software purchase himself
      SOFTSERV   software consulting firm contract
      SOFTHIRE   software consulting firm hiring of manpower/;

PARAMETERS
  P(K)   prices of final goods net of materials and capital costs
         /HARD      =  900
          SOFT      = 1800/

  W(I)   supply of labor
         /ENGIN     = 300
          ANALYSTS = 160
          PROGRAM  = 1000
          SALES    = 400/

  QFLOOR(I)   reservation wage rates
         /ENGIN     = 37.5
          ANALYSTS = 70
          PROGRAM  = 25
          SALES    = 25 /     ;
```

```
TABLE
  AP(I,J)  unit requirements of primary goods
                 HARDBUY  SOFTBUY   SOFTSERV  SOFTHIRE
    ENGIN         20        0         0         0
    ANALYSTS       0        4         0         4
    PROGRAM        0       24         0        26
    SALES         2.4      12         0         6;

TABLE
  AI(INTER,J)   unit requirements of intermediate goods
                HARDBUY   SOFTBUY   SOFTSERV   SOFTHIRE
    CONSULT       0         0         1          0 ;

TABLE
  BF(K,J)   unit outputs of final goods
                HARDBUY   SOFTBUY   SOFTSERV   SOFTHIRE
    HARD          1         0         0          0
    SOFT          0         1         1          0  ;

TABLE
  BI(INTER,J)   unit outputs of intermediate goods
                 HARDBUY   SOFTBUY   SOFTSERV   SOFTHIRE
    CONSULT        0         0         0           1  ;

VARIABLES
   OBJ

POSITIVE VARIABLES
  D(K)   quantities of final goods demanded
  X(J)   level of operations of activities
  GMINUS(I)   unemployment of labor;

EQUATIONS
  OBJECTIVE     total value of final goods
  FINALBAL      market balance for final goods
  INTERBAL      market balance for intermediate goods
  PRIMBAL       market balance for primary goods;

OBJECTIVE..        OBJ =E= SUM(K,P(K)*D(K)) + SUM(I,QFLOOR(I)*GMINUS(I));
FINALBAL(K)..      D(K) =L= SUM(J,BF(K,J)*X(J));
INTERBAL(INTER).. SUM(J,AI(INTER,J)*X(J))-SUM(J,BI(INTER,J)*X(J)) =E= 0;
PRIMBAL(I)..       SUM(J,AP(I,J)*X(J)) + GMINUS(I) =E= W(I);

MODEL UNEMPL/ALL/;

SOLVE UNEMPL USING LP MAXIMIZING OBJ;
```

LEONTIEF

```
* Program LEONTIEF solves the input-output problem with given labor
* supply specified in the data box on page 259 in Chapter 20.

SET
  I  /AGRI,MINING,CONSTRUCT/;
  ALIAS  (I,J);
```

```
PARAMETERS
  B(I)  capital charge
        /AGRI      = 0.2
         MINING    = 0.2
         CONSTRUCT= 0.3/

  D(I)  final demand in millions of dollars
        /AGRI      = 9.0
         MINING    = 12.0
         CONSTRUCT= 15.0/

  N(I)  labor requirements in persons per million dollars
        /AGRI      = 0.15
         MINING    = 0.10
         CONSTRUCT= 0.20/

  W(I)  labor supply (in thousands of persons)
        /AGRI      = 4.397
         MINING    = 3.015
         CONSTRUCT= 6.275/ ;

TABLE
  M(I,J)  input-output coefficients
                  AGRI      MINING      CONSTRUCT
    AGRI          0.10       0.30         0.25
    MINING        0.25       0.15         0.18
    CONSTRUCT     0.20       0.20         0.12 ;

VARIABLES
  CAPCHARGE   total capital charge

POSITIVE VARIABLES
  X(I)        gross output in millions of dollars ;

EQUATIONS
  OBJECTIVE    calculating total capital change
  GOODSBAL(I)  goods balance for sector I
  LABORBAL(I)  labor balance for sector I ;

OBJECTIVE..    CAPCHARGE = SUM(I,B(I)*X(I));
GOODSBAL(I).. X(I)-SUM(J,M(I,J)*X(J)) =G= D(I);
LABORBAL(I).. N(I)*X(I) =L= W(I);

MODEL LEONTIEF/ALL/;

SOLVE LEONTIEF USING LP MINIMIZING CAPCHARGE ;
```

LEONTIEF1

Program LEONTIEF1 elaborates on LEONTIEF, assuming the presence of a vector of reservation wages.

```
*Program LEONTIEF1 solves the problem with data box on page 260 in
*Chapter 20. If you have student GAMS change the name to LEON1.

SET
  I  /AGRI,MINING,CONSTRUCT/;
  ALIAS  (I,J);
```

```
PARAMETERS
  B(I)  capital charge
       /AGRI      = 0.2
        MINING    = 0.2
        CONSTRUCT= 0.3/
  D(I)  final demand in millions of dollars
       /AGRI      = 9.6
        MINING    = 12.5
        CONSTRUCT= 15.5/
   N(I)  labor requirements in persons per million dollars
       /AGRI      = 0.15
        MINING    = 0.10
        CONSTRUCT= 0.20/
   QFLOOR(I)  reservation wage
       /AGRI      = 1.67
        MINING    = 1.50
        CONSTRUCT= 0.75/
   W(I)  labor supply (in thousands of persons)
       /AGRI      = 4.397
        MINING    = 3.015
        CONSTRUCT= 6.275/ ;

TABLE  M(I,J)  input-output coefficients
                   AGRI      MINING      CONSTRUCT
    AGRI           0.10       0.30          0.25
    MINING         0.25       0.15          0.18
    CONSTRUCT      0.20       0.20          0.12 ;

VARIABLES
  POTENTIAL   capital change minus wage sum foregone
POSITIVE VARIABLES
  X(I)        gross output in millions of dollars
  GMINUS(I)   unemployment (in thousands of persons) ;

EQUATIONS
  OBJECTIVE   defining the POTENTIAL
  GOODSBAL(I) goods balance for sector I
  LABORBAL(I) labor balance for sector I ;

OBJECTIVE..   POTENTIAL =E= SUM(I,B(I)*X(I))-SUM(I,QFLOOR(I)*GMINUS(I));
GOODSBAL(I).. X(I)-SUM(J,M(I,J)*X(J)) =G= D(I);
LABORBAL(I).. N(I)*X(I)+GMINUS(I) =L= W(I);

MODEL LEONTIEF1 /ALL/ ;

SOLVE LEONTIEF1 USING LP MINIMIZING POTENTIAL ;
```

CASHMAN

```
* Program CASHMAN solves the text example in Chapter 21.

SETS
  T  time periods /1,2,3,4/
  K  arcs         /12,13,14,23,24,34,21,31,41,32,42,43,44/;
```

```
PARAMETER
  P(T)   payments
       /1  300
        2 -100
        3 -400
        4  300/;

TABLE M(T,K)  incidence matrix
    12     13     14     23     24     34     21   31     41   32   42   43   44
1   1      1      1      0      0      0    -.95 -.89  -.82   0    0    0    0
2 -1.04    0      0      1      1      0      1    0      0  -.95 -.89  0    0
3   0   -1.09     0   -1.04     0      1      0    1      0    1    0  -.95   0
4   0      0   -1.16     0   -1.09 -1.04     0    0      1    0    1    1    1;

VARIABLES
  PROFIT;

POSITIVE VARIABLES
  X(K);

EQUATIONS
  OBJECTIVE
  CASHFLOW(T);

OBJECTIVE..      PROFIT =E= X("44");
CASHFLOW(T)..    SUM(K,M(T,K)*X(K)) =E= P(T);

MODEL  CASHMAN  /ALL/;

SOLVE CASHMAN USING LP MAXIMIZING PROFIT;
```

PORTFOLIO

The program PORTFOLIO introduces a new concept, that of multiple solve statements that we haven't seen before. Note that in the scalar part of the program the variable LAMBDA was set equal to 0.0005 by assignment. At the end of the program we find a solve statement followed by a new assignment of LAMBDA equal to 0.0006, followed by another solve statement, etc. The effect of these statements is to solve a sequence of problems, each with a different value of LAMBDA, whose solutions enable us to trace out the efficiency frontier of portfolios as a function of degree of risk that the user is able to assume.

```
* Program PORTFOLI solves the Markowitz portfolio problem in
* Chapter 22.

SETS
  N     months / 1*12 /
  I     individual stocks / KODAK, IBM, FORD /
  ALIAS (I,J) ;

TABLE P(I,N)  prices of stocks
          1    2    3    4    5    6    7    8    9    10   11   12
  KODAK   40   42   44   40   46   48   50   41   48   38   40   40
  IBM    120  118  120  116  122  115  123  124  117  119  118  116
  FORD    60   61   58   52   54   49   55   37   38   40   39   45

PARAMETER EP(I)  expected price of stock I;
  EP(I) = SUM(N,P(I,N))/12;
  DISPLAY EP;
```

```
PARAMETER  COV(I,J)  covariance between stocks I and J;
  COV(I,J) = SUM(N, (P(I,N) - EP(I))*(P(J,N) - EP(J))/12);
  DISPLAY COV;

SCALAR LAMBDA attitude toward risk;
  LAMBDA = 0.0005;

VARIABLES
  POTENTIAL  potential function to be maximized;

POSITIVE VARIABLES
  X(I)     investment in stock I
  CASH     holding of cash
  EXP      mathematical expection of portfolio
  VAR      variance of portfolio;
EQUATIONS
  OBJECTIVE
  DEFEXP
  DEFVAR
  BUDGET;

OBJECTIVE..      POTENTIAL =E= EXP+CASH-LAMBDA*VAR;
DEFEXP..         EXP =L= SUM(I,EP(I)*X(I));
DEFVAR..         VAR =G= SUM((I,J),COV(I,J)*X(I)*X(J));
BUDGET..         SUM(I,P(I,"12")*X(I))+CASH =L= 15000;

* OPTION LIMROW=0, LIMCOL=0;

MODEL PORTFOLI /ALL/;

SOLVE PORTFOLI MAXIMIZING POTENTIAL USING NLP;

* LAMBDA=0.0006;
* SOLVE PORTFOLI MAXIMIZING POTENTIAL USING NLP;

* LAMBDA=0.0007;
* SOLVE PORTFOLI MAXIMIZING POTENTIAL USING NLP;

* LAMBDA=0.0008;
* SOLVE PORTFOLI MAXIMIZING POTENTIAL USING NLP;

* LAMBDA=0.0009;
* SOLVE PORTFOLI MAXIMIZING POTENTIAL USING NLP;

* LAMBDA=0.0010;
* SOLVE PORTFOLI MAXIMIZING POTENTIAL USING NLP;

* LAMBDA=0.0015;
* SOLVE PORTFOLI MAXIMIZING POTENTIAL USING NLP;

* LAMBDA=0.0020;
* SOLVE PORTFOLI MAXIMIZING POTENTIAL USING NLP;
```

DIAGONAL

```
* This is DIAGONAL for calculating the approximation to the covariance
* matrix using Sharpe's beta model.  The only purpose of this program
* is to display the approximate covariance matrix for the text example.
```

```
SETS
  N  months /1*12/
  I  individual stocks /KODAK, IBM, FORD/
  ALIAS(I,J);

TABLE  P(I,N) prices of stocks
            1    2    3    4    5    6    7    8    9   10   11   12
  KODAK    40   42   44   40   46   48   50   41   48   38   40   40
  IBM     120  118  120  116  122  115  123  124  117  119  118  116
  FORD     60   61   58   52   54   49   55   37   38   40   39   45 ;

PARAMETER EP(I)  expected price of stock I;
  EP(I) = SUM(N,P(I,N))/12;
  DISPLAY EP;

PARAMETER  COV(I,J)  covariance between stocks I and J;
  COV(I,J) = SUM(N,(P(I,N)-EP(I))*(P(J,N)-EP(J))/12);
  DISPLAY COV;

PARAMETER DOW(N)  dow jones index
  /1  1950
   2  1960
   3  1965
   4  1980
   5  1985
   6  2010
   7  2050
   8  2020
   9  2010
  10  1980
  11  1940
  12  1900/;

PARAMETER EDOW, VARDOW;
  EDOW = SUM(N,DOW(N))/12;
  VARDOW = SUM(N, SQR(DOW(N)-EDOW))/12;
  DISPLAY EDOW, VARDOW;

PARAMETER BETA(I), ALPHA(I);
  BETA(I) = SUM(N,(P(I,N)-EP(I))*(DOW(N)-EDOW))/(12*VARDOW);
  ALPHA(I) = EP(I)-BETA(I)*EDOW ;
  DISPLAY BETA,ALPHA;

PARAMETER EPI(I,N), VAREPS(I) ;
  EPI(I,N) = P(I,N)-ALPHA(I)-BETA(I)*DOW(N) ;
  VAREPS(I) = SUM(N,SQR(EPI(I,N)))/12 ;
  DISPLAY EPI, VAREPS ;

PARAMETER COVBETA(I,J), COVEPS(I,J), APPROX(I,J) ;
  COVBETA(I,J) = BETA(I)*BETA(J) ;
  COVEPS(I,I) = VAREPS(I) ;
  APPROX(I,J) = COVBETA(I,J)*VARDOW + COVEPS(I,J) ;
  DISPLAY COVBETA, COVEPS, APPROX ;
```

Index

INDEX

1

NAME

A

B

C

D

E

F

G

H

I

J

K

L

M

N

P

R

S

T

W

INDEX

2

SUBJECT

A

B

C

D

L

M

N

O

P

Q

R